Dictionary of
Telecommunications

Dictionary of Telecommunications

S. J. Aries

Butterworths

London Boston Sydney Wellington Durban Toronto

First published 1981

© Butterworth & Co. (Publishers) Ltd, 1981

British Library Cataloguing in Publication Data

Aries, Sidney John
  Dictionary of telecommunications
  1. Telecommunication systems—Dictionaries
  I. Title
  621.38′03′21   TK5102   80-41449
  ISBN 0-408-00328-6

Filmset by Reproduction Drawings Limited, Sutton, Surrey.

Printed and Bound by Robert Hartnoll Ltd., Bodmin, Cornwall.

Preface

For a number of years I have been closely associated with various national and international committees concerned, among other things, with the production of standard glossaries of technical terms. Definitions produced in this way are authoritative and concise, and hence are excellent for use in specifications and similar contexts. Usually, however, they are drafted by experts for use by other experts, and some of them are therefore of little help to anyone unfamiliar with the subject. With this in mind it was decided to produce a dictionary that would provide a definition of each term and supplement it with explanatory material whenever such treatment seemed to be appropriate. Some of the terms in this book are therefore covered by short essays including diagrams where necessary; Nyquist rate and waveform testing are examples of this treatment. The definitions for less complex concepts are also supported by notes on current practice where this is thought to be helpful. Non-technical terms for facilities are included and there are also entries on the scope, constitution and purpose of a number of international organisations concerned with telecommunications. The work takes due account of the terminology used in North America and so should be useful to a wide readership of English-speaking students, technicians, engineers and others interested in its subject.

The form of presentation adopted is to place each definition in normal reading order, e.g. the definition for transversal equaliser appears under T and not under E. Cross-references are provided to draw the reader's attention to related terms and definitions that should assist the understanding of a given concept. Technical terms used in a definition are normally defined elsewhere in the book, and are printed in *bold italic* type where this is likely to be helpful. An appendix giving many of the abbreviations and acronyms used in the literature has been added, to guide a reader to the definition of a concept known only by its abbreviation.

This book is associated with the *Dictionary of Electronics* by S. W. Amos and the *Dictionary of Audio, Radio and Video* by R. S. Roberts (under the general editorship of S. W. Amos). These subjects are closely related to telecommunications and share many technical terms. For this reason the authors collaborated to prepare a list of English and American terms to be defined, to decide in which dictionary each should appear and what depth of treatment each should receive. It was agreed that some terms for common concepts should appear in all three dictionaries to make them largely self-contained, but that detailed explanations of fundamental terms should be confined to the *Dictionary of Electronics*. Nevertheless some basic terms relevant to newer techniques, such as fibre optics, are covered in detail in this volume.

The preparation of this book has been a stimulating and rewarding task, but it has absorbed most of my leisure time for several years. It is therefore a pleasure to record my appreciation and thanks for the help and understanding so freely given by my wife Elisabeth.

S.J.A.

A

A-condition In a *start-stop system,* the significant condition of the element that precedes a character signal or block signal. The A-element prepares the receiving equipment for the reception of the code elements.

A-digit selector A term used in the UK in connection with a *director system* having a three-digit code. The A-digit selector is operated by the first digit of the wanted exchange code to select a free director.

A-law encoding *Encoding* in accordance with the CCITT Recommendation G711. This specifies a segmented *encoding law* employing **non-uniform quantising** to attain the desired *compression* characteristic. A-law encoding is used with the 30-channel PCM systems complying with CCITT Recommendation G732, i.e. the systems used mainly in Europe.

ARAEN Designation for a set of equipment kept by the CCITT and used for comparative measurements of the transmission performance of telephone systems. The apparatus consists essentially of a transmission path which may be subdivided into a sending end, receiving end and junction. Other apparatus supplies room noise and intercommunication facilities. ARAEN is used as part of *NOSFER* and *SRAEN* for measurements based on the comparison of loudness and of *articulation*, respectively.

ARQ system See *van Duuren ARQ system.*

abbreviated address calling In telegraphy or data transmission, the establishment of a wanted *connection* using fewer characters than those in the full address.

abbreviated calling or **abbreviated dialling** A service whereby each of a selected set of frequently required numbers can be called by dialling a few digits instead of the complete number. Also termed *short-code calling (dialling)* and *speed calling.* The selected numbers are held in a *store*, and the exchange equipment makes the required translation between the dialled code and the wanted number. Some PABXs offering the facility provide both a library of external numbers available to all extensions and smaller libraries, the codes for which can be allocated to

1

individual extensions.

absent extension advice   A PABX facility enabling an extension user to advise callers of his absence by dialling a suitable code so that incoming calls are temporarily diverted to the switchboard, an answering machine or a recorded announcement.

absent extension diversion   A PABX facility enabling an extension user to divert incoming calls temporarily to any other extension indicated when the service is invoked, or to a permanently nominated extension, or to one of a group of specified extensions. The service may be initiated by dialling an appropriate code and cancelled by dialling another.

absolute gain (also known as *isotropic gain*)   Of an antenna, for a given direction: the ratio (usually expressed in *decibels*) of the power that would be required at the input of an ideal *isotropic radiator* to the power actually supplied to the given antenna so that the *radiation intensity* in the *far-field region* in the given direction would be the same. If no direction is quoted, that corresponding to maximum radiation is assumed. If the antenna is lossless its absolute gain is equal to its *directivity* in the same direction. See also *partial gain* and *relative gain*.

absolute power [voltage] level   The magnitude of the power [voltage] of a signal at a specific point in a transmission system, usually expressed in *decibels* with reference to a power of one milliwatt [voltage of 0.775 volt RMS]. The value of 0.775 volt is chosen because it corresponds to a power dissipation of 1 milliwatt in a resistance of 600 ohms, the nominal characteristic impedance of many telephone lines. It follows that power and voltage levels will correspond exactly if measured at a point in a circuit where the impedance is in fact 600 ohms. See also *signal level*.

absorber circuit   A circuit provided in a radio-telegraph transmitter to absorb power during the space periods of on/off keying, thereby minimising fluctuations in the load on the primary power supply.

absorption   (1) In radio-wave propagation, the reduction in power of a radio wave owing to its interaction with matter; see *ionospheric absorption*. (2) In line transmission, the loss in signal power resulting from the dissipation of energy in extraneous media.

absorption cross-section   Of an antenna, see *effective aperture*.

absorption frequency meter   A frequency meter working on the principle that maximum power is absorbed by a calibrated *tuned circuit* when this resonates with the unknown frequency. In *waveguide* applications the tuned circuit is a cavity-type resonator.

2

absorption loss   In an *optical fibre*, loss of optical power owing to its interaction with impurities such as water and transition metal ions in the dielectric material. Absorption is a frequency-dependent phenomenon, so its effects can be reduced by careful choice of operating wavelengths.

absorption modulation   *Amplitude modulation* of the output of a radio transmitter by means of a variable-impedance circuit that is caused to absorb carrier power in accordance with the modulating wave.

absorptive attenuator   A length of *waveguide* containing a dissipative material. Also known as *resistive attenuator*.

abstract symbol   A representation of a concept in a manner that has not been generally agreed, so that the meaning and use of the symbol have to be defined for each application.

accentuated contrast   In *facsimile*, a method of operation whereby all picture elements having a luminance exceeding an intermediate reference level are transmitted as nominal white, those having a luminance level less than the reference being transmitted as nominal black.

acceptable interference   A level of radio interference that would normally be classed as harmful but, by agreement between the authorities operating the radio service in question, is deemed to be acceptable. Usually such a level is only acceptable for an interim period until the performance can be upgraded or until a temporary service is withdrawn.

access code   The single digit, or assembly of digits, that must be dialled by a PABX extension user to obtain a particular service. Access codes are used at the beginning of a call following the receipt of dial tone and also after register recall when an established call exists. Standardisation of these codes is clearly desirable, and one proposal being considered is shown in *Table A.1.*

Table A.1

Service		Access code
PABX operator		0
Public exchange		9
Dial answer night service		8
Inter PBX circuit access		7
Call back		61
Diversion of calls	Activate	62
	Cancel	64
Incoming access barred	Activate	63
	Cancel	65
Number repetition		66
Abbreviated dialling		1x (or 1xx)

3

access line (US) Designation sometimes used in place of *subscriber's line*.

access switch In automatic switching, a *selector* that is used to enable centralised units such as *registers* to gain access to less centralised units such as *relay* sets.

accessibility See *availability*.

accumulator (1) A *register* used to store the output of an *arithmetic logic unit*. (2) A battery composed of one or more secondary cells.

acknowledgement signal unit In *common-channel signalling*, a signal unit used in connection with *error control* to convey information regarding the correct or erroneous reception of one or more signal messages.

acoustic coupling In data transmission, a method of coupling terminal data equipment to a telephone handset using *transducers* and sound waves.

active line See *available line*.

active satellite See *communication satellite*.

activity factor (US) Of a speech channel during the *busy hour*, the decimal fraction of the busy hour that the circuit is expected to be occupied by speech, silent periods in the conversation being ignored.

adaptive equaliser A device that automatically compensates for the distortion experienced by a *digital signal* or a *digitally modulated signal* in its passage through a transmission system. Adaptive equalisers are used in data modems to minimise *intersymbol interference* caused by transmission impairments such as *amplitude/frequency distortion*, phase non-linearities and echo. A typical device consists of a variable *waveform corrector* which continuously adjusts itself in accordance with information derived from the received data signal.

adaptive multiplexer (US) In data transmission, *time-division multiplex* equipment that makes efficient use of the transmission capability of the common channel by allocating *time slots* to terminals only at times when they have traffic to transmit. If all the time slots are in use, a terminal wishing to transmit receives a busy signal until time slots become available for its use.

Adcock antenna An *antenna* consisting of two identical vertical elements spaced by half a wavelength or less in a horizontal plane and connected in phase opposition to give the antenna a figure-of-eight *directivity pattern*.

add-on conference A PABX facility enabling an extension user to set up calls one by one to a number of extensions and to connect each extension in succession in the conference. Further extensions can be added at the discretion of the originating extension at any time during the progress of the call.

add-on third party See *three-party conference*.

address (1) The destination for a message. (2) The location of data in a *store* (memory).

address-complete signal A *signal* (2) sent back from a terminal register to indicate that all the *address information* has been received. If the signal also serves to indicate that the call should be charged if answered, it is known as an *address-complete signal (charge)*. If, however, its subsidiary function is to prevent charging it is termed an *address-complete signal (no-charge)*.

address-incomplete signal A *signal* (2) sent back from a terminal register to indicate that insufficient *address information* has been received to enable a call to be set up. The signal is transmitted following the receipt of an *end-of-pulsing signal* or because the time allowed for reception of the *address signal* has elapsed. It is normally used to initiate release of the traffic-carrying means involved in the call attempt.

address information At some point in a network, all the information (usually in the form of digits) that identifies the called party or defines the onward routing for a call. The digits sent by the caller are often changed as a result of *digit absorption* or *translation* as the call is progressively set up through the network.

address sequencing In *common-channel signalling*, a procedure for ensuring that address messages are processed in the right order when the order in which they are received is incorrect (for example, owing to an error-correcting operation in the course of their transmission over a signalling link).

address signal A *signal* (2) sent in the forward direction containing some or all of the *address information*.

adjacent-channel selectivity Of a radio or television receiver, a measure of the ability of the receiver to reject signals in the channels adjacent to the one to which it is tuned.

advice of change of extension accessibility A PABX facility enabling the supervisor or administration to arrange for calls to an extension to be diverted to the switchboard or a recorded announcement if the extension number has been changed or it is temporarily out of service.

advise-cost-and-duration call (US: *time-and-charge-request call*) A call made via an operator with a request for advice of the cost and duration after completion.

aerial See *antenna*.

aerial cable A cable supported on poles or similar overhead structures and used instead of *open-wire* lines. Aerial cables may incorporate a steel catenary wire moulded in the sheath to give a figure-of-eight section or may be lashed to a separate wire. The supporting wire is called a *messenger cable* in the US.

alarm An audible and/or visible signal used to draw the attention of maintenance personnel to the existence of some abnormal condition in the system.

alarm indication signal A special *signal* (2) used in digital transmission systems to advise downstream equipment that the performance of a *digital section* has become unacceptable and that it has been taken out of service. The signal replaces the normal traffic signal and serves both to prevent the activation of prompt alarms in following sections and to indicate the circuits that should be taken out of service.

alarm sender A device located in an unattended exchange and used to send alarm signals to the *parent exchange*.

Alford loop An *omnidirectional antenna* consisting of four insulated conductors, each half a wavelength long, arranged in the form of a horizontal square and symmetrically fed at two opposite corners by balanced transmission lines.

all-figure numbering or **all-number calling** (US) The use of telephone codes consisting of numbers only.

all-or-nothing relay A term standardised by the IEC and applied to two-position *relays* (e.g. the great majority of relays used in telecommunications) to distinguish them from measuring, protective and other types.

allotting In automatic switching, the process whereby the idle circuit or device that is to be used next is preselected.

almost differential quasi-ternary code A code developed in the USSR for converting binary information to a three-level line signal. The conversion rules are quite complex and are given in the CCITT Orange Book Vol III-3, p. 673.

alphabet (1) In general, all the letters used in a language, including those having distinguishing signs but excluding punctuation marks. (2) In telegraphy or data transmission, a table giving the correspondence between characters and the sets of *signal elements* used to represent them. Thus international telegraph alphabet no. 2 specifies the correspondence between each character (including functional commands) and the two-condition, five-unit code combination used to represent it.

alphabetic telegraphy *Telegraphy* applying to written information, texts and similar matter. Each character, or group of characters, in the message to be transmitted is represented by a *signal element*, or group of signal elements, according to a defined *telegraph code*.

alphabetic word See *word*.

alternate digit inversion In *pulse code modulation*, the practice of

6

complementing alternate digits of the *binary numbers* generated by the encoder. The technique is used, for example, with a *symmetrical binary code* to prevent low-level input signals or idle channels from giving rise to the generation of long strings of zeros, which could cause timing difficulties in intermediate regenerators. It should not be confused with *alternate mark inversion*, which could well be used subsequently to convert the binary signal generated by the encoder into a three-condition (pseudo-ternary) signal for transmission to line.

alternate mark inversion   A process used in digital transmission whereby alternate *marks* are normally constrained to be of equal amplitude but of opposite polarity, and *space* is of zero amplitude. The process may be used to convert a binary-coded PCM signal into a three-condition (or pseudo-ternary) signal having a negligible DC content. Such a signal is known as a *bipolar signal* in the US. A mark that has the same polarity as a preceding mark in an AMI signal gives rise to an AMI violation or *bipolar violation*. See also *modified AMI signal*.

alternate routing   See *alternative routing*.

alternating code   See *paired disparity codes*.

alternating current signalling   The use of alternating currents for the transfer of information relating to the set up, control and release of a call.

alternative code   See *paired disparity codes*.

alternative routing (US: *alternate routing*)   A method of *routing* whereby less desirable or less direct routes are selected at a switching point when congestion is encountered on the *primary route*.

amount of traffic carried   See *traffic volume*.

amplifier   A device that enables an input signal to control an independent source of power in such a way that the output bears some desired relationship to the input. Usually the intention is to increase the power of the signal without appreciably changing its *waveform*, i.e. without introducing a significant amount of *distortion*.

amplitude   The magnitude of a variable quantity, e.g. the voltage of a signal wave, at a given instant.

amplitude/amplitude distortion (US: *waveform amplitude distortion*)   That part of *non-linearity distortion* that manifests itself as an undesired variation of the ratio of the amplitude of the output signal to the amplitude of the input signal as the latter is varied over a range of values. In other words the *gain* (or *loss*) of the device changes with the instantaneous *signal level*. Because this form of distortion is accompanied by the production of *harmonics* and *intermodulation* products, the ratio concerned is that between a single-frequency sinusoidal input signal and the fundamental component of the resulting output signal.

amplitude change signalling   In telegraphy, an old term describing the use of different magnitudes of an alternating (or direct) current to represent the various signal conditions of a *telegraph code*.

amplitude characteristic   See *amplitude/frequency characteristic*.

amplitude distortion   See *amplitude/frequency distortion*.

amplitude/frequency characteristic   A graph showing how the absolute magnitude of the output signal of a system or device varies with changes in the frequency of the input signal, the amplitude of the latter being held constant at a value within the linear operating range of the device or system. By extension the term is often applied to a plot of *gain* or *attenuation* against frequency, although *gain/frequency characteristic* and *attenuation/frequency characteristic* are more precise terms. The term *frequency response* is often used loosely for any one of these characteristics.

amplitude/frequency distortion   *Distortion* caused by an undesired *amplitude/frequency characteristic*. Usually the desired characteristic is flat over the frequency range of interest so that, for example, the *gain* of an amplifier or the *attenuation* of a line is independent of the frequency of the input signal.

amplitude keying   The process in which the magnitude of a signal is varied between a set of discrete values.

amplitude modulation   The process in which the magnitude of a *carrier* wave is varied in accordance with a *modulating signal*.

amplitude quantised control   Of synchronisation in a *digital network*, a method in which the working range of *phase* errors between *clocks* is divided into a number of sub-ranges, any error falling in a given sub-range causing the control signal to assume an amplitude particular to that sub-range.

amplitude shift keying   See *amplitude keying*.

analogue control   Of synchronisation in a *digital network*, a method in which the control signal is varied over a continuous range of values (within the working limits) in accordance with the actual *phase* error between the *clocks*. If the control signal is directly proportioned to the phase error, the method is described as *linear analogue control*.

analogue error detection   See *data signal quality detection*.

analogue signal   A signal, some characteristic of which is varied continuously (i.e. smoothly as opposed to variation in steps) to convey information. In this definition it is the method of conveying the information that distinguishes an analogue signal from a digital one. It follows that a carrier can be amplitude modulated by a continuously varying quantity to produce an analogue signal, or it may be amplitude modulated in accordance with digital data (i.e. keyed) to produce a *digital signal*. The latter term is something of a misnomer, and *digitally modulated signal* would be more meaningful. However, usage of the short form is very widespread.

analogue signalling The transmission of *signals* (2) over an analogue transmission *channel*. The signals may be digital in form, i.e. they may consist of pulses of alternating current, but the signalling method is nevertheless described as analogue to distinguish it from true *digital signalling*, in which a *data link* is employed.

analogue switching Switching in which the inlets and outlets are analogue transmission *channels*.

analogue telegraphy Old term applied to forms of *telegraphy* such as facsimile which generally employed *analogue signals* for the transmission of the material.

analogue-to-digital converter A device that converts an input *analogue signal* into a *digital signal* conveying essentially the same information. Sometimes called a *digitiser*.

analysis meters Overflow meters used in connection with teletraffic studies of a switching system or network.

AND gate A *logic element* having one output and two or more inputs, and having the property that the output will stand at its defined logic 1-state if, and only if, all the inputs stand at their defined logic 1-states. See also *logic convention*.

anechoic chamber A room in which the walls, ceiling and floor are lined with sound-absorbing material and so constructed that virtually no reflections of sound waves occur.

angle modulation *Modulation* in which the electrical angle of a carrier wave is the characteristic that is varied by the modulating signal. The term thus embraces both *phase modulation* and *frequency modulation*.

angular aperture Of a reflecting surface of an antenna, the solid angle subtended at the focus by the periphery of the aperture of the reflecting surface.

anisochronous signal A *digital signal* in which the time interval separating any two signal *transitions* is not necessarily related to the interval separating any other two transitions.

anisochronous transmission A form of *digital transmission* in which there is always an integral number of *unit intervals* between any two significant instants of a given block or character, but for which there is not necessarily the same relationship between two significant instants located in different blocks or characters. Also known as *non-synchronous*

9

transmission.

anomalistic period   Of a *communication satellite*, the interval of time between two consecutive passages of the satellite through its *apogee*.

anomalous propagation   The propagation of radio waves as a result of abnormal conditions in the earth's atmosphere; see for example *tropospheric duct*.

answer-back code   A unique series of characters allocated to a particular telegraph or data terminal and used as a response to a *who-are-you signal*.

answer signal   A *signal* (2) sent in the backward direction when a call is answered. Such a signal may also initiate, or inhibit, call *charging*. If a specific answer signal capable of inhibiting charging does not exist in a system, charging can be prevented by omitting the backward signal when the call is answered.

antenna   The generic term for that part of a radio system that is used to radiate *radio waves* into free space and/or to abstract energy from incoming radio waves. The term *aerial* is no longer used for this concept in international vocabularies. (*Note* For convenience many of the definitions of the various types of antenna are written in terms of their transmitting properties, but it should be understood that they apply equally to their receiving characteristics unless otherwise stated.)

antenna amplifier   An *amplifier* specially designed to boost the signal(s) received from an antenna. Such an amplifier should have a low input noise figure and be connected close to the antenna in order to obtain the best possible *signal-to-noise ratio*.

antenna array   An assembly of *radiating elements* spaced and fed in such a way that the antenna has some desired directional characteristic.

antenna bay   One of the parts of an antenna array fed by a single branch of the main feeder.

anti-clockwise polarisation   See *counter-clockwise polarised wave*.

anti-induction network   A network used with early telegraph circuits to reduce *crosstalk* between the circuits.

anti-node   Of a *standing wave*, a point, line or the surface at which some specified variable (e.g. voltage or current) has its maximum value.

anti-resonance   See *parallel resonance*.

anti-resonant circuit   See *rejector circuit*.

aperiodic antenna   An *antenna* designed to operate over an extensive frequency range, and therefore having characteristics that are substantially independent of frequency. Also termed *non-resonant antenna*.

aperture   (1) Of a facsimile transmitter, a hole through which light passes and which effectively determines the dimensions of the *scanning spot* (1). (2) Of a facsimile receiver, a hole whose image is focused on the recording medium. Light varying in intensity in accordance with the received signal is passed through the opening to affect the photosensitive medium. (3) Of an antenna, a surface at or near the antenna on which assumptions regarding *field strength* can be made in order to calculate its expected *radiation pattern*. For a *directional antenna* the aperture is typically that part of a plane surface normal to the direction of maximum radiation through which the majority of the radiation passes. (4) The open end (or mouth) of a *horn* antenna or similar device. (5) The dimensions of a mouth, *parabolic reflector* or similar item, or of an *antenna array*.

aperture antenna A *directional antenna* having a *directivity pattern* determined by the dimensions of a *horn, lens* or similar device.

aperture distortion In *facsimile* or television, distortion caused by the finite size of the *scanning spot* and resulting in lack of sharpness and loss of detail. *Figure A.1* shows how the *rise time*

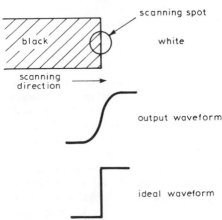

Figure A.1   Aperture distortion

of the waveform generated by scanning across a black-to-white transition is degraded by the size of the scanning spot.

aperture illumination The distribution of the electromagnetic field across the relevant part of an *aperture antenna*, e.g. a *parabolic reflector*.

aperture illumination diagram A graphical representation of the distribution of the electromagnetic field over the *aperture* of an *antenna*.

aperture illumination efficiency Of an *antenna* with a specified planar *aperture* (3), a measure of the efficiency of illumination given by the ratio of the actual antenna gain to the gain that would be obtained if the *aperture illumination* were perfectly uniform.

aperture illumination function A mathematical expression describing a component of the electromagnetic field at each point on the *aperture* (3) of an *antenna* in terms of the coordinates of the point.

apogee That point in the elliptical orbit of a *communication satellite* at which it is at its maximum distance from the centre of the earth. The altitude of the apogee is quoted with reference to a specified hypothetical surface serving to represent the surface of the earth.

Appleton layer See *F layer*.

arc of visibility An arc formed by the points in space at which a *geostationary satellite* could be seen, at a specified minimum angle of elevation above the horizontal, by all the *earth stations* in the network.

area code (US) See *trunk code*.

arithmetic logic unit A general-purpose logic unit that can be externally controlled to perform various arithmetical and other functions.

array, array antenna See *antenna array*.

articulation In telephony, a measure of the success with which sounds can be transmitted over a given assembly of apparatus, usually expressed as the fraction or percentage of the sounds correctly recognised by the listener. The term is appropriately qualified to include the type of sounds transmitted, i.e. word articulation, *logatom* articulation or sound articulation. The latter term relates to the number of vowel or consonant sounds recognised in a random sequence of logatoms.

articulation reference equivalent Of a telephone system, a figure obtained by comparing the *transmission performance* of the system with that of the CCITT's standard at a sound *articulation* of 80 per cent. Tests are made alternately on each system, the attenuation between the sending and receiving ends being adjusted until the articulation falls to 80 per cent in each case. If A_1 and A_2 are the values of attenuation in the system under test and the SRAEN respectively, then by definition the articulation reference equivalent is given by $(A_2 - A_1)$.

artificial antenna A device used for testing purposes and consisting of a non-radiating network having the impedance characteristic of a real antenna over a specified frequency range. Also known as *dummy antenna*.

artificial black [white] signal In *facsimile*, a signal generated locally for testing purposes and corresponding in all respects to a normally received black [white] signal.

artificial dielectric A medium of low effective permittivity and density containing a three-dimensional arrangement of *scattering* elements and behaving as a sensibly uniform dielectric to *radio waves*.

artificial ear A device used to measure the performance of earphones and consisting essentially of a microphone in an enclosure which simulates the acoustic impedance presented by the average human ear.

artificial earth See *counterpoise*.

artificial line A network having essentially the same electrical characteristics as a line over a specified range of frequencies. Also known as a *line simulator*.

artificial mouth A device used to test telephone transmitters and consisting of an electroacoustic transducer capable of producing a sound field resembling that produced by an average human talker.

artificial traffic *Traffic* generated by automatic means and used to test the performance of *exchanges* etc. Also known as *test traffic*.

aspect ratio In *facsimile* or television, the ratio of the width to the height of a picture, document or *scanning field*.

assigned fill See *fill*.

assistance call A call made with the help of an operator, even though the caller could have dialled the call personally.

assistance code The digits that have to be dialled to obtain access to an operator.

assistance traffic Calls requiring the intervention of an operator.

associated signalling In *common-channel signalling*, that method of operation in which signals relating to the traffic carried by a group of circuits between two exchanges are transmitted over a *signalling link* terminating in those exchanges.

asymmetric-sideband transmission See *vestigial-sideband transmission*.

asynchronous network A *digital network* in which the *clocks* need not be synchronous or *mesochronous* for satisfactory operation.

atmospheric absorption In radio-wave propagation, loss of energy suffered by a wave as a result of dissipation in the atmosphere.

atmospheric duct See *tropospheric duct*.

atmospherics (US: *static*) Radio-frequency *interference* caused by natural electric discharges occurring below the *ionosphere*.

attenuation The general term for a decrease in the magnitude of a signal resulting from its transmission through equipment, lines

13

or other transmission paths. Numerically attenuation may be expressed as the scalar ratio of the received power to the transmitted power. Usually, however, it is expressed as ten times the logarithm of that ratio — see *decibel*.

attenuation coefficient or **attenuation constant** (US) The coefficient that determines the decrease of a field quantity (such as the voltage) of a wave propagating along a transmission path. It is usually expressed in *nepers* per unit length, and it represents the real part of the *propagation coefficient*.

attenuation distortion See *amplitude/frequency distortion*.

attenuation equaliser A network having an *attenuation* varying with frequency in such a way (e.g. inversely) that it can be used to correct *amplitude/frequency distortion* caused, for example, by a preceding cable transmission path.

attenuation plan See *transmission plan*.

attitude-stabilised satellite An artificial satellite whose orientation with respect to the earth is kept substantially constant by a gyroscopic system located on board.

audio Pertaining to the range of frequencies in which acoustic waves are audible to the human ear.

audio frequency Any frequency corresponding to that of a sound wave audible to the average human ear. Usually the range is considered to extend from about 15 Hz to around 20 000 Hz.

aural transmitter (US) The equipment used to transmit the sound signal from a television broadcasting station.

aurora Sporadic luminous ionisation in the upper atmosphere near the earth's magnetic poles caused by particles from the sun interacting with the earth's magnetic field. The occurrence of aurora can severely affect the propagation of radio waves directed through the auroral regions, the effects being particularly acute in the VHF and UHF bands.

auto-manual exchange A set of manual switchboards serving a group of automatic exchanges and usually located in one of them. The switchboards provide operator assistance to the subscribers served by the automatic exchanges and handle any calls that have to be completed manually.

auto-switching centre A partial *tandem exchange*.

autodialler (US) A device that automatically dials one of a set of previously recorded telephone numbers when the relevant button is pushed.

autofax A *facsimile* system whereby material may be stored on tape and later automatically transmitted over the PSTN to the addressees. The system makes it possible for a number of documents to be scanned and stored on tape during the day when the network is busy and tariffs are high, the documents being automatically transmitted to the addressees during the night when network loading and tariffs are low.

automatic A qualifying term indicating a process, system or device that is capable, under specified conditions, of functioning without the intervention of a human operator.

automatic alarm call A service whereby a subscriber or PBX extension user can arrange for a call giving an appropriate announcement to be made automatically to his number at any time in the following 24-hour period. Also known as *automatic wake-up service*.

automatic call back See *camp on with recall*.

automatic call distribution An arrangement whereby calls incoming to a manual switchboard are automatically presented in cyclic order of arrival to the next free (in service) answering position.

automatic error correction That property of a transmission system which enables a certain proportion of errors in the received signal to be detected and automatically corrected.

automatic frequency control In a superheterodyne receiver, a system designed to keep the receiver in tune with a wanted transmission. Mis-tuning results in the production of a control voltage, which is used to adjust the frequency of the *local oscillator* so as to minimise the tuning error.

automatic gain control In a receiver, a system whereby the gain of the RF and IF stages is automatically adjusted with the object of minimising changes in the level of the output signal with changes in the level of the received signal. Also known as *automatic volume control*.

automatic identified outward dialling A facility used with *automatic message accounting* whereby the identity of a calling station is automatically forwarded from a PBX over a separate data link.

automatic message accounting (US) A system whereby information relating to calls is automatically collected, recorded and processed for billing purposes. The term is appropriately qualified to indicate the office at which the process is carried out, viz *central automatic message accounting* (CAMA) or *local automatic message accounting* (LAMA).

automatic number analysis The process of comparing a dialled number with a caller's *class of service* so that appropriate action can be taken, e.g. NU tone returned or the call diverted to an operator.

automatic number identification A facility whereby the *directory number* or *equipment number* of a calling station is obtained automatically, for use in message accounting.

automatic number sender   See *callmaker*.

automatic numbering transmitter   A telegraph transmitter that can automatically transmit a serial number before each message.

automatic retransmission   In telegraphy, a method of operation in which received signals are automatically recorded and retransmitted after a short interval.

automatic sequential connection   A facility provided by some data networks whereby a single terminal may be automatically connected in a predetermined sequence to the DTEs at a number of specified addresses.

automatic supervision   A PABX facility whereby the calls in a queue, those held by the operator and those extended by the operator to an extension that has not answered, are automatically brought to the operator's attention at the end of a specified time interval, for example every 30 seconds.

automatic switch to night service   A PABX feature whereby the switchover to night service occurs automatically at any time when there is no operator's instrument plugged in to the switchboard. Sometimes called *operator not working*.

automatic switching system or **automatic system**   A system in which all the operations required to set up, supervise and release connections required for calls are performed automatically in response to signals from a calling device.

automatic ticketing   The facility whereby information relating to calls is automatically recorded for billing purposes.

automatic transmitter   Telegraph apparatus that forms signals automatically from a storage device, usually a perforated tape.

automatic transmitter with controlled tape-feed mechanism   An *automatic transmitter* in which the movement of the tape is controlled by pulses from a synchronising device so that it can form part of a *time-division multiplex* system.

automatic volume control   See *automatic gain control*.

automatic wake-up service   See *automatic alarm call*.

auxiliary route   A route other than a *basic route*.

availability (US: *accessibility*)   Of a switching network, a statement of the number of outlets (trunks) of a desired group to which an inlet has access via the network, i.e. the number of outlets that can be tested for the *busy* or *idle* condition. If this number is unaffected by the state of the network and its other sources, *constant availability* is said to exist. In all other cases the term *variable availability* is used. If any free inlet can gain access to any outlet regardless of the state of the system, *full availability* is said to be provided. It will be seen that this is equivalent to constant availability with access to all the outlets of the desired group. *Limited availability* describes an arrangement in which

16

only some of the outlets of the group can be reached from an inlet.

available line   In *facsimile*, that part of a *scanning line* specifically occupied by *picture elements*. Sometimes known as *active line*.

avalanche multiplication   In a *photodiode*, the increase in photo-current that occurs when the diode is operated at a bias approaching its breakdown voltage. In this condition carriers created by absorbed *photons* gain sufficient energy as they travel through the high-electric-field region of the junction for them to create additional electron-hole pairs when they collide with substrate atoms. This mechanism can increase the photo-current by a factor of 100 relative to the current at low bias voltage, when no multiplication takes place.

avalanche noise   In a *photodiode*, gain-dependent noise produced by the random nature of the *avalanche multiplication* process. The effect of this process is to increase the noise current due to *quantum noise* by a factor F_i whose value depends on the diode material, its structure and the avalanche multiplication factor M. For a typical silicon diode F_i is approximately equal to $M^{0.4}$.

avalanche photodiode   A *photodiode* designed to make use of *avalanche multiplication* and consisting essentially of a PN junction diode having a high breakdown voltage and a structure that minimises the excess noise factor due to the avalanche effect. The performance of an avalanche photodiode can be improved in respect of high-frequency *quantum efficiency* by the use of a more complex structure. See *reach-through photodiode*.

axial ratio   Of a wave having *elliptical polarisation*, the ratio of the major axis to the minor axis of the ellipse described by the tip of the *electric field vector*. Also known as *ellipticity ratio*.

B

B-wire connector   A small cylindrical device that may be slipped over the cut ends of two wires and crimped to establish a reliable connection between them. The inner part, containing sharp tangs to pierce the conductor insulation, is enclosed in a brass sleeve, which is compressed by the crimping tool to force the tangs into contact with the conductor. The completed joint is enclosed in a plastic sleeve.

babble   The total *crosstalk* from a number of interfering sources.

babyphone   A PABX facility whereby calls can be made to an extension that is in the off-hook condition, to check, for example, whether a baby is crying.

back scatter A radio wave produced as a result of *scattering*, and propagating in a direction approximately the reverse of that of the incident wave.

back wave (US) The wave emitted by a radio telegraph transmitter during the spacing portions of a character and between characters. Also called a *spacing wave*.

backfire antenna An antenna consisting of a *fed element* together with a *reflector* and possibly one or more *directors* disposed in front of a large reflecting surface so that the whole acts as an open-ended resonator. Radiation takes place from the open end of the resonator in a direction opposite to that of the wave generated by the fed element and its reflector. Owing to the resonant effect, this arrangement gives more gain than would be obtained by the use of the fed and parasitic elements only.

backward busying A facility for automatically busying the far end of an *incoming* trunk when the busy condition is applied to its incoming end or when it is faulty.

backward clearing The progressive release of the circuits and devices used for a call, starting at the remote end of the connection relative to the direction of call set-up.

backward holding In automatic switching, the process of keeping one or more switches in the operated position by applying a condition to the hold wire of subsequent switching equipment.

backward lobe Of an antenna, a radiation lobe whose direction is sensibly opposite that of the *main lobe*.

backward round-the-world echo See *round-the-world echo*.

backward set-up A method of operation in which a multi-link connection is established on a link-by-link basis in the direction from the called party to the calling party, once signalling activities have established that the call can mature (e.g. the number called is that of a non-barred subscriber whose equipment is free). Sometimes called *backward retrospective set-up*. In some versions of the process the relevant circuits are selected and reserved substantially in parallel with the signalling of the *address information*, but are not interconnected until it has been established that the call can mature.

backward signal A *signal* (2) sent in the direction from the called party to the calling party.

balance return loss (US: *hybrid balance*) A measure of the effectiveness with which a *balancing network* simulates the impedance of the *two-wire circuit* at a *hybrid coil*. More generally, a measure of the degree of balance between two impedances connected to two conjugate sides of a hybrid set, network or junction. Balance return loss is usually expressed in *decibels* and its value is given by the expression

$$20 \log_{10}(Z_B + Z_L)/(Z_B - Z_L)$$

where Z_B is the impedance of the balancing network and Z_L that of the line.

balanced codes General class of *codes* (1) having the property that signals produced in accordance with them have a zero DC content and contain relatively little low-frequency energy.

balanced-disparity code See *NBMB balanced disparity coding*.

balanced mixer A microwave *mixer* (1) constructed from a *hybrid junction* so that the effect of *local oscillator* noise is minimised.

balanced modulator A form of amplitude modulator so constructed that the *carrier* is balanced out and the output contains the *sidebands* only.

balanced transmission line A transmission line formed of two similar conductors having the same resistance per unit length and equal impedances to earth.

balancing network A network constructed from lumped circuit elements and designed to simulate the impedance of a uniform line over a specified frequency range.

balun A term derived from balanced-to-unbalanced transformer, usually describing a *passive* device with *distributed constants*, used for example to couple a balanced antenna to an unbalanced (coaxial) transmission line.

band A range of frequencies between specified limits. The classification adopted internationally is based on numbered bands each extending from 0.3×10^N Hz to 3×10^N Hz, where N is the band number as shown in *Table B.1*.

Table B.1

Band number	Frequency limits (upper included, lower excluded)	Name and abbreviation, where applicable
0	0.3 to 3 Hz	
1	3 to 30 Hz	
2	30 to 300 Hz	
3	300 to 3000 Hz	
4	3 to 30 kHz	Very low frequency (VLF)
5	30 to 300 kHz	Low frequency (LF)
6	300 to 3000 kHz	Medium frequency (MF)
7	3 to 30 MHz	High frequency (HF)
8	30 to 300 MHz	Very high frequency (VHF)
9	300 to 3000 MHz	Ultra high frequency (UHF)
10	3 to 30 GHz	Super high frequency (SHF)
11	30 to 300 GHz	Extra high frequency (EHF)
12	300 to 3000 GHz	

band number In *common-channel signalling*, that part of the address label used for routing the signal message at message transfer points and sometimes to identify the circuit group containing the traffic circuit to which the signalling information relates.

band rejection filter or **bandstop filter** A filter having the inverse characteristic to that of a *bandpass filter*.

bandpass Qualifying term applied to amplifiers and other networks having a response characteristic that is substantially uniform across a defined frequency range.

bandpass filter A selective network offering little *attenuation* to signals in a defined range of frequencies known as the *pass band*, but attenuating signals outside this band.

bandwidth (1) Of a defined *band*, the difference between the limiting frequencies. (2) Of a device or system, the range of frequencies within which the performance with respect to some specified characteristic falls within given limits. For an *amplifier*, for example, the bandwidth is often taken as the range over which its gain is within 3 *decibels* of its maximum value. (3) Of a signal wave, the range of frequencies outside which some characteristic of the wave is everywhere less than a given fraction of its value at a reference frequency. See also *effective bandwidth* and *Nyquist bandwidth*.

bandwidth compression In television transmission, a technique enabling the *bandwidth* normally required for the transmission of a picture of given quality to be reduced by not transmitting redundant information. In a scene in which there is relatively little movement, for example, it is possible to transmit only information relating to those parts of the scene that differ from the previous frame.

bank Of a *selector*, an assembly of fixed contacts over which wipers may move.

bank-and-wiper switch (US) See *selector*.

barred code One or more digits relating to a service or an exchange to which some subscribers are not given automatic access.

barred trunk service A restricted service in which the facility for originating trunk calls is excluded.

barretter A resistor having a high temperature coefficient of resistance and generally consisting of a wire enclosed in a gas-filled envelope.

barrier code (US) A prefix digit used to prevent misdialled local calls from resulting in an extra charge to the subscriber.

barrier frequency See *cut-off frequency* (2).

base station A radio station in the mobile service providing communication with mobile stations and possibly other base stations.

baseband That band of frequencies which contains the signal(s) used to modulate a *carrier* immediately prior to its transmission by line or radio. For example, a *supergroup* or a band of frequencies occupied by a television signal.

basic group In carrier telephony, twelve channels assembled in the frequency band 60−108 kHz.

basic mastergroup In carrier telephony, five supergroups assembled in the frequency band 812−2044 kHz.

basic network (1) The minimal network required between two exchanges to enable traffic to be carried within the specified *grade of service* and *transmission performance* limits. (2) In the US the term is used to describe an electric network designed to simulate the iterative impedance of a line at a given termination, i.e. a *matched termination*.

basic noise *Noise* present in a transmission system in the absence of any signal.

basic numbering-plan area (US) See *national numbering-plan area*.

basic path attenuator See *path attenuation*.

basic route A route forming part of a *basic network* (1).

basic supergroup In carrier telephony, five groups occupying the frequency band 312−552 kHz. The groups constitute the lower *sidebands* of real or virtual *carriers* having frequencies of 420, 468, 516, 564 and 612 kHz.

battery Strictly, two or more primary or secondary cells connected together. Now commonly used to describe a single cell, however.

battery testing In automatic switching, the process of checking whether the test wire of a circuit has a potential different from *earth* (usually that of the exchange battery), the presence of such a potential having a designated significance, usually 'free'.

batwing antenna An antenna consisting of a conducting surface resembling the unfolded wings of a bat and containing an axial slot one wavelength long.

baud The unit of *modulation* rate in telegraphy and data transmission, corresponding to a *unit interval* having a duration of one second.

beam Of a *directional antenna* system, the radiation in a *lobe* (usually the major lobe), or the region in space through which the radiation passes.

beam axis The direction of maximum radiation in a *lobe*.

beam steering The technique whereby the direction of the major *lobe* of a *directional antenna* system can be altered, usually by changing the relative phases of the currents fed to the individual units of the system.

beam width The angular width of a *beam* within which the radiation exceeds some specified fraction of the maximum value, for example the half-power beam width.

bearer A unidirectional transmission path, i.e. a *channel*. The term is normally used in the context of data transmission.

beat frequency oscillator In *superheterodyne reception*, an adjustable-frequency *oscillator* the output of which can be mixed with that of the final intermediate-frequency amplifier to produce an *audio-frequency* beat when the receiver is tuned to an unmodulated signal.

beating The phenomenon in which two or more periodic quantities having slightly different frequencies produce a resultant having periodic variations in amplitude.

beaver-tail antenna A *beam* antenna arranged so that the (horizontal) width of the beam is significantly greater than its vertical dimension.

beep tone See *intrusion tone*.

bel The basic unit of a logarithmic scale used for expressing ratios of powers. The bel was invented by American telephone engineers in the 1920s and was named after Sir Alexander Graham Bell, the father of the telephone. Two powers P_1 and P_2 are related by N bels when $\log_{10} (P_1/P_2) = N$. The number of bels is thus simply the common logarithm of the power ratio. It follows that an amplifier having a power gain of 100 000 can be said to have a gain of 5 bels. The unit is inconveniently large and its tenth part, the *decibel*, is always used in practice. A more extensive treatment of logarithmic units is therefore given under that reference. See also *transmission units*.

bellboy (US) See *radiopaging*.

Bellini-Tosi antenna A receiving antenna the *directivity* of which can be adjusted in the horizontal plane. It consists of two independent crossed vertical loops at right angles to one another and having their ends connected to the field coils of a radio *goniometer*. The output coil can be rotated between the field coils to turn the directivity pattern of the antenna. This form of antenna is very effective in the VLF and LF bands.

Beverage antenna A *directional antenna* consisting of a horizontal conductor connected to the receiver at one end and to *earth* via its characteristic impedance at the other end. Also known as a *wave antenna*. The conductor is several wavelengths long and is suspended above the ground at a height that is small compared with the wavelength. The antenna has maximum *directivity* in the direction of its length.

bias distortion In two-condition telegraphy, distortion such that the marking conditions are either longer or shorter than the corresponding spacing conditions. Bias distortion is known as *positive* if the marking pulses are lengthened with respect to the ideal value.

biased automatic gain control See *delayed automatic gain control*.

biased telephone ringer A telephone bell the clapper of which is biased to one side (electrically or mechanically) so that it will operate on alternating current or on DC pulses of one polarity, but not on pulses having the opposite polarity.

bid An attempt to seize a *circuit* in a *traffic* group. The number of bids per circuit per hour is thus a measure of the traffic pressure on a route.

biconical antenna An *antenna* formed of two opposed conducting cones having a common axis and their vertices adjacent; see

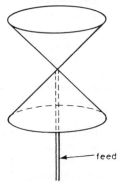

Figure B.1　Biconical antenna

Figure B.1. It is fed at the vertices by *coaxial cable* or *waveguide* and has a circular *radiation pattern* in the plane perpendicular to the axis.

bidirectional A qualifying term indicating that transmission can occur in two directions although the transmission parameters such as *bandwidth* or bit rate may not be the same in both directions.

bilateral control Between two *synchronisation nodes* in a digital network, a method of operation whereby the frequency of the *clock* at each node is influenced by timing information derived from the clock at the other node (compare with *unilateral control*).

binary character Either of two symbols, letters, figures or other characters forming a set of two characters.

binary code A *code* (1) in which each element can assume either of two possible states. Information is thus represented only by *binary characters*.

binary-coded decimal Any system for representing each of the decimal numbers 1 to 9 by means of a unique sequence of *binary digits*. In the simplest BCD code each figure is represented by four digits giving the equivalent *binary numeral*. Thus 9 becomes 1001, 2 becomes 0010 and 38 becomes 0011 1000.

binary counter A device giving one output pulse for each successive pair of input pulses. Also known as a *binary divider*.

binary digit One of two digits forming a set. Usually one of the two digits 0 and 1 used in the *binary numeration system*.

binary divider See *binary counter*.

binary notation A widely used term for the method of representing numbers described under *binary numeration system*. More generally, any system of notation using two symbols only.

binary number A term used loosely instead of *binary numeral*.

binary number code A *code* (1) in which successive values of a quantity are represented by *binary numerals* taken in order. Such a code may be used to represent the ascending quantised levels of samples in *pulse code modulation*; see also *symmetrical binary code*.

binary numeral A representation of a number according to the *binary numeration system*. For example, the binary numeral 101 is equivalent to the Roman numeral V, and both numerals represent the number of fingers on one hand.

binary numeration system (US: *binary number system*) A system of positional notation using the radix 2 and the digits 0 and 1 to represent numerals. In this system each position in the numeral, reading from right to left, represents an ascending power of the radix 2, i.e. 1, 2, 4, 8, etc. The values of the digit positions in which a 1 appears are added to obtain the number represented. Thus the binary numerals 010, 101 and 10101 are equivalent to the decimal numerals 2, 5 and 21 respectively.

binary serial signalling rate The reciprocal of the duration of a signalling element (in seconds), expressed in bits per second.

bipolar code See *alternate mark inversion*.

bipolar coding with zero extraction An extension of the *alternate mark inversion* principle in which strings of zeros are replaced by code groups designed to improve the timing content of the signal. An example of a code formed according to this principle is B6ZS, in which any sequence of six zeros is represented by a code group readily recognised at the receiver because it contains AMI violations.

bipolar signal See *alternate mark inversion*.

bipolar violation See *alternate mark inversion*.

bistable element The generic term for a *logic element* that can store one *bit* of information. Also known as a *toggle*. The element can be set to store the 1-state and can be reset to store the logic 0-state. See also *flip-flop*.

bit An abbreviation for *binary digit*, i.e. one of the two possible members of a binary set. (*Note*   The term should not be used as the unit of selective information in a binary scale, since the *shannon* has been adopted for this concept. Such usage does persist, however.)

bit sequence independence   A term applied to a *digital path* or *digital section* to indicate that it can transmit any sequence of bits at its specified bit rate.

bit stealing (US)   See *speech digit signalling*.

biternary coding   The conversion of a unipolar binary signal into a three-level pseudo-ternary signal by digital integration, i.e. by taking pairs of symbols in succession and adding their analogue values. The same result can be closely approached by passing the signal through a suitable filter whose *rise time* is greater than one bit period. Hence biternary coding is a digital equivalent of a form of *partial response coding*.

black-and-white reception   Deliberate enhancement of the contrast in facsimile reception to yield a black-and-white copy.

black recording or transmission   (1) In an amplitude-modulated facsimile system, recording or transmission in which the maximum values of signal amplitude correspond with the darkest areas of the picture. (2) In a frequency-modulated facsimile system, recording or transmission in which the lower signal frequencies correspond with the darkest areas of the picture.

black signal   In *facsimile*, the signal produced by scanning the darkest areas of the original document.

blanketing area   The area in the vicinity of a powerful transmitter in which the *field strength* is so strong that it interferes with normal reception over a wide band of frequencies.

blanketing frequency   In ionospheric propagation, for a given radiated power the frequency below which abnormal ionisation in one layer (e.g. the *E layer*) prevents any appreciable reflection from a higher layer (e.g. one of the *F layers*).

bleeper   See *radiopaging*.

block   (1) In telegraphy and data transmission, a group of *digits* transmitted and received as an entity and usually encoded for the purpose of *error control*. (2) In *common-channel signalling*, a fixed number of *signal units* transmitted and received as an entity in a *synchronous system*. (3) As a verb, to prevent traffic-carrying means from being used, by busying them.

block codes   In data transmission, *error control* codes in which k *parity bits* check only the n *information bits* in an $(n + k)$ bit *block*. Usually the information bits are transmitted first. The $(n + k)$ bit block is also known as a *code word*, and each word can be independently decoded. Block codes are very suitable for use in error detection and retransmission systems since data is checked, deleted and retransmitted in blocks.

block signal   In data transmission, a group of *signal elements* representing a *block* (1).

blocking   In a switching system, the condition in which the setting up of a call is impossible because all the *outgoing trunks* of the required group are busy or because no path can be established through the system to an idle trunk of the required group. The action taken when blocking occurs depends on system design; see *loss system* and *delay system*.

blocking ratio   See *call congestion ratio*.

blocking signal   A *signal* (2) transmitted to busy-out a circuit at its distant end. Also termed *test busy signal*. The signal may be continuous, in which case its cessation indicates that the circuit is again available for use. Alternatively an *unblocking signal* has to be sent for this purpose.

Bode equaliser   A variable-attenuation equaliser so designed that the *equalisation* introduced at all frequencies in its range can be varied in the same proportion by a single control.

bolometer   An electrothermal instrument that may be used to measure radiant power, for example in a *waveguide*. The primary detector is a temperature-sensitive resistor such as a *thermistor*, and the instrument depends for its operation on a comparison of the rise in temperature caused by an unknown amount of radiant energy with that caused by a measured amount of direct-current or audio-frequency energy.

bond   A low-resistance electrical connection between conducting structures such as racks and metal cable sheaths, made in order to keep them at the same potential, usually that of the *earth*.

boresight   A term used in connection with a highly directional *antenna* to describe the axis along which maximum radiation or pick-up should occur. Such an axis determined from design considerations or established by optical means is called a *reference boresight*. An axis determined by actual electrical measurements is termed an *electrical boresight*. The angular difference between these directions is known as the *boresight error*.

Bose-Chaudhuri codes   *Error detecting codes* in which blocks of $2^m - 1$ bits are formed in such a way that k errors can be corrected by the inclusion of no more than *mk parity bits*. Typically such a code, consisting of 31-digit blocks each containing 21 message digits and 10 check digits, would be capable of detecting quadruple errors or of correcting double errors.

bothway A qualifying term applied to traffic or circuits to indicate that call set-ups can occur in both directions.

bounce An effect occurring in the AC transmission of television signals whereby abrupt changes in the DC component of the input video signal cause damped oscillatory changes in mean signal level. The term is also applied to the resulting changes in picture brightness.

bouncing busy hour (US) The *busy hour* for any single day which, taken over a number of days, is normally not time-consistent.

branch feeder See *feeder* (1).

branch jack A *jack* giving access to a circuit without interrupting it.

break-before-make See *changeover contact unit*.

break contact unit Of a *relay*, two contact members arranged so that operation of the relay breaks the connection between them.

break jack A *jack* having auxiliary contacts through which a circuit may normally be connected. Insertion of a plug breaks the circuit and establishes connections between the contacts of the plug and one side of the circuit.

break pulse A pulse generated by opening and then closing a circuit.

breakdown (after intrusion) The act of disconnecting an existing call by forced release so that an incoming call, which has been offered and accepted, can be connected.

Brewster angle The angle of incidence at the surface of a dielectric for which a wave polarised in the plane of incidence is transmitted without reflection. If the surface in question consists of an ionospheric layer (which is an imperfect dielectric), the *pseudo-Brewster* angle is that at which the *reflection coefficient* has its minimum value.

bridge duplex circuit Old telegraph circuit in which the Wheatstone bridge principle was used to prevent the receiver at either end from being affected by the currents transmitted from the same end.

bridging The connection of a device or circuit in parallel with a transmission line. Usually the bridging circuit has a relatively high input impedance so that it has an insignificant effect on the signals in the transmission line.

bridging amplifier In a CATV type system, an amplifier with a high input impedance which can be connected across a trunk *feeder* (1) to provide a *distribution point* (2) or across a branch feeder to energise a spur feeder.

bridle wire (US) Designation given to the insulated wire used on an *open-wire* line to connect pole-mounted apparatus to the line conductors.

broadband   Qualifying term not amenable to precise definition, but implying operation over a band of frequencies regarded as wide in a given context; see below.

broadband antenna   A resonant *antenna* designed to function satisfactorily over a wide band of frequencies, e.g. the larger part of the VHF band.

broadband interference   A disturbance having a spectral energy distribution such that the response of the measuring instrument does not vary significantly over a range of frequencies equivalent to a specified number of receiver bandwidths.

broadcast relay system   Term used in the UK for systems distributing sound and television programs over a cable network to subscribers.

broadcast videography, broadcast videotex   See *teletext*.

broadside array   A *linear array* or *planar array* having a direction of maximum radiation at right angles to the line or plane of the array.

broker's call   See *refer back*.

buffer   The generic term for a device included in a circuit to provide isolation and/or to prevent some undesired reaction between the devices or circuits it couples together.

buffer amplifier   An *amplifier* used primarily to prevent changes of impedance in the circuit connected to its output from affecting the circuit connected to its input.

buffer store   An intermediate *store* normally used to hold data for a relatively short period.

buffering   See *fibre buffer*.

bug key   A semi-automatic *Morse key* in which movement of an arm to one side produces correctly spaced dots and movement to the other side produces a single dash.

build-up time   See *rise time*.

bunched frame alignment signal   In *pulse code modulation*, a *frame alignment signal* in which the signal elements occupy a group of consecutive digit time slots, as in the standard 30-channel system.

bundle   (1) A group of pairs in a cable. (2) A number of *optical fibres* with or without individual coatings but grouped together in a single enclosure. A bundle in which the coordinates of each fibre are the same at the two ends of the bundle is known as an *aligned bundle* or a *coherent bundle*. An incoherent bundle is sometimes called a *light conduit* or *light guide*.

buried cable   Designation for local line cables directly buried in the ground, as opposed to *underground cable*.

Burrus diode   A type of *light-emitting diode* specially developed for single fibre applications in *optical fibre* communication and named after its inventor. The diode features low thermal resistance, high current density, and an etched hole to locate the end of the optical fibre close to the primary light-emitting area in order to minimise coupling losses.

burst   In a TDMA system, a discrete group of digits transmitted by a single *earth station*. See *reference burst* and *standard burst*.

burst acquisition   In a TDMA system, the procedure whereby the equipment at an *earth station* is synchronised with an incoming *reference burst* so that the station can commence transmission of its own *standard bursts* without interfering with the bursts from other stations.

burst interference or **burst noise**   In data transmission, *interference* or *noise* of sufficient amplitude and duration to cause a sequence of digits to be incorrectly received.

burst isochronous transmission   A method of transmission that can be used when the signalling rate in the information bearer channel is higher than the input data rate. Digits are transferred at the channel rate but the transmission is interrupted at intervals so that the mean transfer rate matches the input rate. The isochronous bursts of data are always separated by an integral number of digit periods. The technique can be used in a public data network where *envelopes* are transmitted over a bearer channel but only the *bytes* within the envelopes are transferred between a terminal and the network.

burst phase control   In a TDMA system, the technique by which an *earth station* is able to keep its *burst* in the correct position in the TDMA frame.

bus   See *highway*.

busied out   See *busy*.

busy   The state of a *selector*, line, etc. when it is in use, has been reserved for use or has been rendered unavailable for traffic, i.e. has been *busied out*.

busy-back (US)   See *busy tone*.

busy-flash signal   A *signal* (2) sent back to indicate that a required route or subscriber is busy.

busy hour   Of an exchange or group of circuits, that uninterrupted period of one hour during which the average intensity of traffic is at a maximum. See also *mean busy hour* and *bouncing busy hour*.

busy-hour to day ratio   The ratio of the *traffic volume* in the *busy hour* to the traffic volume in a day. Some countries use the inverse of this ratio.

busy-line display   A PABX facility whereby an operator can obtain information on the state (busy or free) of the exchange lines, inter-PBX circuits and sometimes of the PABX extensions.

busy-signal system See *loss system*.

busy test The process of testing a line, selector, etc. to see whether it is available for use or is busy.

busy tone An audible signal sent to a calling party to indicate that the called party is *busy* or, in systems that do not employ *equipment engaged tone*, that intermediate apparatus is busy and the call is therefore unable to mature.

busy verification (US) Action taken by an operator to check whether a called station is actually in use or is out of order.

buzz *Interference* of fairly short duration, but lasting for longer than the time specified by the CISPR when measured under the prescribed conditions.

bypass number See *extension diversion bypass*.

byte A fixed number of *binary digits* treated as a unit and usually shorter than a word. A byte is sometimes described by the number of digits it contains, e.g. triplet, octet.

byte serial transmission A form of data transmission in which successive bytes are transmitted in sequence. The individual digits of each byte may be transmitted serially or in parallel.

C

CISPR The International Special Committee on Radio Interference set up under the aegis of the IEC. The CISPR brings together representatives of administrations, broadcasters and other organisations interested in this subject. CISPR operates through a number of committees dealing with various aspects of interference and publishes recommendations relating to methods of measurement, limits, etc. Its work forms the basis of many national standards and of EEC directives dealing with this subject.

cable Generic term for an assembly of insulated conductors laid up in a sheath and having some degree of flexibility.

cable chamber (US: *splicing chamber*) A room, usually located in the basement of an exchange, where the large cables from the external plant are joined to smaller stub cables leading up to the *main distribution frame*.

cable code Generic term for variants of the *Morse code* used mainly on submarine cables. In the cable codes dots, dashes and letter spaces are all represented by equal-length signal elements; see *two-condition cable code* and *three-condition cable code*.

cable entrance facility (US) Term recently proposed in the US as a replacement for *cable vault*. See *cable chamber*.

cable fill The ratio of the number of pairs in service to the total number of pairs in a cable.

cable Morse code (US) See *three-condition cable code*.

cable pressurisation A technique in which dry air within a cable is maintained at a pressure in excess of atmospheric pressure, in order to prevent loss of service due to the ingress of moisture. The practice also provides a means of continuously monitoring the condition of a cable's sheath and joint closures. Two methods of pressurisation are in use. In the *static system* a cable is pressurised, sealed and the pressure is monitored by gauges fitted at exchanges, repeater stations and also at intermediate points. An alarm is activated if the pressure falls below a predetermined figure. This method is used on trunk and junction cables in the UK, the maximum applied pressure being 62 kPa— sufficient to withstand a 5½ metre head of water. The second method, known as *continuous flow*, is more suitable for use in the local line network, where it is difficult to seal cable ends owing to the many spurs and joints and the need for more frequent rearrangement. With this method dry air is continuously pumped into the cables at the exchange and is allowed to leak out of the remote ends of the system. In the UK these usually coincide with the ends of the main cables at *cross-connection points*. Monitoring devices check the rate of flow of air into the cable at the exchange and the pressure at the remote ends.

cable rack A metal structure usually suspended from the ceiling and used to support the cables interconnecting equipment in exchanges and repeater stations.

cable vault See *cable chamber*.

cage element An antenna element consisting of a number of wires so disposed as to resemble an elongated cylinder of circular cross-section.

call (1) As a verb, the action taken by a customer or operator to establish a connection with a wanted party or service. (2) The result of the action described in 1, whether successful or not.

call announcer A device that receives incoming pulses and converts them to spoken words.

call arrival signal A *signal* (2) sent to a quiescent terminal to gain the attention of the wanted subscriber or operator.

call back A PABX facility whereby an extension user, calling a second extension and finding it busy, can dial a code giving access to call back equipment. After receipt of an acknowledgement signal (*switching tone*) the caller hangs up. If within a specified period the called extension becomes free the equipment

31

automatically rings the calling extension and, if the latter answers, connects it to the wanted extension. The calling extension enjoys normal service during the waiting period. If the calling extension is busy when call back is attempted and does not become free within a specified time, the call back equipment is released.

call-back ringing   A non-standard ringing cadence used to indicate to an extension user that an incoming call is the result of his request for *call back* service.

call chaining   See *series call*.

call circuit   In a *manual switching system*, a circuit used by operators for the transmission of switching instructions.

call congestion ratio   The ratio of the number of calls that cannot be connected immediately, to the total number of call attempts offered to a system in a specified period. Also known as *blocking ratio*.

call connect systems   Generic title used for marketing purposes in the UK to describe customers' telephone installations providing PBX facilities.

call diversion   Generic term for the process in which a call directed to a given number is automatically diverted to another predetermined number.

call diversion on busy   A PABX facility whereby incoming calls to selected extensions are automatically diverted to another extension or group of extensions if the wanted extension is busy. The service can be applied by the switchboard operator or by the extension user by dialling an appropriate *access code*.

call diversion on ringing tone—no reply   A PABX facility available to selected extensions whereby incoming calls that are not answered within a designated period are automatically diverted to a nominated extension or group of extensions.

call forwarding   A PABX facility whereby a user can automatically divert incoming calls to any other selected extension.

call in suspense   See *operator hold*.

call indicator   A device used at a manual exchange to display in front of an operator incoming called numbers, whether dialled or otherwise transmitted from an automatic exchange.

call information logging   A PABX feature whereby details of chargeable calls are automatically recorded. Normally the extension number, the exchange line number, the time, the call duration and the digits dialled are all recorded. In a multi-user PBX this information can be used to bill individual customers, a process sometimes termed *departmental call accounting*.

call inter-arrival distribution   An expression giving the probable distribution of the time intervals between the instants at which successive calls occur.

call offering   A PABX facility whereby an extension user making a call to another extension engaged on an internal call can cause a distinctive tone (PBX internal call waiting tone) to be heard by the required extension user. This service is obtained by pressing the register recall button and dialling the correct *access code*. The required extension user may dial an acceptance code and speak privately to the intruding party whilst holding the original party, or may terminate his existing call and replace his handset. In the latter case the extension will be immediately re-rung and connected to the intruding extension.

call offering under night service   A PABX facility enabling an extension designated for night service to intrude into an established connection to offer the extension user an incoming exchange line call. The service is obtained by dialling an *access code*, and *intrusion tone* is heard by all three parties after intrusion has taken place.

call packing   A systematic method of allocating calls to paths through a *switching network*, usually by attempting to route new calls via the most heavily loaded part of the network.

call pick-up   A PABX facility whereby any extension telephone can be used to answer a call appearing on another extension, for example in an open-plan office.

call processing   All the functions performed by a common control in setting-up, supervising and releasing a call.

call queuing   An arrangement whereby calls incoming to a switchboard are placed in a queue in order of time of arrival, the call at the head of the queue being presented to the first answering point that becomes free to accept traffic.

call rearrangement   A technique for making better use of a *switching network* by rearranging existing connections in order to obtain a free path for an additional call.

call redirection   A telegraph or data network facility whereby calls are automatically readdressed on the request of a called subscriber, the calling terminal being advised of the change.

call sender   Equipment able to store many multi-digit numbers, which can be sent automatically in order to test the functioning of one or more *exchanges*.

call spill-over   In *common-channel signalling*, the effect on a traffic circuit of the arrival at a *switching centre* of an abnormally delayed signal message relating to a previous call, while a subsequent call is being set up on the circuit.

call splitting   Disconnection of the through transmission path between the parties to a call for a purpose such as *trunk offering*.

call tracing   The process of determining one or both of the telephone numbers belonging to the parties engaged in a call.

call waiting   A facility provided by some systems whereby a call to a busy number results in the return of ringing tone to the caller and the application of a periodic tone (call waiting tone) to both the called and calling party's lines. The called party may then continue with his existing call while holding the new caller, or may speak to the latter while holding the former.

call waiting signal   A tone applied to a PBX extension engaged on a call to advise the user that there is another call awaiting attention. If the call is from another extension user who has invoked the *call offering* service, the signal is called *PBX internal call waiting tone*. If the new call is from an incoming exchange line, however, the tone is called *external call waiting tone* and has a different cadence.

called number identification   See *dialled digit display*.

called party release   A method of operation in which the release of a connection is under the control of the called party so that it begins only when he restores his telephone, data modem, etc. to its quiescent state.

calling device   Apparatus used to generate the signals required to establish connections in an automatic telecommunication system.

calling line identification   A facility whereby the location (i.e. the residential address) of a calling device may be automatically identified.

calling party release   A method of operation in which the release of a connection is under the control of the calling party so that it begins only when he restores his telephone, data modem, etc. to its quiescent state.

calling signal alarm   A switchable PBX facility whereby the arrival of a call causes a bell or buzzer to sound.

callmaker   Subscriber's apparatus capable of automatically generating calling signals corresponding to a selected set of telephone numbers. Also termed *repertory callmaker* and *repertory dialler* (US). In the *card callmaker* available in the UK each wanted number is stored as a pattern of holes in a plastic card. Insertion of a chosen card into the callmaker causes the appropriate calling signals to be sent to line. An alternative version known as the *tape callmaker* can store 400 18-digit numbers on a wide magnetic tape.

calls waiting indicator   A visual indication, provided for a switchboard operator, of the number of calls awaiting attention.

camp on or **camp on busy**   A facility provided by some systems whereby a call that cannot be connected because the wanted terminal is busy, is stored by tne equipment and completed automatically as soon as the wanted number becomes free. Also known as *connect when free, ring when free* and *wait on busy*.

camp on with recall A *camp on* facility in which the calling terminal is released until the wanted connection can be made. Also known as *automatic call back*.

capacitor microphone A microphone in which the transducer consists essentially of a thin metal foil forming one plate of a capacitor.

capacity top Of an *antenna*, a conducting structure connected to the end of a radiating element to change the current distribution therein.

capture effect An effect occurring in a demodulator of angle-modulated signals whereby the stronger of two signals presented to it effectively controls its output.

carbon microphone or **carbon telephone transmitter** A microphone consisting essentially of a flexible diaphragm attached to a container filled with minute granules of carbon. Sound waves impinging on the diaphragm vary the resistance between two electrodes in the container, thereby modulating a direct current passing through it.

carbon noise The random noise produced by a *carbon microphone* in the absence of any sound excitation.

card callmaker See *callmaker*.

cardioid response A heart-shaped curve depicting the performance in a specified plane of a device such as a microphone or an antenna.

carriage return Horizontal movement of the printing mechanism of a page-printing machine to a position corresponding to the start of a line.

carried load See *traffic carried*.

carrier (1) A sinusoidal oscillation or electromagnetic wave available for *modulation*. The term is sometimes applied to a direct current intended for modulation. See also *pulse carrier*. (2) That part of a modulated signal which corresponds with the carrier in some specified respect, e.g. the carrier-frequency spectral components of an amplitude-modulated wave. (3) In *suppressed-carrier operation*, an oscillation generated in the receiver for the purpose of *demodulation*. See also *pilot carrier*.

carrier channel A *channel* consisting of a particular band of frequencies in a carrier system.

carrier compression In a *single-sideband* or *independent-sideband* transmitter, any unwanted change in the amplitude of the *pilot carrier* occurring when a sideband signal is present.

carrier-energy dispersal See *intermodulation-noise dispersal*.

carrier telegraphy   Telegraphy in which signals from a telegraph transmitter are used to modulate a *carrier*.

carrier transmission   That form of transmission in which information is conveyed by modulating a continuous wave known as the *carrier* wave.

carrier wave   See *carrier*.

case shift   In alphabetic telegraphy, changeover of the translating mechanism of a receiver so that letters-case characters are printed instead of figures-case characters, or vice versa.

cassegrain antenna   An *antenna* consisting of a large reflector (whose surface is a paraboloid of revolution) together with a secondary reflector generally hyperbolic in shape and located

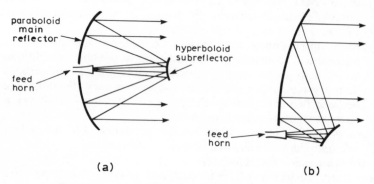

Figure C.1   Cassegrain antennas: (a) symmetrical, (b) offset

between the focal point and vertex of the primary radiator; see *Figure C.1(a)*. Alternative feeding and geometrical arrangements are also used, as in the *offset cassegrain*; see *Figure C.1(b)*.

cathodic protection   A method of protecting the metal sheaths of underground cables from *electrolytic corrosion*, by ensuring that they are held at a lower electric potential than the surrounding medium of soil and water. The required potential may be provided by a source of direct current connected to a *ground bed*, or by using one or more *reactive anodes*.

Ceefax   Designation for the *teletext* service offered by the BBC.

cent call seconds   See *hundred call seconds*.

central battery signalling   Description applied to early telephone systems using a common power installation at the exchange to supply energy for signalling purposes.

central battery system   Description applied to early telephone systems using a common power installation at the *exchange* to supply energy for both signalling and speaking purposes. Also known as *common-battery system*.

central office See *exchange*.

central processor A central unit in an *automatic switching system* generally exercising control over other processors and functional units.

centralised automatic message accounting See *automatic message accounting*.

centralised control of selective answering A PBX feature whereby an alarm is given automatically if selective answering is in use and the number of calls of a particular class awaiting attention exceeds a specified number.

centralised control signalling In a data network, the use of a dedicated channel or channels for the exchange of call control signals relating to a group of data circuits.

centralised dictation A PABX facility whereby an extension user can gain access to and control one of a pool of recording machines for the purpose of dictating letters, memoranda, etc.

centre frequency (1) In *frequency modulation*, the average frequency of the *carrier* when it is modulated by a symmetrical signal. (2) Of a *channel* or *filter*, the mean of the two frequencies defining the channel or filter pass band.

centre holes Holes punched in the middle of a telegraph tape to enable the feed mechanism to move it backwards or forwards. Sometimes called *feed holes*.

centre stable relay A *polarised relay* used in telegraphy and having a *contact unit* with a central neutral position from which it may be moved in either of two directions in accordance with the direction of the current in the coils.

centrex service A service provided by some specially equipped exchanges whereby a subscriber can enjoy many of the facilities normally provided by a separate PABX. The extensions and operator's desk are given numbers in the numbering plan for the exchange area and hence can all be reached by *direct dialling*. Internal calls between extensions can be made without dialling the full code, and many other facilities such as call transfer can be made available.

chad The piece of paper removed when a hole is punched in a paper tape.

chadless perforation Partial perforation so that the small piece of paper that would have formed a *chad* is left hinged to the leading edge of the hole.

changeback In *common-channel signalling*, the process of transferring signalling traffic from one or more standby links to the regular link as soon as the latter has been proved to be serviceable.

changed address interception A facility provided by some

37

telegraph and data networks whereby a calling terminal is automatically advised of a called terminal's new address, and subsequently is either connected to the wanted terminal or is released.

changed number interception In automatic telephony, a service whereby calls to a number that has recently been given up or changed for an administrative reason, are connected to a manual board or a recording machine so that information regarding the change can be given to the caller.

changeover In *common-channel signalling*, the process of transferring signalling traffic from a normal link to one or more standby links, owing to the failure of the regular link or because it must be cleared of traffic.

changeover contact unit General term for an assembly of three *contact members*, one of which is movable so that it can be placed in contact with either of the other two. Such assemblies are known as *make-before-break* (bridging) or *break-before-make* (non-bridging), depending on whether all three members make contact during the changeover operation or not.

channel A means of unidirectional transmission, consisting for example of a defined frequency *band* in an FDM system or of a particular *time slot* in a TDM system. Many channels may thus share a common transmission path. In the US the term is sometimes used in place of *circuit* to indicate a bidirectional transmission facility.

channel-associated signalling The transmission of *signals* (2) relating to the traffic carried by a single *channel*, either in that channel or in a separate signalling channel permanently associated with it and routed in the same transmission system.

channel-busy tone (US) See *congestion tone*.

channel gate A device that enables a *channel* to be connected to a *highway* (or vice versa) at specified instants.

channel switching See *circuit switching*.

channel time slot In *pulse code modulation*, a time slot occupying a defined position in a *frame* (1) and used for the transmission of the *character signals* (2) relating to a particular channel. It may also be used for the transmission of *in-slot signalling* or other information.

channel translating unit Carrier telephone equipment used for the *frequency translation* of twelve audio channels and their assembly into a *group* (1). It can also carry out the inverse operation.

character (1) In alphabetic telegraphy or data transmission, a letter, figure or other symbol forming part of a message. By extension, a command such as carriage return or line feed. The term is also used to describe the information corresponding to a character. (2) In data processing, a letter, digit, punctuation mark or other symbol forming one member of an agreed set of characters used for the organisation, control or representation of data. See also *coded character set*.

character-serial transmission A form of data transmission in which successive characters are transmitted in sequence. The individual elements of each character may be transmitted serially or in parallel.

character signal (1) A group of *signal elements* representing a *character* (1). (2) In *pulse code modulation*, a group of *signal elements* representing the *quantised value* of a sample. Sometimes called a *PCM word*.

characteristic distortion In telegraphy, displacement of signal *transitions* caused by a transmission path with an inadequate *transient response* so that a given transition is affected by the previous transition (or transitions). The effect therefore varies with the pulse length, and short pulses are more distorted than long ones.

characteristic impedance Of a uniform transmission line, the impedance with which the line is endowed by virtue of its geometry and the materials used in its construction. It is the value that the line would have if it were infinitely long or if it were of finite length and terminated with its iterative impedance. Numerically it is the value obtained by dividing the complex voltage between the conductors by the complex current along them at any given point in the line when it is energised and correctly terminated.

characteristic wave impedance The ratio of the transverse component of the electric field to the transverse component of the magnetic field at a point traversed by a travelling electromagnetic wave. This is the same thing as the *wave impedance*, with the sign so chosen that the real part is positive.

charge-to-third-number call (US) A call charged to a number other than that of the called or calling party.

chargeable time clock A device associated with a connecting circuit of a *manual switchboard* to enable the time to be charged for a call to be determined.

charging The process of assigning a fee to a subscriber for the use of a *circuit* or facility.

charging current Of a transmission line, that current which flows into the capacitance of a line when it is connected to a voltage source.

Chebyshev array A *broadside array* in which the elements are so spaced and fed as to produce an array having the property that for a given *side-lobe* level the width of the *main beam* is minimised. Also known as *Dolph – Chebyshev array.*

check bit or **check digit** A redundant digit used in an error-detecting procedure such as a *parity check.*

cheese antenna An *antenna* consisting of a portion of a parabolic cylinder bounded by two parallel plates perpendicular to its axis. The plates are so dimensioned that more than one *mode* (2) can propagate in the parallel-plate region.

Chireix antenna An *antenna* formed by a group of superimposed conductors, each shaped like a right-angled sawtooth. The length of the straight side of each tooth is equal to half the operating wavelength.

choice In a switching system in which the outlets or groups of outlets are always tested in the same order, the designation of an outlet with respect to the order of selection, e.g. first choice.

choke (1) An inductor, generally included in a circuit because it presents a relatively high impedance to the flow of alternating current and a low impedance to the passage of direct current. (2) A *waveguide* device designed to prevent energy in a specified frequency range from following an undesired path.

chopping The process of interrupting a direct current or a beam of light in a regular manner.

cigar antenna An *end-fire antenna* consisting of a number of conducting discs spaced along and perpendicular to a rod passing through their centres. The rod includes a *driven element* at one end.

circuit In telecommunications, a means of bidirectional communication between two points. In its simplest form a circuit can consist of two conductors, as in the case of a normal telephone line. The term also applies to any association of a go and a return *channel*, however these are provided. The channels forming a circuit may be permanently associated, or may be selected and associated only for the duration of a call. In some systems channels are allocated to a circuit only for time intervals during which they are required for the actual transmission of information; see *time-assignment speech interpolation.* The characteristics of the channels, such as *bandwidth* and bit rate, may differ in the two directions of transmission.

circuit number In *common-channel signalling*, that part of the address label used to identify the traffic circuit to which the signalling information relates.

circuit-switched connection In a data network, a connection between two or more terminals established on demand so that a data circuit is exclusively available to the terminals until the connection is released.

circuit switching A method of switching in which a circuit is established and used for the entire duration of a call. This method of operation does not make the most efficient use of the channels forming the circuit; see *message switching, packet switching* and *time-assignment speech interpolation*.

circuit tracing The process of identifying all the traffic-carrying means forming an established telecommunication connection.

circular orbit Of a *communication satellite*, an orbit in which the distance between the satellite and the centre of the earth is constant.

circular polarisation In radio-wave propagation, *polarisation* (1) such that the tip of the *electric field vector* describes a circle in any fixed plane normal to the direction of propagation. A circularly polarised wave may be resolved into two equal-amplitude, linearly polarised waves in phase *quadrature* and having their *planes of polarisation* at right angles to each other. See also *orthogonal polarisation*.

circulating register A storage device in which data is continually moved out of one end and re-entered at the other.

circulator A *waveguide* component consisting of a junction of at least three arms and having non-reciprocal transmission properties so that energy entering one arm is transmitted to the next adjacent arm in a particular direction.

cladding A cylindrical layer of highly transparent material fused to the core of an *optical fibre* and having a refractive index about one per cent lower than that of the core. The cladding layer provides additional strength, but its primary purpose is to contribute to the propagation of the guided waves in the core by virtually eliminating the losses that could otherwise occur owing to leakage of the electromagnetic field through the core boundary.

cladding mode stripper In an *optical fibre*, material applied to the *cladding* to enable optical energy propagating in the cladding to escape.

clamping The process in which some feature of a recurrent *waveform* is held at a reference value.

class of service A classification of customers according to the facilities available, charging rates or similar parameters. Thus class-of-service information may indicate whether a customer is business or residential, has an *individual line* or *party line*, is subjected to restricted service, enjoys special facilities, has *flat-rate service*, etc. The term is also used to describe categories of PBX extensions according to the facilities allocated, restrictions imposed, etc.

class-of-service tone A tone applied to a line to indicate to an operator that a particular *class of service* is appropriate to the call.

classification of exchanges   A five-level classification of *switching centres* based on function and adopted by the CCITT to simplify international discussions. The correspondence between the international terms and those used in the UK and North America is given in *Table C.1*. The CCITT has also classified the four-wire-switched automatic international exchanges into three levels designated CT1 to CT3; see *Figure T.2 (transmission plan)*.

Table C.1

Function of switching centre	Name		
	International	UK	N. America
Exchange directly connected to subscribers	Local exchange	Local exchange	End office or class 5 office
First level of trunk switching	Primary centre	Group switching centre	Toll centre or class 4 office
Second level of trunk switching	Secondary centre	District switching centre	Primary centre or class 3 office
Third level of trunk switching	Tertiary centre	Main switching centre	Sectional centre or class 2 office
Fourth level of trunk switching	Quaternary centre	(None in UK)	Regional centre or class 1 office

clear   To initiate the release of a *circuit* in a controlled manner so that each of the various links and devices is correctly returned to its idle condition.

clear-back signal (US: *hang-up signal*)   A *signal* (2) sent in the backward direction when the called party clears. It can serve several purposes, such as stopping charging or initiating circuit release.

clear-forward signal (US: *disconnect signal*)   A *signal* (2) sent in the forward direction to initiate release of the *circuits* used for a call or a call attempt. Such a signal is sent to the caller's *local exchange*, and subsequent action depends on the release philosophy of the system, e.g. *calling party release, first party release,* etc.

click   In *radio interference*, discontinuous interference lasting less than 200 milliseconds and separated by at least that interval from any subsequent disturbance. A click may contain a number of *impulses*.

42

click noise In certain *pulse code modulation* systems, loud clicks occurring in the received speech as a result of errors affecting the most significant digits of the *character signals* (2).

clip position See *dead sector*.

clipping In telephony, the loss of the initial part of a word, usually owing to the action of a voice-operated switch. See *limiting*.

clock The generic term for equipment that provides timing signals used to control functions such as *sampling* or the *scanning* (1) of subscribers' lines, etc. Various categories of clock are defined. Thus a *master clock* generates very accurately timed signals and usually controls a number of other clocks. A *reference clock* is one of high stability used to govern the frequency of a number of mutually synchronised clocks in a *digital network*.

clock meter A meter with a clock-type face available to customers in the UK for checking the number of units used on one or more dialled calls. It has three hands, one of which is resettable and can record up to 99 units. The other two hands record the cumulative total up to 9999 units, after which each begins another revolution of the face.

clockwise polarised wave (also known as *right-hand polarised wave*) An elliptically or circularly polarised wave such that the *electric field vector* in any plane normal to the direction of propagation rotates with time in a clockwise manner when viewed by an observer looking along the direction of propagation, i.e. away from the transmitting antenna. See also *elliptical polarisation* and *circular polarisation*.

closed-circuit signalling A form of DC *signalling* in which a current flows in the idle condition and is increased or decreased to convey *signalling information*.

closed-circuit television The use of television cameras, monitors and suitable transmission links to provide visual communication between two or more points. Permanent private links may be provided, for example, to distribute educational programmes to a number of reception points. Similarly, temporary links may be established to enable conferences or lectures to be relayed to overflow audiences.

closed user group A group of users of either a public data network or a public switched (telegraph) network, who have the facility of communicating with one another but who cannot communicate with any other users of the network.

clover-leaf antenna A non-directional transmitting antenna consisting of three or four similar loops fed in phase and arranged in a horizontal plane around a vertical axis so that the arrangement resembles a clover leaf.

coaxial antenna A *half-wave dipole* antenna formed by exposing a quarter wavelength of the inner conductor of a coaxial cable by folding back the outer conductor over the sheath for the same distance. Also termed *quarter-wave skirt dipole*.

coaxial cable A single *coaxial tube* enclosed in a sheath. By extension, a cable consisting principally of a number of coaxial tubes.

coaxial line, coaxial pair or **coaxial tube** A *transmission line* consisting of two conductors arranged so that one is centred within the other but insulated from it. Also known as *concentric line*.

code (1) A set of unambiguous rules for the representation of data by *symbols* and/or *signal elements*. (2) In a telephone *numbering plan*, one or more digits having a particular significance, usually in connection with *routing* and *switching*.

code combination In telegraphy or data transmission, a group of *signal elements* representing a *character* (1), the *significant condition* of each element being specified by a particular *equal-length code*.

code conversion (1) In digital transmission, the process of converting signals formed in accordance with one *code* (1) into signals formed according to another code. (2) In automatic switching, the conversion of part of a *destination code* into a *routing code*.

code digit A digit having a particular significance in accordance with a defined *code* (2).

code division The separation of a number of transmission paths by the use of different codes used as message labels.

code-division switching The connection of *inlets* to *outlets* by means of coded message labels.

code element See *coded representation*.

code extension character In data processing, a *character* (2) used to indicate that succeeding *coded representations* are formed according to a different code or are taken from a different *coded character set*.

code rate Of an error detection/correction code, a measure of the efficiency of the code given by that fraction of the channel capacity used to transmit *information bits*. Hence if the channel bit rate is 1200 bit/s and the code used requires the transmission of *parity bits* at an average rate of 200 bit/s, the code rate would be 0.83, i.e. an efficiency of 83 per cent.

code switch In automatic switching, a switch developed by L. M. Ericsson as a replacement for the *crossbar switch* and consisting of sets of contacts operated by a coded combination of electromagnets.

code translation See *translation*.

code value See *coded representation*.

code word A *coded representation* consisting of at least two digits, symbols or other characters.

codec An item of equipment containing an encoder and a decoder.

coded character set In data processing, a set of unambiguous rules, essentially in tabular form, that establishes a set of *characters* (2) and the corresponding *coded representation* for each one of them.

coded mark inversion A method of producing a two-level signal in which a binary 0 is represented by one signal level for half a bit period followed by a transition to the other level for the

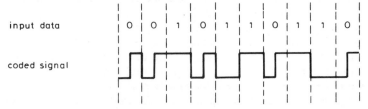

Figure C.2 Coded mark inversion

remainder of the bit period, and a binary 1 is represented alternately by either signal level for a full bit period; see *Figure C.2*.

coded representation The representation of a piece of data in accordance with a *code* (1), or the representation of a character in accordance with a *coded character set*. Thus 'LHR' represents Heathrow in the three-letter code for airport identification, and the binary digits '1000001' represent the capital letter 'A' in the ISO seven-bit coded character set. Also known as *code element* and *code value*.

coded signal In *multi-frequency signalling*, a signal consisting of a multi-frequency pulse in which the particular combination of frequencies represents the digit to be transmitted in accordance with a *signalling code*.

coding See *encoding*.

coherent detection *Local carrier demodulation*, the local carrier (or carriers) having exact phase correspondence to the transmitted carrier (or carriers).

coherent significant instants In parallel data transmission, the instants when a *transition* occurs simultaneously in all the channels.

coil loading See *loading*.

45

coin-denomination tone (US) or **coin-value tone**   A tone sent to an operator to indicate the value of a coin inserted in a coinbox.

coinbox discriminating tone or **coin tone** (US)   A tone sent to an operator to indicate that a call is from a public coinbox.

coinbox identification tone   A tone sent to an operator to indicate that a called number is that of a coinbox.

cold point   That point on a *radiating element* of an antenna at which the potential difference with respect to earth approximates to zero.

collect call (US)   See *reverse charge call*.

collect key (US)   The switchboard key used by an operator to collect the money deposited in a prepay coin telephone.

combined distribution frame   A structure combining the functions of a *main distribution frame* and an *intermediate distribution frame*, usually in a small exchange.

combiner   (1) In a CATV-type system, a device whereby signals present at two or more inputs are fed to a single output without interaction. (2) Of an antenna, a device permitting several transmitters to use a single antenna simultaneously.

comma-free code   Any *equal-length code* in which no symbols are required to indicate the separation between the *code words*. This is achieved by ensuring that any sequence of symbols formed by portions of two adjacent code words differs in at least one symbol from any valid code word.

common answering   A switchboard feature such that a common *call indicator*, together with identification of the type of calling signal, is *multipled* to every position capable of answering calls. See also *individual answering* and *selective answering*.

common-battery system   See *central battery system*.

common-channel signalling   The use of a dedicated channel for the transfer of *signalling information* relating to a plurality of other channels. Also known as *label addressed signalling* because the various signal messages are identified by labels. A typical common-channel *signalling link* can meet the signalling needs of over two thousand speech circuits, and may also be used for the transfer of information required for network management purposes.

common trunk   In a *grading* arrangement, a *trunk* accessible to all groups of the grading.

communication satellite   A vehicle placed in an orbit around the earth and used to relay signals between *earth stations*. In common usage the first word is often omitted from the term. A *passive satellite* merely reflects radio signals beamed towards it, whereas an *active satellite* receives, amplifies and retransmits such signals. See also *orbital test satellite*.

Communications Satellite Corporation (COMSAT) The privately owned common-carrier company that represents the United States in INTELSAT. COMSAT has the largest investment share in INTELSAT, and performs technical and operational functions on the latter's behalf.

community antenna television system (CATV) A system for the distribution of television signals over a *coaxial cable* network to subscribers living in an area of poor reception. The signals are received at a carefully selected site using sensitive highly directional antennas to minimise *noise* and other interference. In addition to improved reception of the local channels, subscribers may also be able to view channels not normally receivable in their area. In the US operating companies are also allowed to originate programs locally.

companding The application of *compression* followed by *expansion* (1), usually with the object of improving the ratio between the signal and any *noise* or interference introduced into the transmission path between the points at which the processes are applied. See also *lincompex*.

compatible high-density bipolar code (CHDB-n) A modified form of *alternate mark inversion* in which strings of $n + 1$ zeros are replaced by one of two code groups containing timing information (i.e. marks). The particular group used as a substitute depends on the number of marks that have occurred since the previous substitution.

compelled signalling A *signalling* method in which the transmission of each signal in the forward direction is inhibited until an acknowledgement of the satisfactory receipt of the previous signal has been sent back from the receiver terminal.

compilation See *programming*.

completely restricted extension A PABX extension that can make and receive internal calls only.

composite cable A cable containing a mixture of conductor sizes and/or types.

composite circuit (US) A *circuit* that can be used simultaneously for telephony and DC *signalling*, separation being based on frequency discrimination.

compound signal In AC *signalling*, a signal consisting of the simultaneous transmission of more than one frequency.

compound switching The connection of *inlets* to *outlets* using some combination of the techniques of *space-division, time-division, frequency-division* and *code-division switching*.

compression A process in which the range of *amplitudes* of a signal is automatically reduced in a specified manner. This may be achieved by making the gain of an amplifier vary inversely with applied signal level averaged over a specified interval of time. By applying relatively more amplification at low signal level, the *signal-to-noise ratio* can be improved. Similarly a reduction in the amplification applied at high signal levels can prevent overload.

compression of the contrast range In *facsimile*, deliberate or fortuitous modification of the facsimile signals so that the ratio between the luminance of the whitest and blackest parts of the reproduced copy is less than that on the original document.

compression ratio The ratio of the *gain* applying at a reference signal level to that at a higher stated signal level.

compunication See *teleprocessing*.

computer word (also known as *machine word*) A group of characters stored in one location in a functional unit such as a *central processor*, and capable of being treated as a unit.

concentration In switching, the use of a *switching stage* having a larger number of inlets than it has outlets so that the intensity of the traffic offered to subsequent units is increased. Equipment used in this way is termed a concentrator. A *line concentrator* provides for the concentration of traffic from subscribers' lines, whereas a *trunk concentrator* has trunks connected to its inlets.

concentric line See *coaxial line*.

conditional selecting See *conjugate selecting*.

conducted interference *Interference* propagated along circuit conductors, e.g. interference entering a receiver via its mains lead.

conduit (1) In the US, a structure containing one or more *ducts* (1). (2) A flexible or rigid tube of metal, plastic, etc., used to provide mechanical protection for cables and wires in buildings, ships, aircraft, etc.

conference call or **conference connection** (US) A call established between at least three stations so that each party is able to converse with all the others.

Conference of European Posts and Telecommunications (CEPT) An organisation formed by the Postal and Telecommunications Administrations of Europe as a forum for the discussion and harmonisation of tariff and operational matters. Plenary Assemblies are held every two years, with member countries taking responsibility for management administration in rotation. CEPT works through two Commissions (Postal and Telecommunications), each of which has a number of subsidiary committees and working groups. Its interests have extended into the technical field, and on the telecommunications side working groups study questions relating to telegraphy, telephony, radio communication, television transmission, communication satellites, etc. Much of this work clearly parallels that of the CCIR and the CCITT, but CEPT does not publish recommendations or reports; instead it seeks to establish consensus views for formal discussion in the appropriate fora of the ITU or the Universal Postal Union.

conformal antenna An antenna whose shape is primarily determined by the need to conform with a surface such as that formed by part of an aircraft or a ship's hull.

confravision The audio-visual conference service available in the UK. Specially equipped studios in major cities can be linked by audio and vision circuits so that participants can see and speak to one another. The service is also available to certain countries overseas.

confusion signal In *common-channel signalling*, a message sent back to indicate that an exchange is unable to act on a signal received from the previous exchange because the message is considered unreasonable.

congestion In a telecommunication network, the condition in which an unacceptable number of call attempts fail owing to an insufficiency of circuits or equipment.

congestion signal A *signal* (2) sent in the backward direction to indicate that there is insufficient equipment for an attempted call set up to be completed. Subsequent action depends on system design, and the call may be either aborted or rerouted.

congestion tone (US: *channel-busy tone*) A tone indicating that a wanted number is unavailable owing to congestion. Some systems use *busy tone* for this purpose.

conjugate selecting A method of *selecting* that takes account of the state of all the interswitch links and *crosspoints* involved in setting up a connection in a *switching network* or a part thereof. Also known as *conditional selecting*.

connect signal See *seizing signal*.

connect-through (US) An administrative practice whereby a cable *pair* joining a subscriber's premises to the *local exchange* is left intact if the subscriber discontinues service.

connect when free See *camp on*.

connected call A call established, without regard to the state of the called number, e.g. busy or no answer.

connecting stage Term proposed in connection with symbols for switching systems to describe an arrangement of inlets and outlets using only one *crosspoint* to connect an inlet to an outlet, but in which several connections can exist concurrently.

connection An association of *channels* and other traffic-carrying devices that together provide for the transfer of information—usually between two terminal points. As with

49

'section' and 'link', the term has a specific meaning in some ITU terminology. Thus *international television connection* describes the overall transmission facility between send and receive broadcasting studios, *switching centres* or standards converters.

consonant articulation   A measure of the *articulation* efficiency of a circuit, expressed as the percentage of sounds correctly recognised by the listener when the speech units used are consonants, or consonants combined with vowels into meaningless syllables.

constant available power source   In telephony, apparatus serving as a source of test signals and having a purely resistive internal impedance and an open-circuit terminal voltage independent of frequency over its working range.

constant-disparity code or **constant-ratio code**   A binary *equal-length code* that has the same number of 1s in each character. Such a code may be used to detect a single error in the reception of a character, since its disparity will be changed by the error.

constraint length   Of a *convolutional code*, the length of a *block* multiplied by the number of blocks containing *information bits* that are checked by the *parity bits* in a given block.

contact or **contact element**   In general, a conducting part designed to act with another similar part to make or break an electrical connection. Specifically in a *relay*, the small piece of special material (often a precious metal) attached to the end of the spring and intended to make contact with the contact on another spring.

contact follow   The distance travelled by two *contact members* after they have made contact.

contact member   A piece of conducting material, usually in the form of a flat spring, serving as the mount for a *contact*. Also termed *contact spring*.

contact sensing and operating   A PABX feature enabling the user of an authorised extension to control the operation of appliances or equipment at a suitably equipped terminal. The user dials a code followed by the number allocated to the relevant contacts, and then hears a tone denoting their state—i.e. whether open or closed. By dialling a further code the user can change this state. Sometimes called remote control (of appliances).

contact spring   See *contact member*.

contact unit   An assembly of two or three *contact members* that together provide means of making, breaking or changing over an electrical connection. Often abbreviated to 'contact' in common usage.

continuity check   In *common-channel signalling*, a check carried out on a *circuit* or circuits in a connection to establish that a path

50

exists for the transmission of speech, data, etc.

continuous interference An electromagnetic disturbance arising from *impulsive noise, random noise* and/or other causes and lasting for more than 200 milliseconds.

continuous loading See *loading*.

continuous noise In *interference* measurement, a disturbance whose effects cannot be resolved into separate impulses by the measuring system employed.

continuous receiver or **continuous recorder** *Facsimile* apparatus in which the recording medium consists of a continuous strip that is advanced by a constant pitch between lines, so that several documents can be recorded without the need to change the medium.

continuous RQ In data transmission, a method of *error control* in which blocks of data are transmitted without interruption until a negative acknowledgement signal is received over the return channel. Receipt of this signal causes the transmitter to go back and retransmit the erroneous block and any subsequent blocks sent prior to the receipt of the error indication. Although this method requires the retransmission of at least two blocks for every erroneous block detected, it is nevertheless capable of yielding a high throughput efficiency compared with an *idle RQ* system.

continuous signal In analogue signalling, a *signal* (2) that is transmitted continuously as long as the condition it represents persists.

continuously variable slope delta modulation See *delta modulation*.

contoured beam antenna A *shaped beam antenna* designed in such a way that when its beam illuminates a given surface the lines of equal *power flux density* form specified contours on that surface. The term is used in connection with *communication satellite* antennas, and the contours on the surface of the earth are known as *footprints*.

contrast range In *facsimile*, the ratio between luminance of the whitest and the blackest parts of a picture.

control character In telegraphy or data transmission, a character serving to initiate, modify or stop a control operation such as carriage return or rewind.

controlled-carrier modulation See *floating-carrier modulation*.

conversation time That part of the total time taken for a call that is available to the parties for conversation. More precisely it is the interval between the instant at which the *answer signal* is detected at the point where the call duration is recorded and the instant at which the *clear* signal is detected at the same point.

51

convolutional code In data transmission, an *error control* code in which the *parity bits* in a given *block* check both the *information bits* in that block and information bits in some other blocks as well. Also termed *recurrent code*.

cooption See *three-party conference*.

coordination contour A line on a map produced for the purpose of *frequency coordination*, showing the extent of the *coordination distance* in all azimuthal directions from the site of a proposed new radio station.

coordination distance The computed azimuthal distance from a projected radio station within which an existing station operating in a shared frequency band could interfere with (or experience *interference* from) the new station, under the condition assumed in the calculation. Usually worst-case parameters are assumed; for example, the antenna of a terrestrial radio link is supposed to be pointing directly towards a new *earth station* site. Different values of coordination distance are obtained by appropriately varying the parameters used. In the case of an *earth terminal*, for example, the distance computed for reception is generally greater than that calculated for interference caused by the terminal's transmitter, because the terminal's receiver is much more sensitive to interference than is the receiver of a terrestrial radio link.

copolar diagram The *directivity pattern* of an antenna with respect to the *polarisation* (2) for which it was designed.

copolarised See *direct polarisation*.

cord circuit A circuit provided at switchboard positions and used to establish connections.

cordless switchboard A switchboard in which connections are established by the manual operation of keys.

core Of an *optical fibre*, the central region having a higher refraction index than that of the surrounding medium or cladding, and basically serving to propagate the guided waves.

corner See *waveguide corner*.

corner reflector A reflecting surface consisting of three flat planes at right angles to one another and used to reflect radio waves in a direction parallel with that of their incidence.

corner reflector antenna An *antenna* consisting of one or more radiating elements located in the interior angle of a corner formed by two reflecting surfaces.

correcting signal In a *synchronous system*, a special signal transmitted for the purpose of synchronisation.

correction from signals In a *synchronous system*, the use of the normal incoming signal for the purpose of *synchronous correction*.

cosmic noise Radio *noise* caused by natural phenomena outside the earth's atmosphere. Also known as *extraterrestrial noise* or *galactic noise*.

counter-clockwise polarised wave (also known as *left-hand polarised wave*) An elliptically or circularly polarised wave such that the *electric field vector* in any plane normal to the direction of propagation rotates with time in a counter-clockwise manner when viewed by an observer looking along the direction of propagation, i.e. looking away from the transmitting antenna. See also *elliptical polarisation* and *circular polarisation*.

counter-EMF cell A low ampere-hour capacity cell connected in series opposition with an exchange battery in order to reduce the voltage applied to the equipment. Several such cells may be used, and each can be individually switched out of circuit depending on the state of charge of the battery.

counterpoise A system of conductors located above the ground and forming part of an antenna system, usually as a replacement for, or supplement to, an earth system.

country code A code consisting of one, two or three digits characterising a country in *direct distance dialling*. Country codes formed in accordance with the *world numbering plan* begin with a single digit identifying a particular geographical area known as a world numbering zone. Thus the digit 1 identifies all the countries in the North American zone, and the digit 7 identifies all the countries in the USSR. For these two zones the single digit serves as the country code. In South America, however, each country has either a two-digit or a three-digit code beginning with the digit 5. The use of an alternative *international prefix* in direct distance dialling makes it possible to employ a shorter code—known as a regional country code—for calls to certain other countries in a defined group. Thus calls between some countries in South America may be made using a single-digit country code instead of the two-digit or three-digit code that must be dialled from Europe. No country code need be dialled for calls between countries covered by an integrated numbering plan, because this provides a unique *trunk code* for each separate *numbering plan area* in the zone.

coupled reperforator and tape reader Telegraph apparatus providing for the automatic retransmission of all the received signals, including the last one.

coupling Generic term for a linkage between two *circuits* whereby energy is transferred from one to the other.

coverage area In mobile communication, an area surrounding the *base station* in which the signal strength is sufficient to provide reliable communication for a specified percentage of the time (usually 90 per cent).

cradle switch See *switch-hook*.

critical angle In an *optical fibre*, the angle made between the normal to the inner surface and the meridional ray that is just

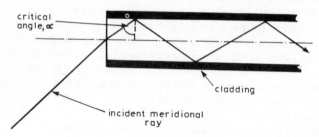

Figure C.3 Critical angle

internally reflected; see *Figure C.3*. This angle determines the maximum angle at which divergent rays can be accepted for transmission along a fibre; see *numerical aperture*.

critical frequency (1) For a radio wave vertically incident on an ionospheric layer, the frequency below which the wave will be reflected from the layer and above which it will pass through the layer. Its value depends on the degree of ionisation existing at the time in question. Also known as the *penetration frequency*. (2) Of a *waveguide*, the frequency below which a travelling wave in the *dominant mode* cannot be maintained. Also called the *cut-off frequency*. (3) Of a specified *mode* (2) in a waveguide, the frequency below which a travelling wave in the specified mode cannot be maintained in the waveguide.

critical wavelength The *wavelength* corresponding to the *critical frequency*. Also known as *cut-off wavelength*.

crossbar switch A rectangular array of *crosspoints* with electromechanical means of operation common to each row and column in the matrix.

cross-connection point A flexibility point in a *local line network* at which the incoming *pairs* from *main cables* may be joined in any desired order to the outgoing pairs of the *distribution cables*. Many methods of cross-connection using terminal strips, jumpers, straps, pins, etc. have been devised and used. Present UK practice is to use *B-wire connectors* to join pairs directly or via a *jumper* wire.

crossfire (US) American term for *interference* in a telegraph channel caused by signals in another telegraph channel, i.e. telegraph *crosstalk*. As with crosstalk, crossfire is measured at both the sending end and receiving end of a circuit.

54

crossmodulation Undesired *amplitude modulation* of a wanted signal by one or more other signals as a result of their passage through a non-linear circuit or device. In a broadcast receiver crossmodulation may take place if a strong unwanted signal overloads the receiver's input circuits. The programme of the undesired station will then be heard as a background to the wanted programme.

cross-office check A test carried out on a circuit across an exchange to confirm that a transmission path for speech, data, etc. exists.

crossover frequency Of a frequency-dividing network, a frequency at which equal power is delivered to each of two outputs, it being assumed that these are correctly terminated.

crossover network A frequency-selective network that divides the input frequency spectrum into two or more adjacent *bands* for connection to different loads.

crosspoint Generic term for a switching element, which may be mechanical or electronic in nature and which may be operated to extend the speech and signal paths of a *connection*.

crosspolar diagram The *directivity diagram* of an antenna with respect to a *polarisation* (2) orthogonal to that for which the antenna was designed.

crosspolarisation discrimination A measure of the purity of *polarisation* (2) of an *antenna* system, usually expressed in *decibels*. For a receiving antenna it is the ratio of the power available at an output port due to radiation from a far-field source of specified polarisation to the power available at the same port when the source is changed to the *orthogonal polarisation*. For a transmitting antenna it is the ratio of the power transmitted with a specified polarisation to that transmitted in the orthogonal polarisation when the antenna is excited by energy having the reference polarisation only. By extension the term is also applied to overall transmission links, so that the quoted ratio includes the effect of both the transmitting and receiving antennas and *depolarisation* occurring in the transmission path owing to precipitation or other causes.

crosspolarisation interference In a radio system using *dual-polarisation transmission*, co-channel interference between a pair of orthogonally polarised signals. Such interference is the overall result of *depolarisation* occurring in the radio path and that contributed by the antenna systems.

crosspolarisation isolation ratio Of a *dual-polarised antenna*, the ratio (generally expressed in *decibels*) of the power radiated in a reference *polarisation* (2) when one port of the antenna is excited, to the power radiated in the same direction and polarisation when the other port is excited, the input power being the same in both cases.

crosspolarised antenna   See *dual-polarised antenna*.

crosstalk   The unwanted transfer of energy from a *circuit* known as the *disturbing circuit* into another circuit known as the *disturbed circuit*.

crosstalk attenuation or **crosstalk coupling**   The ratio of the power at a sending point in the disturbing circuit to the power coupled into the disturbed circuit under specified terminated conditions.

crossview   In a multipair broadcast relay system, the effect on a wanted television picture of the undesired transfer of energy from one or more *pairs* carrying other television signals.

crushing   An unwanted change in the contrast gradient of a television picture at one end of the luminance range. *White*

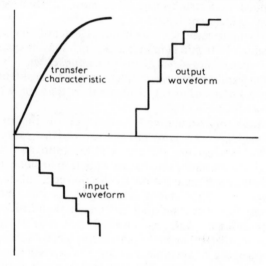

Figure C.4   Crushing

crushing is a loss of contrast between the brightest picture elements, whereas *black crushing* affects the darkest elements in the scene. Crushing is usually caused by a non-linear transmission facility, as shown in *Figure C.4*.

curtain antenna   An *antenna array* in which the radiating elements are arranged in a vertical plane.

customer digital switching system   Generic designation used in the UK for digital *private automatic exchanges*.

cut-off attenuator   A fixed or variable length of *waveguide* used at a frequency below its *cut-off frequency* (1) so that it acts as a *reactive attenuator*.

cut-off frequency (1) The frequency marking a transition between a pass band in which the *attenuation* is relatively low and a stop band in which it is substantially higher; for example, the frequency above which the attenuation of a *low-pass filter* exceeds a specified value. In the case of a *waveguide* it is usually called the *critical frequency*. (2) Of a radio wave propagated between specified points via ionospheric layers, the frequency below which the wave is unable to penetrate a particular layer at that angle of incidence which would have permitted transmission by reflection from a higher layer. Also called *barrier frequency*.

cut-off mode See *evanescent mode*.

cut-off waveguide A *waveguide* operated below its *critical frequency* (2). Also known as *evanescent waveguide*.

cut-off wavelength See *critical wavelength*.

Cutler feed A form of *antenna* feed in which the *waveguide* passes through the reflector at its vertex and then splits into two branches, each of which turns through 180° so that its open end faces the reflector.

cylindrical array A two-dimensional *antenna array* whose elements are arranged with their centres on a cylindrical surface.

cymomotive force Of a transmitting *antenna* in a given direction, the product of the *field strength* and the distance, the latter being sufficiently large for the reactive components of the field to be negligible. At medium and low frequencies with propagation taking place along the ground, the result is corrected to take out the effect of *attenuation* due to the finite conductivity of the ground. Numerically the cymomotive force corresponds to the field strength in millivolts per metre at a distance of one kilometre when the propagation path is lossless.

D

D layer A layer of ionised air occurring during daylight hours in the *D region* of the ionosphere, i.e. from around 50 km to about 90 km above the surface of the earth. The D layer is the lowest and most weakly ionised layer affecting the propagation of radio waves. It reflects waves having frequencies below 50 kHz, and partially absorbs higher-frequency signals.

D region That part of the *ionosphere* bounded by altitudes of about 50 and 90 kilometres. The D region has a lower electron density than the E and F regions, and is responsible for most of the *attenuation* of radio waves in the frequency range of 1 to 100 megahertz.

damped oscillation An oscillation whose *amplitude* decreases with time.

dark current Of a *photodiode,* the leakage current that flows in the absence of optical stimulation and is caused by the reverse bias applied to the device.

data channel A unidirectional transmission path used for data. In the US the term is also used to describe a *data circuit*.

data circuit A transmission facility between two points providing for the transmission of data in both directions but not necessarily at the same rate.

data-circuit terminating equipment A functional unit joining a data transmission line to the terminal equipment at a *data station*. The unit establishes and controls each connection, and provides for code or signal conversion where necessary.

data compression A technique for making more efficient use of a communication *channel* by substituting short *code words* for frequently used characters.

data connection A number of *data circuits* interconnected by switching equipment on a tandem basis to provide data transmission between *data terminal equipments.* The *data-circuit terminating equipments* at the terminals are deemed to form part of the connection. If one of the circuits is provided by means of a *packet switching* network, the overall connection is termed a *virtual data connection*.

data link Two or more *data stations* connected by a network suitable for information to be exchanged between them. In *common-channel signalling* the term describes an association of two *data channels* operating at the same data rate but in opposite directions.

data scrambler A device used in long digital transmission systems to convert an input *digital signal* into a pseudo-random sequence free from long runs of *marks, spaces,* or other simple repetitive patterns. This facilitates *timing extraction* and reduces the accumulation of *jitter*.

data signal quality detection In data transmission, an *error control* process in which one or more parameters of a received data signal are monitored for conformance with prescribed limits. The qualities that may be tested include the *amplitude* of the signal, the *signal-to-noise ratio* and the amount of *waveform distortion* present in the signal. Such tests do not directly indicate the occurrence of *digital errors* but rather the likelihood that errors will have occurred. They introduce a certain amount of *redundancy* (1), since they can give rise to unnecessary retransmission when errors are not in fact occurring. Used in combination with an *RQ system*, however, quality tests can be very effective in dealing with long error bursts, which would otherwise require the use of an *error detecting code* having a high degree of redundancy.

data signalling rate   The *digit rate* expressed in normalised form in *binary digits*. For a serial channel it is given by $T^{-1} \log_2 n$, where n is the number of significant conditions and T is the interval of time occupied by a single symbol, i.e. the *minimum interval*.

data sink   Equipment that receives data signals after transmission.

data source   Equipment that supplies data for transmission.

data station or **data terminal**   An assembly consisting of *data terminal equipment* joined to *data-circuit terminating equipment*.

data terminal equipment   A functional unit that serves as a *data sink, data source*, or both, at a *data station*. It also provides for the control of information transfer in accordance with a *data link* protocol.

data transfer rate   The average number of *bits, characters* (1) or *blocks* (1) transferred between corresponding data equipment, e.g. *data source* and *data sink*, per unit of time.

data transmission   The conveyance of data from a *data source* to one or more *data sinks* by means of signals sent over a telecommunication network.

datagram   In a public data network, an entity of data containing sufficient information to enable it to be routed from the *data source* to the desired *data sink* without the need for any prior communication between the source or sink and the network.

dataplex   Generic term used in the UK for data services that involve *multiplexing*.

datavision   See *teletext*.

day to busy-hour ratio   The ratio of the *traffic volume* in a day to the traffic volume in the *busy hour*. Some countries use the inverse of this ratio.

dead sector   In a facsimile transmitter, that part of a scanned area (such as the surface of a drum) that is used only for registering or securing the document to be transmitted. Also known as *clip position*.

decadic signal   In *analogue signalling*, a signal consisting of a train of identical pulses corresponding in number with the value of the digit it represents.

decay time   Of a pulse, the interval between the instants at which the instantaneous value of a pulse passes through specified upper and lower limits, namely 90 per cent and 10 per cent of the peak value unless otherwise stated. In the case of a pulse of radio-frequency energy, or of a carrier modulated by a pulse, it is the instantaneous value of the envelope of the signal that is considered. Also known as *fall time*.

decibel   A dimensionless, logarithmic unit equal to one-tenth of a *bel*. The decibel is thus one-tenth of the common logarithm of a number expressing a ratio of two powers, and we may write:

$$\text{Number of decibels} = 10 \log_{10} (P_1/P_2)$$

In conditions of equal impedance (the usual case for input and output quantities in telecommunications) a power ratio is equal to the square of the corresponding voltage or current ratio. Hence:

$$
\begin{aligned}
\text{Number of decibels} &= 10 \log_{10} (P_1/P_2)^2 \\
&= 20 \log_{10} (V_1/V_2) \\
&= 20 \log_{10} (I_1/I_2) \text{ in the case of a ratio of} \\
&\qquad \text{two currents } I_1 \text{ and } I_2
\end{aligned}
$$

The decibel is a very convenient unit for stating values of parameters such as *attenuation, signal-to-crosstalk ratio* and *signal-to-noise ratio*. It is also widely used to express the value of a given quantity with reference to a specified value of the same quantity. Thus a statement that a particular power level P_x is thirty decibels above a reference power of one milliwatt means that $10 \log_{10} (P_x/1) = 30$. From this P_x is seen to be equal to 1000 milliwatts, i.e. 1 watt. The standard way of writing such statements is to enclose the reference quantity in brackets following the quoted level, i.e. $P_x = 30$ dB (1 mW). The figure '1' in the reference can be omitted, but care should be exercised in cases where the reference is more complex, e.g. a ratio. For many reference quantities used in telecommunications a condensed notation is usually applied. In particular, the example above would be written as $P_x = 30$ dBm, since dBm is the abbreviation for dB (1 mW). Other abbreviations for reference quantities will be found in the Appendix.

Although the decibel was first defined in terms of power, and hence in terms of quantities linked with power in a well defined manner, modern practice has extended its use beyond these limits. An example of such practice is the expression in decibels of a ratio of two voltages V_1 and V_2 which appear across unequal impedances. The number of decibels, N, is still derived from the formula $N = 20 \log_{10} (V_1/V_2)$, but this number will no longer represent the corresponding power ratio. In other words it is no longer possible to calculate that ratio directly from the formula $N = 10 \log_{10} (P_1/P_2)$. In such circumstances it is important that any expressions in decibels should be accompanied by a statement clarifying the usage. Two examples will illustrate the use of the decibel.

(a) The strength of an electromagnetic field may be stated in terms of a power density or of the corresponding value of either the electric or the magnetic field. It is usual to give the value of the electric field E in decibels with reference to a field of one microvolt per metre (1 μV/m). The power carried by an electromagnetic field is proportional to the square of the electric field strength. It follows that a statement that a certain field strength has a value of 40 dB (μV/m) simply means that $20 \log_{10} E \, \mu$V/m $= 40$. From this the field strength is seen to be 100 μV/m.

(b) The intensity of a sound is directly related to the power carried by the sound wave, and this power is proportional to the square of the corresponding sound pressure level. It is usual to express such levels in decibels with reference to a pressure of twenty micropascals, since this corresponds with the threshold of hearing of the average human ear. The statement that a certain sound pressure level $L_x = 80$ dB (20 μPa) therefore means that $20 \log_{10} (L_x/20 \, \mu$Pa) $= 80$. From this L_x is found to be 200 000 μPa or 0.2 Pa.

decineper A *transmission unit* equal to one-tenth of a *neper*.

decision feedback In data transmission, a method of *error control* in which a decision on the accuracy or otherwise of received data is taken by the receiver based on *parity checks*; see *idle RQ, continuous RQ* and *van Duuren ARQ system*.

decision instant In the reception of a *digital signal*, the instant at which a decision is made by a receiving device as to the probable value of a *signal element*.

decision value In *pulse code modulation*, a value defining a boundary between two adjacent ranges of input-signal amplitude in the process of *quantising*.

decoding (1) In general, a process applied to a signal produced by encoding, whereby the information conveyed by the signal is restored to its original form. (2) In *pulse code modulation*, a process in which a reconstructed sample is generated for each *character signal* (2) applied to the decoding device.

de-emphasis A process that reduces the *amplitude* of the higher-frequency components of a complex wave with respect to the amplitude of others. This is the inverse of the process of *pre-emphasis*, so the signal is restored to its original form.

deferred alarm See *non-urgent alarm*.

definition In *facsimile* or television, a measure of the sharpness of detail in a reproduced picture.

dejitteriser A device for reducing *jitter* in a *digital signal*, consisting essentially of an elastic store into which the signal is written and from which it is read at a rate determined by the

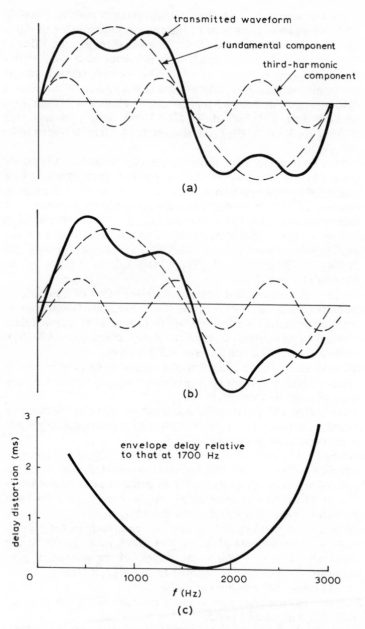

Figure D.1 Delay distortion: (a) wave consisting of fundamental and third harmonic; (b) distorted wave due to excess delay of third-harmonic component; (c) delay distortion characteristic

62

average rate of the incoming signal. Such a device is largely ineffective in dealing with low-frequency impairments such as *waiting time jitter.*

delay (1) Of a signal, a measure of the amount of time by which the signal is retarded, usually expressed in fractions of a second but sometimes given as a number of pulses, cycles, characters, etc. (2) Of an amplifier or receiver to a sudden excitation by step function or sine wave, the time elapsing between the instant when the excitation is applied and the instant when the response first attains half the steady-state amplitude.

delay-dialling signal (US) A *line signal* sent back by the incoming exchange following receipt and recognition of a *seizing signal*, to acknowledge the latter and to indicate that the *register* equipment is not yet attached or ready to receive *address signals.*

delay distortion or **delay frequency distortion** *Distortion* of a received signal waveform caused by a transmission system with a *phase/frequency characteristic* that is not linear over the frequency range required for transmission. The effect arises because not all the frequency components of the wave are transmitted through the system in the same time, some being more delayed than others so that the output waveform is distorted; see *Figure D.1(a)* and *(b)*. Numerically, the term delay distortion is sometimes applied to the difference in units of time between the *group delay* at one frequency and that at a reference frequency. A plot of this delay against frequency is called a *delay distortion characteristic*; see *Figure D.1(c).*

delay equaliser or **delay frequency equaliser** A network intended to compensate for *delay distortion* by making the time of transmission through a system substantially constant over the relevant frequency band.

delay line Any real or artificial line, or equivalent device, used to introduce a desired *delay* (1) in the propagation of a signal.

delay modulation A method of encoding binary data to form a two-level signal. A binary zero causes no change of signal level unless it is followed by another zero, in which case a *transition* takes place at the end of the first bit period. A binary one causes a transition from one level to the other in the middle of the bit period. See *Figure D.2.*

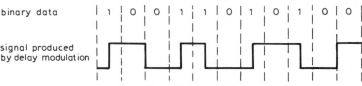

Figure D.2 Delay modulation

63

delay system In automatic switching, a system in which a call attempt that cannot be completed owing to internal congestion is permitted to wait until a free path becomes available. Also termed *waiting system*.

delay working In a manual system, a method of operation used when there are insufficient *circuits* to permit the immediate connection of calls. Details of each call attempt are recorded by the operator, and the calling circuit is released until a free circuit is available for completion of the call.

delayed-answer supervision A facility provided on some switchboards whereby, if a call is unanswered after a specified period of time (e.g. 30 seconds), the continuous lamp signal is replaced by a flashing signal.

delayed automatic gain control Automatic control of the *gain* of a receiver or amplifier applied only to signals whose magnitude exceeds a given threshold value.

delayed call A call attempt placed in a waiting queue because it has encountered congestion.

Dellinger fade-out A sudden fade-out of radio signals in the band from about 1 MHz to around 30 MHz, owing to partial or complete absorption in the *ionosphere* as a result of abnormal solar radiation affecting the transmission paths in the sunlit hemisphere.

delta impulse See *unit impulse*.

delta modulation A form of *differential pulse code modulation* in which the actual value of each *sample* of an *analogue signal* is compared with the integrated value of the preceding samples, a single digit being transmitted to indicate the sign of the difference.

Figure D.3(a) is a simplified block diagram to illustrate the

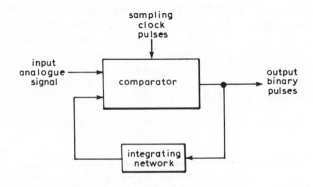

Figure D.3(a)   Delta-modulation encoder

64

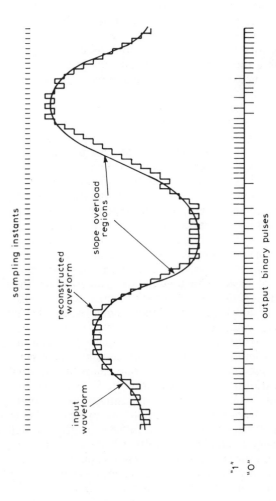

sampling instants

reconstructed
waveform

slope overload
regions

input
waveform

output binary pulses

"1"
"0"

Figure D.3(b)   Delta modulation: comparison of waveforms

65

principle of operation of a basic delta-modulation encoder. The instantaneous value of the input analogue signal is compared at each sampling instant with the value of the reconstructed waveform obtained from an integrating network in the feedback loop. A positive binary pulse is produced if the analogue sample is greater than the reconstructed waveform, or a negative pulse if it is smaller. In this way the difference between the input signal and the reconstructed waveform is minimised and the latter tends to follow the former, albeit in a series of discrete steps; see *Figure D.3(b)*. The integrator in fact serves to decode the output signal locally, so that the distant decoder can consist of no more than an integrating network followed by a *low-pass filter* to eliminate noise.

The diagram necessarily depicts a low sampling rate. In practice the input signal must be sampled at a rate four or five times as fast as that used in PCM if acceptable quality is to result. Even so, the *digit rate* is only about half that of PCM in which each quantised sample is represented by eight digits. In addition to the resulting gain in transmission capacity, delta modulation enjoys a number of other advantages over PCM. It is much simpler to implement, does not require *synchronisation* (2) except for multiplex purposes, and is more tolerant of *impulsive noise*. These features combine to make it an attractive proposition for use in *pair gain systems* in the *local line network*.

Figure D.3(b) also illustrates in exaggerated form one of the deficiencies of basic delta modulation, namely *slope overload distortion*. This is the inability of the reconstructed waveform to track the waveform of the input signal when the latter's instantaneous value is changing rapidly. Such changes are proportional to the amplitude of the input signal and are also more severe when high-frequency components are present. This limits the dynamic range of signals that can be handled without excessive distortion. One solution would be to increase the sampling rate, which would incidentally also lower the quantisation distortion produced in the process. This would negate one of the principal advantages of this modulation method, however, and there are other ways of overcoming the problem. In essence these all result in a continuous adjustment of the size of the steps used to form the reconstructed waveform, so that it is able to match the input signal much more closely. The processes are known generally as adaptive delta modulation. In one version, termed *continuously variable slope delta modulation*, the digits produced in the encoding process are examined through a four-bit 'window', and every time a run of four like digits occurs a pulse is applied to an integrating network having a syllabic time constant. The voltage that builds up on the network causes the step size to be steadily increased until the reconstructed waveform 'overtakes' the original and the opposite digit is produced, thus breaking the continuous run. In the absence of input pulses the voltage stored by the network decays and the step size is reduced to a minimum—the condition appropriate to idle channel conditions. It will be noted that this process includes a form of *companding* in which the dynamic range of the coder/decoder combination is adjusted to track the input signal amplitude rather than compressing the signal range to suit the channel's characteristics as in analogue transmission systems.

delta-sigma modulation A variant of *delta modulation* in which the integral of the input signal is encoded rather than the signal itself. This may be achieved by preceding a normal delta modulation encoder by an integrating network; see *Figure D.4*.

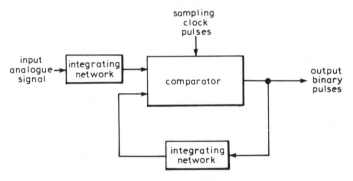

Figure D.4 Delta-sigma modulation encoder

Since the integral of the input signal is encoded, the decoder should properly include a differentiating network. As explained under the previous definition, however, a normal decoder consists essentially of an integrating network and filter. Since the integrating and differentiating networks would be complementary they can be dispensed with, and the delta-sigma decoder can consist of nothing more than a filter. In a practical encoder it is possible to move the integrating network so that it is located between the device deriving the error signal and the quantiser, i.e. within the block labelled 'comparator' in *Figure D.4*. It is then possible to dispense with the integrating network in the feedback loop. As a result the encoder contains no more components than a basic delta modulation encoder, and the decoder is simpler. Consideration of *Figure D.4* shows that a better term for this system would be *sigma-delta modulation*.

demand-assignment In *communication satellite* systems, the allocation of circuits to users only at those times when they are actually required for traffic; see *SPADE*.

democratic network See *mutually synchronised network*.

demodulation The process by which an original modulating signal is recovered from a modulated wave, i.e. the reverse of the *modulation* process.

density In *facsimile*, a measure of the light-reflecting properties of an *elemental area*.

departmental call accounting See *call information logging*.

dependent exchange A *local exchange* that gains access to its *group switching centre* via another exchange.

depolarisation In propagation, the transfer of energy from a specified *polarisation* to other polarisations. Specifically, the depolarisation factor is the ratio of the power of the reference component of a polarised signal to the power of the component having an *orthogonal polarisation*. Depolarisation in the *troposphere* may be caused by rain or ice crystals. See also *crosspolarisation discrimination*.

derivative equaliser A *waveform corrector* that compensates for distortion in a received signal by introducing a correcting signal that is a linear function of the derivative of the distorted signal. In this way it is possible to correct for *amplitude/frequency distortion* and *phase/frequency distortion* simultaneously.

descrambler In digital transmission, a device for restoring a binary signal from a *data scrambler* to its original form.

deserialiser (US) See *serial to parallel converter*.

designated extension answering A facility provided at PABXs not having switchboards, whereby incoming calls can be answered by one extension or one of several selected extensions, before being transferred to the required extension.

designated extension group pick-up A PABX facility enabling any extension in a defined group of extensions to pick up and answer incoming calls arriving at any unattended extension in the group. Pick-up is effected by dialling a special code followed by the pick-up number allocated to the called extension. The number 0 is not used as a pick-up number for any specific extension, and it may be dialled to cause the system to search for the first ringing extension regardless of its pick-up number.

designated extension night service A PABX facility whereby a selected extension can be associated with a group of exchange lines for the purpose of receiving incoming calls on any of them. The extension selected as the night service terminal retains normal PBX services and is provided with a *call waiting* indication.

despotic network A *synchronised network* in which a single master *clock* controls all the other clocks in the network.

despun antenna Of a rotating *communication satellite*, an *antenna*, the direction of whose *main beam* with respect to the satellite is continually adjusted so that it illuminates a fixed area on the surface of the earth.

destination code A combination of digits that uniquely identifies a particular subscriber's station or other terminal in a network.

detached manual board A switchboard located in another building than that housing the associated equipment.

detection The process of recovering information from an electromagnetic wave. This includes the *demodulation* of modulated waves and determination of the presence of a signal, for example in simple *on/off keying*.

deviation distortion In an FM receiver, distortion caused by lack of *bandwidth*, inadequate *amplitude modulation* rejection, or lack of linearity in the *discriminator*.

deviation ratio The ratio of the maximum *frequency deviation* to the maximum modulating frequency in an FM system.

deviation sensitivity Of an FM receiver, the smallest value of *frequency deviation* that produces a specified output power.

deviative absorption In ionospheric propagation, absorption of those radio waves experiencing appreciable bending at frequencies near the *critical frequency* (1) of an ionospheric layer.

dial A device used to generate the pulse signals needed for the establishment of a desired connection in an *automatic system*.

dial answer night service A PABX facility whereby any incoming call can be caused to ring one or more bells located at selected points. The call can then be answered by any extension user dialling the correct *access code*, and it may be transferred as required using the enquiry and automatic transfer services.

dial conference A PABX facility enabling an extension user to call several other parties, all of whom are then able to speak and listen to each other.

dial long lines (US) Designation for a class of *range extender* equipment providing improved *signalling* and *supervision* on lines exceeding the normal loop resistance limit.

dial-mobile telephone system A mobile communication system in which mobile stations can establish connections with fixed telephone stations by dialling.

dial pulsing Interruptions of the direct current path at the sending end by the operation of a dial.

dial tone In automatic telephony, an audible signal connected to a calling subscriber's line or a PABX extension when the equipment is ready to accept dialled or keyed information.

dialled digit display   A PBX switchboard feature showing the digits that have been dialled by the operator. Also known as *called number identification*.

dialling   Strictly, the production of signalling digits as a result of the rotation and release of a dial. The term is sometimes used to describe the production of signalling digits by other means, e.g. a pushbutton dial.

dialling duration   The time taken to dial a complete number, measured from the commencement of dial tone to the end of the last pulse train.

dialling-in   The process whereby an operator dials or keysends digits over a circuit to a distant automatic exchange.

dialling-out   The process whereby a subscriber or operator dials one or more digits to gain access to an operator at a distant exchange.

dialling pattern (US)   The *numbering plan* applying to a particular automatic exchange.

diary service   A PABX facility whereby an extension user can record a message and arrange for it to be automatically played back to him at any time on any date up to one year ahead.

dicode   A *pseudo-ternary code* in which the three signal levels are formed by representing each positive transition in the input binary signal by a positive pulse, and each negative transition by a negative pulse. If rectangular pulses of one bit duration are used, the resulting signal is the same as that given by a *twinned binary code*.

dielectric antenna, dielectric radiator or **dielectric rod antenna** (also termed *polyrod antenna*)   An *end-fire antenna* consisting of a shaped piece of dielectric material whose dimension in the direction of radiation is long compared with the wavelength. The *directivity pattern* is produced by the propagation of a surface wave on the dielectric rod.

dielectric lens   Of a *microwave* antenna, a structure of dielectric material used to refract radio waves. See *E-plane lens, H-plane lens* and *zoned antenna*.

dielectric waveguide   A rod of dielectric material surrounded by air.

differential detection   See *differential encoding*.

differential duplex transmission   An early system of direct-current *duplex* telegraphy in which discrimination between the sent and received signals was obtained by the use of differential relays and *balancing networks*.

differential echo suppressor   See *echo suppressor*.

differential encoding   A form of encoding in which the *transitions*

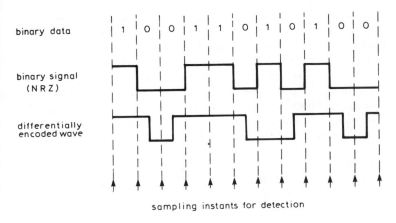

Figure D.5 Differential encoding

in a wave are used to represent **binary digits**. Thus a transition may be used to represent a '0' and no transition a '1', as shown in *Figure D.5*. Such a signal can be inverted without affecting its interpretation. For a serial channel synchronous operation is required, the information being recovered by sampling the received signal and comparing the polarity of adjacent samples to see whether a transition has occurred—a process known as *differential detection*.

differential gain   Of a video transmission system, a measure of the extent to which the gain of the system varies with the instantaneous amplitude of an input signal, i.e. a measure of *amplitude/amplitude distortion*. It is expressed by the difference between unity and the ratio of the output amplitudes of a small high-frequency signal at two specified levels of a low-frequency input signal on which it is superimposed. By multiplying the difference by 100 the differential gain can be given as a percentage. Alternatively it can be expressed in *decibels* by multiplying the common logarithm of the ratio itself by 20.

differential phase   Of a video transmission system, a measure of the extent to which the output phase of a small high-frequency signal changes with variations in the instantaneous level of a low-frequency signal on which it is superimposed. Differential phase is an important parameter in the case of NTSC colour signals, because small changes of phase of the colour subcarrier with changes of luminance level lead to the reproduction of incorrect hues.

differential phase detection   Of a phase-modulated signal conveying digital information, a method of *detection* in which

71

the phase of each symbol is compared with that of the previous symbol.

differential pulse code modulation A version of *pulse code modulation* in which an *analogue signal* is sampled, the difference between the actual value of each sample and its predicted value (derived from the previous sample or samples) being quantised and converted by encoding to a *digital signal*.

diffraction A phenomenon whereby the paths of electromagnetic and sound waves are bent as they pass the edges of objects in their path. Diffraction effects extend the range of line-of-sight transmissions slightly beyond the radio horizon.

digipulse telephone (US) A pushbutton telephone containing equipment that converts calling signals from the keypad into pulses similar to those generated by a rotary dial.

digit A number selected from a finite set; for example, a 0 or 1 in a binary set or one of the figures 0–9 in a telephone number. A digit may be represented by a discrete condition of a signal, e.g. its phase, amplitude or frequency at a given instant. In equipment it may be represented by a condition of a ferrite core or element of magnetic tape. A position in time or space into which the representation of a digit may be placed is called a *digit position*.

digit absorbing selector A *selector* arranged so that it does not carry out any switching function on receipt of one or more dialled *digits* in a train, but behaves normally on receipt of subsequent digits.

digit absorption In automatic switching, the process whereby *digits* are received, interpreted and rejected if not required for switching purposes.

digit deletion Rejection of part of the *address information* during the call set-up process.

digit position See *digit*.

digit rate The number of *digits* of a specified radix transmitted per unit of time.

digit registering In automatic switching, the process whereby signals representing *digits* are received and stored for interpretation and action.

digit time slot An interval of time allocated to a single *digit*.

digital block A *digital path* together with associated *digital multiplex equipment*.

digital connection Two or more *digital paths* connected by means of a *digital switch* or switches.

digital demultiplexer Equipment that separates a composite *digital signal* formed by *time-division multiplexing* into its component tributary signals.

72

digital error In digital transmission, a single incorrect *digit* in the received signal. It should be noted that more than one digital error can be produced at the output of certain types of device when an erroneous digit is applied at the input; see *error multiplication*.

digital filling The addition of a fixed number of digits per unit time interval to a *digital signal* in order to change its *digit rate* to a higher nominal value. The added digits are not used for the transmission of information. Filling could be required, for example, if it was desired to use a standard 8.448 Mbit/s *digital path* for the transmission of a lower-rate digital signal representing an encoded FDM *supergroup*.

digital loop carrier systems US designation for *pair gain systems* that effectively combine the techniques of *concentration* and *time-division multiplex* transmission; see *subscribers carrier system* and *subscriber loop multiplex*.

digital multiplex equipment See *muldex*.

digital multiplex hierarchy An ordered scheme for the combination of *digital signals* by the repeated application of *digital multiplexing*. Details of one hierarchy recommended by the CCITT and based on the 2.048 Mbit/s signal formed by a standard 30-channel PCM system are given in *Table D.1*.

Table D.1

Multiplex level	No. of channels	Gross bit rate
Primary	30	2.048 Mbit/s
Second-order	120	8.448 Mbit/s (4 × 2.048)
Third-order	480	34.368 Mbit/s (4 × 8.448)
Fourth-order	1920	139.264 Mbit/s (4 × 34.368)

It will be noticed that the gross digit rate of each order is slightly higher than the sum of the preceding tributary rates, i.e. $4 \times 2.048 = 8.192$ not 8.448. The extra *digit time slots* in the multiplexed signal are provided to accommodate digits required for *frame alignment, justification* and network management purposes.

digital multiplexer Equipment that combines a number of input *digital signals* into a single digital signal by *time-division multiplexing*.

digital multiplexing A process in which a number of tributary *digital signals* are combined by *time-division multiplexing*. If the tributary signals are synchronous it is possible to combine them by *pulse interlacing* to form a signal having a rate equal to the sum of the tributaries' rates. It is necessary, however, for the demultiplex equipment to be able to recognise which digits belong to which tributaries, so a *frame alignment signal* has to be transmitted for this purpose. Extra time slots are therefore provided in the output signal by giving it a higher rate than the sum of the tributaries' rates. If the tributary signals are **plesiochronous** it is also necessary to provide additional time slots for the purpose of *justification*. The process of digital multiplexing can be repeated so that a number of composite digital signals—each consisting of a combination of a number of lower-rate signals—can themselves be combined into a single composite signal of higher rate. This leads to the concept of a number of orders of multiplexes designated primary, second-order, third-order and so on; see *digital multiplex hierarchy*.

digital network A network employing both digital transmission and digital switching.

digital path A complete transmission facility for a digital signal of defined rate between two points (usually digital *distribution frames*) at which terminal equipment or digital switches may be connected. A digital path may comprise one or more digital sections and is normally bidirectional. The term is usually qualified, e.g. 2048 kbit/s digital line path or 8448 kbit/s digital radio path.

digital phase modulation See *phase-shift keying*.

digital section A complete transmission facility for a *digital signal* of defined rate between two consecutive digital *distribution frames*. A digital section is bidirectional unless otherwise stated.

digital signal A signal in which the information is conveyed in a coded form by means of a number of discrete signal conditions. See also *analogue signal*.

digital signalling The use of a digital transmission channel for the transfer of information relating to the establishment, control and release of calls.

digital speech interpolation A technique for improving the utilisation of long-distance digital systems used for the transmission of speech. The process is similar to *time-assignment speech interpolation* but operates on the digitally encoded speech signals. The technique can more than double the capacity of a digital transmission system, and it is likely to be brought into use at some earth stations in the *global satellite communication system* during the mid 1980s.

digital sum A concept used in connection with the study of signals produced by various codes. The pulse levels in the signal are given signed values, so that in a typical three-level *line signal* a positive pulse would have the value $+1$, space would be represented by 0 and a negative pulse by -1. The digital sum is then the sum of all the pulse values from some arbitrary time origin up to the instant under consideration. It is clear that its value at any instant will be equal to the difference in the number of positive and negative pulses that have been transmitted, and that it is therefore a measure of the accumulated imbalance of the signal. In order to restrict the amount of low-frequency energy in the signal, the running digital sum must be kept within low limits and many codes have been devised to satisfy this requirement; see *four binary – three ternary code (4B3T)* and *MS43*.

digital sum variation The difference between the maximum and minimum value of the *digital sum* of a coded signal.

digital switch Equipment capable of establishing connections between *circuits* carrying *digital signals*—usually, for example, between channels provided by the *time slots* of standard PCM transmission systems. Such a switch normally requires a combination of *time-division switching* and *space-division switching* techniques. In the US the term is sometimes used to describe a complete exchange.

digital-to-analogue converter A device that converts an input *digital signal* into an *analogue signal* conveying essentially the same information.

digital transmission The transmission of information in the form of *digital signals*.

digitally modulated signal The signal resulting from the *modulation* of a *carrier* wave by a *baseband* digital signal.

digitiser (US) See *analogue-to-digital converter*.

digram coding A method of coding binary data in which pairs of *binary digits* are treated as units.

digroup See *primary block*.

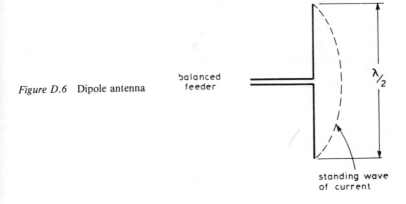

Figure D.6 Dipole antenna

balanced feeder

$\lambda/2$

standing wave of current

diplex operation   The use of a single *circuit, carrier* or *antenna* for the simultaneous transmission or reception of two signals.

diplexer   A three-port frequency-dependent device that may be used as a separator or a combiner of signals. Typically the signals from two television *antennas* for different frequency *bands* may be combined on to one downlead and then separated by a second diplexer for connection to the receiver inputs.

dipole antenna   A centre-fed, rectilinear, symmetrical *antenna* producing a *directivity pattern* similar to that of an elementary electric dipole. In its simplest form it consists of a single straight wire a half-wavelength long, so excited that the *standing wave* of current is symmetrical about its midpoint and has a *node* (2) at each end; see *Figure D.6*. A dipole radiates uniformly in all directions in a plane normal to its axis, and this type of element often forms a fundamental unit of an array. Also known as *doublet antenna*.

dipulse   A positive pulse followed immediately by a negative pulse.

dipulse code   A three-level code in which one binary state is represented by zero signal level and the other one by a *dipulse* transmitted within a single digit period. This has the effect of increasing the *amplitude* of the high-frequency components in the signal, which helps to offset any *amplitude/frequency distortion* caused by a transmission line.

Dirac pulse   See *unit impulse*.

direct back scatter   A back-scattered radio signal received directly from the region in which *scattering* is taking place. Also termed *short-distance back scatter*.

direct control system   In automatic switching, a system in which functional units that control the establishment of connections are associated with a given call for its duration and respond directly to the *signals* (2) generated by a calling device.

direct-current signalling   The use of direct currents for the transfer of information relating to the set-up, control or release of a call.

direct dialling   The process whereby a subscriber or operator sets up a call by dialling, without the intervention of an intermediate operator.

direct dialling-in   A facility permitting a caller to gain access to a PABX extension without the assistance of the PABX operator. Also known as *direct inward dialling*.

direct distance dialling   The establishing of long-distance calls automatically by means of *signals* (2) produced by the calling device of a customer or operator.

direct exchange line   See *exclusive exchange line*.

direct exchange night service   A PABX facility whereby a selected

76

extension can be directly connected to an exchange line to provide a night service terminal. The extension loses normal PBX services.

direct extension night service A PABX facility whereby an extension can be associated with an incoming exchange line to act as a night service terminal. Normal PBX services are retained, and an incoming call waiting indication is provided at the terminal.

direct inward dialling See *direct dialling-in*.

direct junction circuit A circuit between two local exchanges.

direct orbit Of a *communication satellite*, an *orbit* such that the projection of the satellite on a plane through the equator rotates in the same direction as the earth.

direct outward dialling A facility whereby PABX or CENTREX extensions can dial outside numbers without assistance from the PABX or centrex operator.

direct-point repeater (US) A *telegraph repeater* in which the incoming signal actuates a *relay* that repeats the signal directly into an outgoing line.

direct polarisation Of an *antenna*, that polarisation (whether *linear polarisation, circular polarisation* or *elliptical polarisation*) which the antenna is intended to radiate or receive. Two antennas having normally the same polarisation are said to be *directly polarised* or *copolarised*.

direct printer Apparatus used with telegraph systems employing unequal-length *cable codes* or the *Morse code* and producing a printed output directly from the received signals.

direct ray The shortest possible path for a radio wave between a transmitting antenna and a receiving antenna.

direct recording In *facsimile*, the production of a visible record by the received signal, without any intermediate processing.

direct service area The area within which subscribers' lines are directly connected to an exchange without the use of a *cross-connection point*.

direct voice calling See *voice calling*.

direct wave A radio wave propagated along a *direct ray*.

direction of polarisation (1) For a linearly polarised wave propagated in space, the direction of the *electric field vector*. (2) For an elliptically polarised wave propagated in space, the direction of the major axis of the ellipse traced by the electric field vector. See *linear polarisation, elliptical polarisation*.

directional antenna An antenna that radiates (or receives) radio waves more effectively in some directions than others.

directional coupler In a CATV type of system, a *splitter* in which the attenuation between the input and at least one output is higher in the reverse direction of transmission. Such couplers are used as *subscriber's tap* units giving relatively low forward loss while protecting the network from any spurious signals (e.g. oscillator harmonics) generated by the subscriber's installation. Also known as *directive feed*.

directional phase shifter A passive *waveguide* device with the property that the *phase* shift introduced for waves transmitted in one direction differs from that introduced by transmission in the opposite direction.

directive feed See *directional coupler*.

directive gain (US) Of an *antenna*, for a specified direction: a rating given by the product of 4π and the ratio of the *radiation intensity* in the given direction to the total power radiated by the antenna. It seems likely that this concept will be covered by the term *directivity* in future US standards.

directivity Of an *antenna*, for a specified direction, the ratio in *decibels* of the *radiation intensity* produced in the given direction to the average value of the radiation intensities in all directions in space. If the direction is not specified it can be assumed to be that of maximum radiation. The directivity as thus defined is independent of antenna losses and is equal to the *absolute gain* in the same direction only if the antenna is lossless.

directivity diagram or **directivity pattern** Of an antenna, a graphical representation, using an appropriate coordinate system, of the *directivity* of the antenna. Such diagrams are usually prepared for planes or cones containing the antenna, and they may be produced for a field component of specified *polarisation* (1). See also *radiation pattern*.

director (1) Of an antenna, a *parasitic element* located in front of the *driven element* with respect to the direction of maximum radiation and serving to increase the gain in that direction. (2) In automatic switching, a *register-translator* in a *director system*.

director exchange A *local exchange* employing the *director system*.

director system Designation for the older *step-by-step automatic system* used in large multi-exchange areas in the UK.

directory number All the digits required to designate a subscriber's station in a directory for the relevant area.

discone An *antenna* consisting of a cone with a disc mounted symmetrically near its apex, the elements being fed in antiphase.

disconnect signal See *clear-forward signal*.

discriminating selector A *selector* in which *digit absorption* is used to discriminate between calls to be completed locally and those to be routed elsewhere.

discriminator Generic term for a circuit or device producing an output signal of varying *amplitude* in response to an input signal varying in frequency or *phase*.

discriminatory engaged signals A PABX facility whereby an extension user can be advised of the type of call (internal or external) on which a required extension is engaged. The facility is normally provided by using a non-standard *busy tone* for internal extension-to-extension calls.

dish Of an *antenna*, a concave reflector usually shaped like part of a sphere or a paraboloid of revolution.

disparity The excess of 1s over 0s in a binary word. Hence the three words 00100, 01010 and 10111 have disparities of -3, -1 and $+3$ respectively. The term is also used to describe the imbalance of coded signals, i.e. the excess of *marks* over *spaces* in a binary signal or the *digital sum* of a three-level signal.

distinctive engaged tone An audible signal differing from standard *busy tone* and used in connection with the *intrusion* service on some PABXs. An extension user, on calling another extension that is not protected against intrusion and is engaged on an internal call, hears the tone and (provided he enjoys a suitable *class of service*) may then attempt intrusion.

distinctive ringing tone A variation of the standard ringing cadence used with some PABXs to indicate to a called extension user that the call is an internal one. See also *call back ringing*.

distortion Any unwanted change in a signal *waveform* occurring as a result of its transmission through a system or device intended to produce an output signal that is a faithful replica of the input signal. The principal causes of distortion are (a) non-linearity between input and output (see *harmonic distortion* and *intermodulation*), (b) variations in *gain* or *attenuation* with frequency (see *amplitude/frequency distortion*), and (c) non-linearity of the *phase/frequency characteristic* (see *delay distortion*).

distortionless condition In line transmission, the ideal condition in which the *characteristic impedance* is purely resistive so that neither the *attenuation* nor the *delay* (1) varies with the frequency. This condition obtains when $L.G = R.C$, the letters representing the distributed constants for inductance, leakance, resistance and capacitance, respectively.

distributed connection In logic circuitry, the parallel connection of the outputs of a number of *logic elements* in order to achieve an AND or an OR operation without the use of an explicit element. The output terminals of elements intended for this type of connection are typically open-collector or open-emitter outputs which require connection to an external load.

distributed constants In uniform *transmission lines* or *waveguides*, parameters that exist along the whole length of the line or guide. In the case of a two-conductor transmission line the distributed constants of interest are the series resistance, series inductance, shunt conductance and shunt capacitance per unit length of line.

distributed frame-alignment signal In *pulse code modulation*, a *frame-alignment signal* in which the *signal elements* are distributed in non-consecutive *digit time slots* as in the standard 24-channel system.

distribution cable In a *local line network*, designation given to a cable to a *distribution point* or between two *cross-connection points*.

distribution frame A structure providing for the termination of wires and cables and their interconnection in any desired order.

distribution network That part of a *local line network* which connects the *flexibility cabinets* to the *distribution points* (1).

distribution pedestal (US) A *distribution point* (1) in a network using *buried cables*.

distribution point (1) In a *local line network*, the final point from which *pairs* are run to individual subscribers' premises. In the US the term *ready access terminal* is used for this concept. (2) In a CATV network, a point from which signals are taken from the trunk network (or sometimes the *head end*) to feed branch or spur cables serving subscribers.

distribution terminal (US) A *distribution point* (1) in a network using *aerial cables*.

district switching centre UK designation for a switching centre in the *trunk transit network* that is directly connected to a number of *group switching centres* and to at least one *main switching centre*; see *Figure T.4* and also *classification of exchanges*.

disturbance Any undesired irregular phenomenon occurring in a communication *channel*.

disturbance voltage The voltage produced by a disturbance when measured under closely specified conditions.

dither A pseudo-random signal added at the input to a *quantising* device and subtracted at its output in order to reduce the impairments resulting from quantisation.

diverse routing The use of different transmission paths for subdivisions of a group of *circuits* so that an interruption of one path does not affect all the circuits in the group.

diversity The generic term for the technique of providing more than one path for the establishment of a *channel* or *circuit* in order to improve the reliability of a service.

diversity reception Radio reception in which the effects of *fading,* rain, *atmospherics*, etc. are minimised by providing more than

80

one means of receiving the transmitted information. See *space diversity reception* and *frequency diversity reception*.

divided code ringing or **divided ringing**   A form of ringing in which one half of the bells on a *party line* are connected between one wire and *earth*, the other half being connected between the second wire and earth.

Dolph – Chebyshev array   See *Chebyshev array*.

dominant mode   In *waveguide* transmission, the *mode* (2) of propagation with the lowest *critical frequency* (3); also known as *fundamental mode* or *principal mode*. Apart from the *evanescent mode*, this is the field configuration of the lowest-frequency wave that will propagate in the guide, as determined by its dimensions in terms of wavelength.

don't answer call (US)   A call on which ringing is started but the caller hangs up before it is answered.

dot   A unit-duration marking condition in the *Morse code*.

dot cycle   Of a two-condition telegraph signal, one cycle of a periodic variation between the two conditions, comprising a unit-duration marking condition followed by a unit-duration spacing condition.

dot frequency   In *facsimile*, the fundamental frequency of the square wave that would be generated by scanning alternate black and white *picture elements*. For an uninterrupted sequence this equals half the number of picture elements transmitted per second.

dot signal   In telegraphy, a signal composed of a continuous sequence of alternate *marks* and *spaces* of equal duration, also known as *reversals*.

dotting speed   Of a telegraph channel, an old term describing the maximum reversal rate that could be clearly resolved at the receiver.

double-cord switchboard   A switchboard on which incoming and outgoing lines are terminated by *jacks* that may be interconnected by a cord circuit having an 'answering plug' at the end of one cord and a 'calling plug' at the end of the other.

double-current cable code   A *two-condition cable code* in which positive current and negative current represent the two conditions.

double-current transmission   The use of positive current and negative current to represent the *mark* and *space* conditions in telegraphy.

double-ended synchronisation   At a specified *synchronisation node* in a digital network, a method of synchronisation in which *synchronisation information* at the specified node is obtained by comparing the phase difference between the local clock and the digital signal incoming from the other node, with the phase difference at the other node between its local clock and the digital signal incoming from the specified node. Information regarding this latter phase difference is transmitted to the specified node by means of a data signal. Compare with *single-ended synchronisation*.

double modulation A process in which a *sub-carrier* is first modulated with an information-carrying wave, the resulting modulated sub-carrier then being used to modulate another carrier having a higher frequency.

double phantom circuit A circuit derived from two *phantom circuits* in such a way that each leg consists of the four wires of one phantom circuit effectively connected in parallel.

double seizure A condition arising from incorrect *seizing*, as a result of the arrival of a second call before *guarding* has been effected.

double-sideband transmission A method of operation in which both *sidebands* produced by the process of *amplitude modulation* are transmitted at the same level.

double superheterodyne receiver A receiver employing two different *intermediate frequencies* in order to minimise *image frequency* and other *spurious responses* while maintaining a high degree of *adjacent-channel selectivity*.

double-talking See *echo suppressor*.

doublet antenna See *dipole antenna*.

doublet (electrical) radiator A hypothetical radiator consisting of a pair of equal and opposite varying electrical charges connected by an infinitely small straight conductor. Also known as *elementary electric dipole, infinitesimal dipole, radiating doublet* and *hertzian radiator*.

doublet (magnetic) radiator A hypothetical radiator consisting of equal and opposite magnetic poles separated by infinitesimal distance.

down time The time during which a system is out of use owing to a fault.

downward modulation A form of *amplitude modulation* in which the instantaneous magnitude of the modulated wave is never greater than the amplitude of the unmodulated carrier. See also *negative modulation*.

drift In *common-channel signalling*, an effect caused by lack of synchronism between an incoming and an outgoing *signalling channel* at a terminal, and manifesting itself as a lack of correspondence between transmitted and received *signal units* over a long period.

drift compensation The process of adjusting the timing

relationship between received *signal units* and the backward acknowledgment of them, where *drift* has occurred.

drive pattern   In *facsimile*, periodic variations in the density of the reproduced material caused by errors in the position of the recording spot due to defects in the scanning mechanism.

driven element   Of an *antenna*, an element that is energised by a transmitter either directly or via a *feeder* (2). In a receiving installation the term is applied to an element connected to a receiver. Also known as *primary radiator, driven radiator* and *fed element*.

dropwire   A *pair* used to connect an overhead *distribution point* to a subscriber's premises. To meet the need for a high strength/weight ratio, copper-coated steel conductors are used in the UK.

drum factor   Of a *drum receiver* or *drum transmitter*, the ratio of the length of the drum usable for scanning, to its diameter.

drum receiver   *Facsimile* apparatus in which the recording medium is attached to a rotating drum, which is scanned helically by a recording head.

drum transmitter   *Facsimile* apparatus in which the document to be transmitted is attached to a rotating drum, which is scanned helically by a reading head.

dual-polarisation transmission   The radiation of two signals having the same nominal frequency but opposite senses of *polarisation* (1), i.e. there is *orthogonal polarisation*. This technique—sometimes called *frequency reuse by dual polarisation*—effectively doubles the traffic-carrying capacity of a frequency band, and will be used in the 4 and 6 GHz bands by the Intelsat V satellites. For satisfactory separation of the signals at the receiving site, both transmitting and receiving antennas must have an adequate degree of polarisation purity. See also *crosspolarisation interference* and *depolarisation*.

dual-polarised antenna   An antenna intended to radiate or receive radio waves with mutually *orthogonal polarisation* and having two ports, either at the antenna end or at the transmitter/receiver end of the feed line.

dual-tone multifrequency pulsing   Pulsing in which each digit or signal is represented by a specific pair of *audio frequencies*, one selected from a set of four below 1000 Hz and the other from a set of four above 1200 Hz.

duct   (1) An underground pipe in which cables may be installed. (2) In radio-wave propagation, see *tropospheric duct*.

duct motor   A device used to pull a lightweight draw-rope into a duct prior to cabling. One version consists of two mechanically coupled bags that can be alternately inflated to grip the wall of the duct. After inflation of the leading bag the coupling contracts, drawing the second bag forward. This is then inflated, the leading bag is deflated and the coupling is extended to push the leading bag forward.

dummy antenna See *artificial antenna*.

duobinary coding A method of producing a three-level signal by precoding the input binary signal so that *spaces* become transitions and *marks* are represented by no transition, and then passing the resulting signal through a filter having approximately half the *Nyquist bandwidth*. The operation is represented diagrammatically in *Figure D.7*. Owing to the relatively slow rise

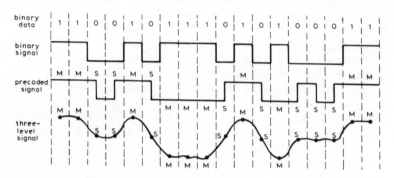

Figure D.7 Duobinary coding

time of the filter, adjacent transitions of opposite sense largely cancel one another out and the signal assumes the intermediate value. Hence this value represents the space condition of the original binary signal, and marks are represented by either of the extreme signal values. The original information can be recovered at the receiver by full-wave rectification followed by slicing at the half-amplitude level. The effect of the operation is that successive marks separated by an even number of spaces are always represented by the same extreme signal level, whereas those separated by an odd number of spaces are represented by opposite levels. Any violation of this relationship in the received signal will be the result of an error, so the code has inherent error-detection capability.

duplex A qualifying term denoting a capability for simultaneous transmission in both directions over a *link* or *circuit*.

duplexer A device permitting an antenna to be used simultaneously for transmission and reception.

dynamic impedance The impedance of a parallel-tuned circuit at resonance. Also called *dynamic resistance*, because the *resonant*

84

frequency is usually taken as that at which the dynamic impedance becomes purely resistive.

dynamiciser See *parallel-to-serial converter*.

E

e and m signalling A method of transferring *signals* (2) between transmission and switching equipment over two leads. The name derives from the designation of the leads, the e lead being used to send signals to the switching equipment and the m to the transmission equipment.

E bend A length of *waveguide* with a smooth change in the direction of the line of centres such that the *direction of polarisation* of the electric field is parallel to the plane in which the centres lie. Also known as *E-plane bend*.

E layer Any layer of more intense ionisation occurring in the E region of the *ionosphere*. The height of the principal layer is around 100 km, and this layer has been known as the Heaviside layer or the Kennelly-Heaviside layer in the past. Ionisation density decreases during the night, and the E layer may sometimes disappear altogether. See also *sporadic E layer*.

E mode Designation formerly used in the UK for *TM mode*.

E_{mn} **mode** Designation formerly used in the UK for TM_{mn} mode; see *TM mode*.

E-plane bend See *E bend*.

E-plane lens A structure for converging (or diverging) radio waves and consisting of a number of thin parallel conducting plates arranged so that they are parallel to the electric vector.

E-plane sectoral horn A *sectoral horn* flared so that the electric field of the *dominant mode* of the waveguide feeding the horn is perpendicular to the parallel sides of the horn.

E-plane T junction See *series T*.

E region See *ionosphere*.

Early Bird See *global satellite communication system*.

earth (US: *ground*) A deliberate or accidental electrical connection with the earth or a large conducting body serving as the earth, e.g. a ship's hull or the chassis of a vehicle. Earth connections serve to establish a reference potential level and are used to carry earth currents in communication circuits.

earth mat An arrangement of conductors associated with an *antenna* and laid on the ground to serve as a highly conducting *earth*.

earth-phantom circuit An *earth return circuit* using one or more

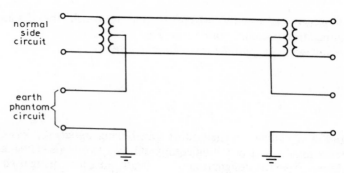

Figure E.1 Earth-phantom circuit

pairs of conductors effectively connected in parallel for one leg; see *Figure E.1*.

earth radius factor   See *effective radius of the earth*.

earth return circuit   A *circuit* using a conductor (or two or more conductors in parallel) for one leg, the return path being provided via connections to *earth*.

earth station   A radio station located on the surface of the earth (or within the major portion of its atmosphere) and forming part of a space communication system. Such a station comprises one or more *earth terminals*.

earth terminal   An antenna together with one or more transmitters, receivers and other ancillary apparatus at an *earth station*. Such an assembly is often loosely described as an antenna.

earth testing   In automatic switching, the process of checking whether the test wire of a *circuit* is at earth potential, the presence of such a potential indicating that the circuit is engaged.

Echo   An experimental *passive satellite* consisting of a balloon with a highly reflecting metallic skin. The satellite was placed in an inclined orbit about 1000 miles above the earth, and was used for test transmissions between the east and west regions of the US and also for a test transmission across the Atlantic.

echo   A delayed signal or sound wave arriving at a given point as a result of reflection, refraction or other indirect propagation, with sufficient strength and delay for it to be distinguished from the received wave. In long-distance radio-wave propagation via the *ionosphere*, echo signals are those that travel the longer path around the world between, for example, a transmitter in Japan and a receiving station in the UK. At higher frequencies such as those in the UHF television bands, echoes are usually produced by reflections from buildings, cranes, etc., and they can cause *ghost* images on television pictures.

86

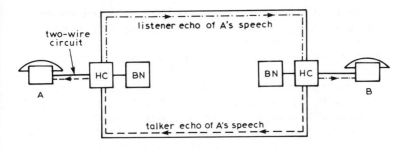

HC : hybrid coil
BN : balancing network

Figure E.2 Echo

In a *line circuit* an echo is produced whenever a signal encounters an imperfectly matched junction such as a poorly balanced two-wire to four-wire connection; see *Figure E.2*. If both ends of the four-wire circuit are poorly balanced it is possible for an echo signal to pass right round the loop and to be heard by the distant party. This is known as *listener echo* to distinguish it from the *talker echo* heard by the speaker. The disturbing effect of echoes in telephone circuits increases with the delay between the original sound and the echo, and is thus a function of circuit length. For circuits under about 3000 km in length the effect of echo can be reduced to acceptable levels by inserting a fixed permanent loss to attenuate the returned echo signal. For longer circuits where the delay exceeds about 45 milliseconds the amount of loss required would be excessive and some form of *echo suppressor* has to be used. This is particularly true of circuits including a *satellite link* in both the go and return channels, since the round-trip delay is then over half a second.

echo canceller A form of *echo suppressor* that compares the signals in the go and return channels, generates a replica of the *echo* signal and subtracts it from the signal in the return path, thereby cancelling the echo. Echo cancellers are more effective than other types of suppressor since they do not impair speech in the return channel or introduce any *speech chopping*. However they are complicated and expensive, and may not always be compatible with other types of device used at the distant end of a circuit.

echo checking In data transmission, a method of verifying the accuracy of received data by returning it to the transmitting end for comparison with the original data. See also *echoplexing*.

echo effect In *facsimile*, a defect due to the occurrence of echoes

87

in the transmission path and manifesting itself by the appearance of one or more additional outlines displaced in the direction of scanning from the main outline.

echo suppressor Generic term for a voice-operated device included in the four-wire portion of a long-distance telephone circuit to prevent the propagation of echoes. Early suppressors worked by introducing a high loss in the return channel (or disconnecting it altogether) whenever speech signals were present in the go channel. This effectively prevented echoes, but meant that the first speaker took control of the circuit and kept it until he stopped talking. Control was retained for a short time after speech ceased, to cover the time taken for the echo to propagate round the loop. This interval of time was described as the *hangover* or *holdover time*. Later designs of suppressors, termed *differential echo suppressors,* operated by comparing the level of the speech in the return channel with that of the speech in the go channel. If the return level is that appropriate to an echo, the suppression loss remains in circuit. If, however, the signal in the return path exceeds a given threshold level the loss is removed. This enables the distant party to break in by speaking more loudly than the original talker. Break-in is not effective until the expiry of the hangover time, and consequently some *speech clipping* of the initial syllables occurs. Echoes are not suppressed when both parties are speaking at once, a condition called *double-talking*. In more sophisticated designs they are nevertheless reduced by special speech-compression circuits. More recently, digital echo suppressors that operate on the bit stream have been developed. Echo suppressors prevent the free bothway flow of information, and must be disabled if a speech circuit is required for simultaneous data transmission. A disabling circuit that is sensitive to a specified tone frequency, but not to speech, is therefore included in all designs complying with the relevant CCITT Recommendation.

echo waveform corrector An adjustable *transversal equaliser* used to correct for *linear waveform distortion*, such as that suffered by a *video-frequency* television signal in its passage through a transmission system.

echoplexing In data transmission, the use of information feedback for *error control* on circuits derived by *time-division multiplex*. With simple information-feedback error control, where a terminal has exclusive use of a circuit, the time between the operation of a key at the sending end and the printing of the corresponding character at the sending end is very small. With echoplexing the round-trip propagation time is longer, however, and this may affect the rate at which information can be transferred over the circuit.

effective aperture or **effective area**   Of an *antenna*, for a given direction, the ratio of the power available at the terminals of a receiving antenna to the *power flux density* of a plane wave incident on the antenna from the given direction and having a *polarisation* (1) that results in maximum power at the antenna terminals. The effective area as thus defined is equal to the sum of the partial effective apertures for any two *orthogonal polarisations*. If no direction is given, that corresponding to maximum received power is assumed. The effective aperture S of a receiving antenna is connected to the *absolute gain* of the same antenna used for transmission by the expression $G = 4\pi S/\lambda^2$, where λ is the wavelength.

effective bandwidth   Of a *bandpass filter* or band-limited transmission system, the *bandwidth* of a hypothetical *filter* with an ideal rectangular response and the same transfer ratio at a reference frequency as the actual filter or system, such that the ideal filter would pass the same amount of energy from a *white-noise* signal source. Also known as *equivalent-noise bandwidth*.

effective height   Of a linear vertical *antenna* less than a quarter-wavelength long, the length of a hypothetical vertical radiator, with its lower end at ground level, that would produce the same radiation field if it carried a current uniform in *phase* at all points along its length and of uniform *amplitude* equal to that of the actual current in the antenna.

effective isotropically radiated power (US: *effective radiated power*)   The product of the power supplied to an *antenna* and its *relative gain* in a given direction with respect to a *half-wave dipole*.

effective length   (1) Of a receiving antenna, the ratio of the magnitude of the open-circuit voltage at the output terminals to the magnitude of the electric field component of appropriate *polarisation* (1) incident on the antenna. (2) Of a transmitting antenna, the length of a hypothetical radiating element that would produce the same electric field as the given antenna at the same distance and in the same direction, if it carried a current uniform in *phase* at all points along its length and of uniform *amplitude* equal to that of the current at the terminals of the given antenna.

effective margin   See *margin*.

effective radiated power (US)   See *effective isotropically radiated power*.

effective radius of the earth   The radius of a hypothetical earth on which the distance to the true line-of-sight horizon would be the same as the distance to the *radio horizon* on the real earth, under assumed conditions of atmospheric *refraction*. Since these vary with geographical location, weather, etc., the relationship between the effective radius and the true radius is given in terms of an earth radius factor *k*. For the standard conditions of refraction *k* has the value of 1.33, i.e. the effective radius is one-third larger than the true value. See also *line-of-sight radio link*.

effective synchronisation link   See *synchronisation link*.

efficiency   Of a *parity check* code, see *code rate*.

egg-box lens   A structure for converging (or diverging) radio waves and consisting of two sets of thin parallel conducting plates, the sets being orthogonally disposed with one of them parallel to the *electric field vector*.

elbow   See *waveguide corner*.

electret   A piece of dielectric material having permanent surface charges that produce an external static electric field, in the same way that a permanent magnet produces a magnetic field. Polarisation of the dielectric is generally produced by cooling the molten material in the presence of a strong electric field—as it were, 'freezing' charges in the material. The resulting internal polarisation may take a number of forms (e.g. atomic, dipole, space charge, or interfacial), but all of them lead to surface charges on the material. The first type of electret device likely to find application in telecommunications is the electret microphone. In this, as in most practical applications, use is made of the electric field between the surface of the dielectric and an electrode. The electret is usually a plastic film about 0.1 mm thick with a metallic layer deposited on one face. The plastic face is located close to another electrode—the back plate of the microphone—and movement of the film varies the voltage induced on this electrode.

electric field strength or **electric field vector**   Of an electromagnetic wave, the force exerted on a stationary charge per unit charge at a given point, usually expressed in volts per metre.

electrical length   Of an *antenna* element, the physical length expressed in *wavelengths*.

electrically alterable store   An erasable *store* whose contents may be changed by electrical means, usually by the application of a reverse voltage.

electrolytic corrosion   Damage to the metallic sheath of an underground cable due to stray earth currents (such as those from an electric traction system) entering and leaving the cable sheath. The damage occurs almost entirely in areas where the current leaves the cable sheath, i.e. where the sheath serves as an anode, and various protective schemes rely on this phenomenon;

see *cathodic protection*.

electromagnetic compatibility   A measure of the ability of systems or equipment to be operated in an electromagnetic environment without their efficiency being impaired by mutual *interference*.

electromagnetic disturbance   Any electromagnetic phenomenon likely to be superimposed on a wanted signal.

electromagnetic interference   Impairment of a wanted signal caused by an electromagnetic disturbance.

electromagnetic noise   An electromagnetic disturbance that does not correspond with any signal, and is usually random and impulsive in nature.

electromagnetic spectrum   The complete range of frequencies or wavelengths of electromagnetic radiation, extending from the longest radio waves to the shortest cosmic rays and including heat and light rays, ultra-violet rays, x-rays and gamma rays.

electromagnetic wave   A wave characterised by time-varying, mutually perpendicular electric and magnetic fields.

electromechanical switching   The connection of inlets to outlets using electrically operated mechanical devices such as *selectors* or *relays*.

electronic crosspoint   A switching element implemented by solid-state semiconductors or other static devices.

electronic exchange   Designation used to describe exchanges employing modern techniques such as *stored program control* and digital switching. In common usage the term is also applied to exchanges using mechanical switching units such as *reed relays*, rather than true electronic crosspoints.

electronic keying   *Keying* accomplished without the use of mechanical contacts.

electronic switching   The connection of inlets to outlets using *electronic crosspoints* or *time-division* techniques.

elemental area   In *facsimile*, any small part of a *scanning line* having a dimension along the line equal to the nominal line width.

elementary cable section   In a transmission system, the physical means of transmission between the output terminals of one device (such as a *repeater* or *regenerator*) and the input terminals of the next device in the system. A section may thus consist of a length of *coaxial cable* or *optical fibre* (including any necessary joints) together with any tail cables required for connection to the equipment.

elementary electric dipole   See *doublet (electrical) radiator*.

elementary regenerated [repeated] section   An *elementary cable section* and its following *regenerator [repeater]*.

elevated duct   See *tropospheric duct*.

elliptical orbit Of a *communication satellite*, an orbit in which the distance between the satellite and the earth is not constant.

elliptical polarisation In radio-wave propagation, *polarisation* such that the electric field rotates and oscillates in *amplitude* in each period. The extremity of the *electric field vector* will thus describe an ellipse in any fixed plane intersecting and at right angles to the direction of propagation. Elliptical polarisation may be produced by combining unequal-amplitude, linearly polarised waves in phase *quadrature*. If the waves have equal amplitude, the ellipse becomes a circle and *circular polarisation* results. See also *orthogonal polarisation*.

ellipticity ratio See *axial ratio*.

emergency alarm See *urgent fault alarm*.

emergency cells *End cells* provided for use during an emergency discharge.

en-bloc signalling A method of *signalling* in which address digits are transmitted in one or more blocks, each block containing sufficient *address information* to enable *switching centres* to carry out progressive onward routing.

enable input An input to a binary *logic element* exercising overall control of the element's function(s).

encode To represent a character or a message in terms of a *code* (1).

encoding In *pulse code modulation*, the representation of quantised *samples* of an analogue signal by *character signals* (2) according to a defined *code* (1).

encoding law In *pulse code modulation*, a statement defining the relationship between the decision values used in *quantising*; see, for example, *A-law encoding*.

end cells Cells forming part of a *battery* and arranged so that they can be switched in or out of circuit to adjust the overall voltage.

end-delay Of a long-distance *circuit* equipped with an *echo suppressor*, the round-trip propagation time of the echo path.

end distortion In a *start-stop system*, distortion in which the end of each marking pulse is shifted from its correct position with respect to the beginning of the relevant start pulse.

end-fire antenna [array] A linear *antenna [array]* whose direction of maximum radiation lies along the line of the antenna [array].

end-of-pulsing signal (US: *ST signal*) A *signal* (2) sent forward to indicate that the *address signals* have all been transmitted.

end office (US) A class 5 central office in which *subscribers' lines* are terminated; see *classification of exchanges*.

end-to-end signalling In a multi-link connection, a method of *signalling* in which signals are transmitted from one end of the connection to the other, without intermediate storage.

92

engaged test   A test whereby an operator in a manual exchange touches the sleeve of the required *jack* with the tip of a *cord circuit* plug in order to check whether the circuit is in use. If the circuit is engaged a click is heard in the operator's receiver.

engaged tone   See *busy tone*.

enquiry call facility   In a PBX, a facility whereby a user at an extension can suspend and hold an *exchange line call* while he makes a call to another extension.

enquiry character   In data transmission, a *control character* used to request information, such as identity and type of equipment in use, from a station with which a connection has been established.

entraide   A re-entrant link switching system in which some outlets from a given stage are connected back to the inlets of the same or a previous stage so that overflow traffic is fed back and has a second chance to be switched through. Also known as *re-entrant trunking*.

envelope   In a public data network, a group of *binary digits* consisting of a *byte* together with additional digits required for the operation of the network.

envelope delay   See *group delay*.

envelope delay distortion (US)   The difference between the *group delay* at one frequency and the group delay at a reference frequency. It is usually expressed in facsimile transmission as half the difference in microseconds between the maximum and minimum values of the group delay over the frequency band required for transmission.

envelope velocity   See *group velocity*.

equal-length code   In telegraphy or data transmission, a *code* (1) in which each *character signal* is composed of the same number of *signal elements* of the same duration.

equal-ratio channels   In *time-division multiplex* systems, channels that are connected to the common transmission path for equal periods of time.

equalisation   The generic term for the process of correcting undesired transmission characteristics of a *channel*. In line transmission, for example, signal *attenuation* normally increases with frequency. Equalisation in this case can consist of the insertion in the line of one or more networks having the inverse *amplitude/frequency characteristics*, so that over a desired frequency band the overall attenuation of the line is made substantially constant. A device used in this way to prevent *amplitude/frequency distortion* is called a frequency equaliser. A phase equaliser, on the other hand, operates to prevent *delay distortion*. More sophisticated devices that operate to correct simultaneously both phase and frequency distortion are often termed *waveform correctors*. See also *adaptive equaliser* and *transversal equaliser*.

equalising charge An extended charge given to an exchange battery to ensure that the active material in all the plates of every cell is restored to the charged state.

equated busy-hour call A unit of traffic intensity equal to the average number of calls per hour assuming a mean holding time of 120 seconds. Hence thirty EBHC are equivalent to one *erlang*.

equatorial orbit The path traced by a *communication satellite* when its *orbital plane* includes the earth's equator.

equipment engaged tone An audible signal sent to a caller to indicate that a call cannot be completed, owing to congestion in some part of the network. In many systems *busy tone* is used for this purpose.

equipment number In automatic switching, a number uniquely identifying a particular inlet or outlet in a *switching network*.

equivalent availability Of a switching system using *conjugate selecting*, the *availability* of a single-stage reference network which, with the same number of circuits, handles the same traffic with an equal probability of congestion.

equivalent binary content Of a signal generated by a digital source, the signal content expressed in binary terms.

equivalent bit rate Of a *line coded* signal, the number of binary digits that can be transmitted in a unit of time, usually quoted in bits per second.

equivalent build-up time or **equivalent rise time** See *rise time*.

equivalent isotropically radiated power The product of the power supplied to an *antenna* and the *absolute gain* of the antenna in a given direction.

equivalent-noise bandwidth See *effective bandwidth*.

erasable store See *store*.

erlang The unit of *traffic intensity*. If the average number of simultaneous calls in progress in a given period over a particular group of trunks is N, the traffic intensity is said to be N erlangs; i.e. one permanently engaged circuit has a traffic flow of one erlang.

erlang-hour The unit of *traffic volume*, equal to a mean *traffic intensity* of one *erlang* maintained for one hour.

error control In data transmission, a general term for the various techniques used to reduce the incidence of errors in the transfer of data. The simplest method is to return the data to the sending end for verification. However, this procedure requires a full *duplex* circuit and is open to the objection that an error in the return channel can give rise to a false indication, leading to an unnecessary retransmission of a message, block, etc. Moreover, it is possible for a disturbance to affect both forward and return channels, so that an error in the sending channel is 'corrected' by one in the return channel and no retransmission occurs. Other systems rely on some method of detecting errors at the receiving end, followed by a request for retransmission. Such a *decision feedback* system also requires a return channel, but this may be a simultaneous low-capacity channel occupying a different frequency band or it may be provided by temporarily interrupting a channel transmitting data in the reverse direction; see *idle RQ, continuous RQ* and *van Duuren ARQ system*. More sophisticated systems employ codes that enable errors to be detected and corrected at the receiving end; see *error correcting code*. It is also possible to monitor one or more parameters of the received signal to see that it has remained within prescribed limits; see *data signal quality detection*. This method can be combined with an RQ system to provide effective control on circuits where long error bursts can be expected to occur.

error correcting code In digital transmission, a code possessing some property enabling the occurrence of errors to be detected and corrected. For example, the words forming the code can be chosen in such a way that a single error cannot convert one *code word* into another, but merely results in the production of a false word that resembles the unmutilated word more closely than it does any other valid code word. Such a code necessarily has more *redundancy* (1) than a single *error detecting code*. A great many error correcting codes have been devised. Those that treat each fixed-length block of data or code word separately are called *block codes*; see *Hamming codes* and *Bose-Chaudhuri codes*. Other types operate continuously on the bit stream; see *Hargelbarger codes*.

error detecting and feedback system A system employing an *error detecting code* and so arranged that any character or block of data found to be in error automatically initiates a request for retransmission of that part of the signal found to be in error; see *van Duuren ARQ system*.

error detecting code In digital transmission, a code having some property that enables the occurrence of certain false words to be detected: for example, a *constant-disparity code* having a 3 to 4 ratio of *marks* to *spaces* in each word. A single error (or three, five or seven) in the reception of a word must upset the 3 to 4 ratio, and hence the mutilated word can be detected. Alternatively, only words having an even number of marks can be used to form a code. Again any odd number of errors in a character will result in an uneven number of marks and this can be detected by a *parity check*. In more sophisticated systems error detection is applied to groups of digits called *blocks*. The digits in a block can be arranged in the form of a matrix so that parity checks can be applied to both columns and rows of digits. Such an arrangement gives better protection against burst errors without excessive *redundancy* (1).

error extension or **error multiplication**   A property possessed by some items of equipment such as code converters and *data scramblers*, whereby a single incorrect digit in the input signal can cause more than one *digital error* in the output signal. In the case of a *four binary – three ternary code*, it is easy to see that an erroneous digit in a ternary word may give rise to up to four incorrect binary digits in the output of a decoder. In data scramblers error multiplication usually takes place because the incorrect digit also forms part of a *feedback* signal. The number of errors produced by an item of equipment when a single error is present in the input signal is known as the *error multiplication factor*, and it may be stated as a peak or average value.

error rate   In digital transmission, the ratio of the number of incorrect digits received to the total number of digits received, usually expressed in terms of *binary digits*.

error spread   In *error multiplication*, the number of bit periods in which errors can arise as a result of a single error in the input signal.

Es layer   See *sporadic E layer*.

Eurodata Foundation   An independent organisation established to study and make recommendations regarding Europe's data communication needs. The Foundation was set up in 1977 by seventeen members of CEPT. It has its headquarters in The Hague and is controlled by a general board on which all members are represented. Publications include a yearbook, and information is also available on a commercial basis from a data base.

EURONET   The data transmission network provided for the European Economic Community by the telecommunication authorities of member countries. Although it is a private network intended to give access to data bases holding specialised scientific, technical and economic information, its design should permit it to be used for other traffic if required. The initial network links *packet-switching* exchanges in Frankfurt, Paris, Rome and London. Remote access facilities are being provided by multiplexers in Amsterdam, Brussels, Copenhagen, Dublin and Luxembourg. The geographical coverage will be greatly extended, as users' terminals will be able to gain access to the network via the PSTNs and public data networks as the latter are brought into service.

European fixed-service satellite system (ECS) The *communication satellite* system being established by *Interim Eutelsat* to provide services between fixed *earth terminals*. The principal services to be provided will be intra-European telephony and the distribution of Eurovision television programmes. The first ECS satellite is due to be launched into a geostationary orbit in 1981, and it will be used for trials of the planned services until the second one is launched some two years later. The first satellite will be broadly similar to the *orbital test satellite* OTS II in that it will operate in the 11 and 14 GHz frequency bands with *frequency reuse* by linear *orthogonal polarisation*. It will have twelve 80 MHz *transponders*, six being accommodated on *vertical polarisation* and six on *horizontal polarisation*. The solar power supplies will enable the simultaneous use of nine transponders, with three held in reserve as emergency replacements. Batteries will permit the use of five transponders during an eclipse. The satellite will have three spot beam antennas and one elliptical eurobeam, covering Europe and North Africa. Digital transmission using *time-division multiple access* is planned for the telephony service. Television signals will be transmitted using *frequency modulation* and *sound-in-sync*.

European maritime satellite system (MARECS) The *communication satellite* system being established by *Interim Eutelsat* to provide telecommunication services to ships at sea.

European Space Agency (ESA) The Agency founded in 1975 by bringing together the two earlier organisations ESRO and ELDO, which had been responsible for developing the satellites and launch vehicles used in the European space research program. The Agency was established by the same states that had originally created ESRO, viz Belgium, Denmark, France, Germany, Italy, Netherlands, Spain, Sweden, Switzerland and the United Kingdom. Ireland has also signed the ESA Convention, and Austria, Canada and Norway each participate in one program. The organisation's purpose is to foster and provide for cooperation between European states in space research and technology and their applications. The latter include the provision of scientific, weather and communication satellites. See also *European fixed-service satellite system, orbital test satellite* and *Interim Eutelsat*.

Eutelsat See *Interim Eutelsat*.

evanescent mode A mode of oscillation in a *waveguide* such that the *amplitude* diminishes along the waveguide but the *phase* is unchanged. The frequency of this mode is below the *critical frequency* (2) for the guide, and hence it is sometimes called the cut-off mode.

evanescent waveguide   See *cut-off waveguide*.

even parity   See *parity*.

exalted carrier reception   Of an amplitude-modulated signal, a technique whereby a relatively high-level carrier-frequency wave is used to demodulate the received signal in order to reduce distortion caused by *selective fading* or asymmetry of the *sidebands*. The technique may be used for the reception of single-sideband, vestigial-sideband or double-sideband transmissions. See also *local carrier reception* and *reconditioned carrier reception*.

excess-attenuation testing   Precise determination of the attenuation/frequency characteristic of a *coaxial cable* in order to identify and evaluate attenuation peaks caused by periodic irregularities in the structure of the cable. In practice the periodic irregularities in a cable are invariably capacitive in nature, and they therefore give rise to *echoes* that are in phase *quadrature* with the main signal. Backward echoes converted into *forward echoes* by reflection at a previous discontinuity suffer a further 90° phase shift, and are therefore 180° out of phase with the main signal. As a result the attenuation of the cable peaks at frequencies at which the forward echoes add in phase. It has been found that there is a direct relationship between the value of the excess attenuation (the difference between a peak value and the value obtained by interpolation from the smooth characteristic) and the forward echo giving rise to it. As a result, excess-attenuation measurements can be used to predict the forward-echo performance of a cable. In practice an excess attenuation of 0.43 dB corresponds to a signal-to-forward-echo ratio of about 26 dB. See also *structural return loss* and *through-pulse-echo testing*.

excess-three code   A *binary-coded decimal* code in which a decimal digit n is replaced by the binary numeral for $(n + 3)$.

exchange (US: *central office*)   The generic term for an assembly of equipment providing for the interconnection of incoming and outgoing lines together with the necessary *signalling, supervision*, etc. More than one exchange may be housed in the same building, e.g. a *local exchange* may be cosited with a *tandem exchange*. It would be less confusing if the term *switching centre* were used in these contexts. By common usage, a building housing one or more switching centres together with equipment providing a wide variety of telecommunication services is usually called a *telephone exchange*. See also *classification of exchanges*.

exchange area   The designated area containing the subscribers served by a *local exchange*.

exchange connection A single *circuit* to a local subscriber, however provided. The term is used for statistical purposes.

exchange line call A call from a *private exchange* (PBX, etc.) to a subscriber to the public telephone service.

exclusive exchange line A line providing service to a single subscriber and having only one exchange number. Also known as *direct exchange line*.

exclusive OR element A *logic element* having a number of inputs and only one output. The output will stand at its 1-state if one, and only one, of the inputs stands at its 1-state.

executive assistance A PABX facility available to selected extensions whereby the switchboard can be called directly by pressing an auxiliary button and lifting the handset.

executive intrusion A PABX facility available to selected extensions, whereby a user, finding a required extension engaged on an internal call, may dial a code and intrude on the established connection without causing it to be broken. Conversation with the engaged parties is possible, and if the required extension clears it is automatically re-rung and connected to the intruding extension.

executive/secretary diversion A PABX facility whereby an executive who does not wish to be disturbed can direct incoming calls to his secretary's extension. If, however, an urgent call arrives the secretary can use the *extension diversion bypass* service to override the arrangement, and may then transfer the call to the executive's extension. This combined facility is sometimes called *executive assistance diversion*.

expansion (1) A process in which the range of *amplitudes* of a signal is automatically increased in a specified manner. This can be achieved by making the *gain* of an amplifier vary with the level of the input signal so that higher-level signals are subjected to relatively more amplification. Expansion is the complementary process to *compression* (see *companding*). (2) In switching, the use of a *switching stage* having more outlets than it has inlets, so that the intensity of the traffic offered to subsequent units is reduced.

expansion of the contrast range In *facsimile*, deliberate or fortuitous modification of a facsimile signal so that the ratio between the luminance of the whitest and blackest parts of the reproduced copy is greater than that on the original document.

extension (1) An additional telephone at a subscriber's premises. (2) A telephone connected to a *private branch exchange*.

extension diversion bypass A PABX facility enabling the user of a selected extension, by dialling a special *bypass number*, to obtain access to another extension that has diverted its incoming calls.

extension group hunting A PABX facility whereby a number of extensions can be associated in a group so that an incoming call automatically hunts for, and is connected to, the first free extension. If all the extensions in the group are engaged *busy tone* is returned to the caller. Several variants of the facility are possible. If hunting is initiated by dialling the first number of a group, individual access to the other numbers can be provided, whereas if hunting is initiated by calling any number in the group, individual access is not possible. Another variant, sometimes called *group call*, employs a separate number outside the extension numbering range for the initiation of group hunting. Any individual number in the group, including the first, may then be called.

external call waiting A PABX facility whereby an extension user can dial a code so that a distinctive signal (*external call waiting tone*) will be connected to his extension if an incoming *exchange line call* or inter-PBX call arrives whilst he is busy on another call. The user can then answer the waiting call with security from, and without losing, the original connection. If the user clears without answering the waiting call, his extension is re-rung if the incoming call is still waiting.

extra In the recorded reception of radio-telegraph signals, a spurious *mark* condition usually caused by atmospheric *noise*.

extraordinary wave See *magneto-ionic double refraction*.

extraterrestrial noise See *cosmic noise*.

eye diagram or **eye pattern** In digital transmission, the pattern produced by an oscilloscope when a *baseband* digital signal is applied to the vertical input terminals, the time base being triggered at the *symbol rate*. The trace provides a condensed representation of all possible signal states and transitions, and is

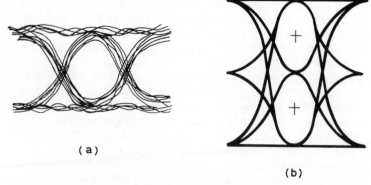

(a)

(b)

Figure E.3 Eye diagrams: (a) binary signal, (b) ternary signal

100

thus a useful indication of system performance. Usually the signal available at the input to a *regenerator* is displayed. *Figure E.3(a)* is a sketch of the eye diagram produced by a two-level signal that has suffered some degradation in transmission. The small cross at the centre of the display indicates both the instant at which a decision has to be taken as to the value of a symbol and the threshold level used in the decision-making process. Clearly, to reduce the possibility of errors due to noise, the eye opening should be as large as possible. Reductions in the opening are caused by intersymbol interference, amplitude irregularities, and timing irregularities such as *jitter*. *Figure E.3(b)* represents an ideal eye diagram produced by a three-level signal.

F

F layer An ionised layer in the upper atmosphere more than 150 km above the surface of the earth. Two separate layers, known as F1 and F2, are usually identified in this region. The lower or F1 layer exists in the day hemisphere, whereas the F2 layer is the higher of the two layers in the day hemisphere and the only layer existing in the night hemisphere. The F1 layer has the form of an extensive ledge, and exhibits some degree of daily and seasonal regularity in behaviour and occurrence.

F region That part of the *ionosphere* lying more than 150 km from the surface of the earth.

facsimile telegraphy (US: *facsimile*) A service providing for the transmission and reproduction at a distance of still pictures, printed matter and similar documentary material. Although this service has traditionally been regarded as a branch of telegraphy, the tendency in the UK today is to adopt the American usage of the single word facsimile. This usage is therefore followed in the references elsewhere in this dictionary. Facsimile systems operate on principles similar to those used in television. The document to be reproduced is systematically scanned to produce a signal representing the tonal density of each successive element of its surface. The signal is transmitted to the distant end (usually by modulating a carrier), where it is used to reproduce a replica of the original document on a suitable recording medium. Systems capable of reproducing a continuous range of tonal densities are classed as *phototelegraphy*, whereas those capable of producing only two levels of intensity are known as *document facsimile systems*.

factor of cooperation In *facsimile*, the product of the total length

101

of a *scanning line* (including the part in the *dead sector*) and the *scanning density*.

fading Variations in the strength of received radio signals due to changes in the propagation conditions with time.

failure In telegraphy, an old term describing an unwanted spacing condition resulting in incorrect recording by a telegraph receiver.

faint-speech amplifier Apparatus provided to assist subscribers afflicted with speech problems, and consisting of a unit that can be switched into circuit to amplify the outgoing speech currents. The gain is initially set by the installer, but small adjustments can be made by the user.

fall time See *decay time*.

fan antenna An antenna consisting of a set of wire elements spread out in a fanwise manner.

fan-beam antenna A *directional antenna* producing a *main beam* having a large ratio of major to minor dimension at any transverse cross-section.

fanning strip A strip of insulating material with symmetrically disposed holes in it through which the individual *pairs* of a cable may be passed for support and identification purposes, e.g. in a *cross-connection point*.

far-end crosstalk *Crosstalk* in which the unwanted energy transferred into the disturbed circuit propagates in the same direction as the wanted signal, and is observed and measured at a terminal remote from the sending terminal of the disturbing circuit. The measurement is usually made by comparing the voltages at the receiving end, the level of the disturbing signal being corrected to take account of the *attenuation* of the disturbing circuit. See also *crosstalk attenuation*.

far-field region Of an *antenna*, that region of the field produced by the antenna where the angular field distribution is essentially independent of the distance from the antenna. In this region the components of the electromagnetic field represent a propagation of energy, and their *amplitudes* vary inversely with distance from the antenna. If the latter has a maximum dimension D that is large compared with the *wavelength* λ, the far-field region is usually considered to exist at distances in excess of $2D^2/\lambda$ from the antenna. Also known as the *Fraunhofer region*, although such usage is now deprecated. The terms *far zone* and *radiation zone* have also been used for this concept.

Faraday rotation In radio-wave propagation, an effect occurring in the *ionosphere* whereby the *direction of polarisation* of an *electromagnetic wave* may be rotated.

fed element See *driven element*.

feed Of an *antenna*, that portion of the antenna connected or

102

coupled to the *feeder* and used to produce the *aperture illumination*.

feed holes See *centre holes*.

feedback The generic term for the process in which a fraction of the output signal of a device or system is returned to the input, usually to modify the overall characteristics. See *positive feedback* and *negative feedback*.

feedback balanced code A *line code* in which the binary information can be represented in alternative ways—usually termed *modes*. The particular mode used at any instant is chosen, with reference to the running *digital sum*, as that which will reduce any imbalance of the output signal; see *MS43*.

feeder (1) General term for a transmission line in a cabled distribution system of the type that transmits one or more signals to a multitude of receiving points, e.g. a *community antenna television system*. A *trunk feeder* is one connecting a *head end* with a *distribution point*, or interconnecting two distribution points. *Branch feeders* connect distribution points to *spur feeders*, to which system outlets are connected. (2) A transmission line connecting an *antenna* with a transmitter.

feeder cable (US) In a *local line network*, one of the large multipair cables extending out from the *local exchange* to the *distribution network*.

feeding bridge Exchange apparatus whose primary purpose is to supply current to a subscriber's telephone.

ferrite-rod antenna A receiving antenna consisting of a number of turns of wire wound on an elongated magnetic core usually in the form of a rod or bar.

fibre buffer The coating of material applied to an *optical fibre* immediately over the optical cladding in order to protect and isolate the fibre.

fibre optics General term for the technology concerned with the transmission of optical waves over *dielectric waveguides*.

field In data processing and transmission, a subdivision of a set of data; for example, a part of a signal unit in *common-channel signalling*.

field intensity In radio-wave propagation, a measure of the *power flux density* expressed by the amount of power traversing unit area normal to the direction of propagation.

field programmable logic array See *programmable logic array*.

field strength In radio-wave propagation, the value of either the electric or magnetic field for a specified *polarisation* (1). Usually the term describes the RMS value of the electric field in microvolts per metre.

field strength pattern A chart showing contours of equal *field* *strength* produced by a transmitter.

figure of merit Of the receiving antenna system of an *earth terminal*, a measure of performance obtained by dividing the gain by the *noise temperature* in absolute units, the ratio being referred to the input of the low-noise amplifier and expressed in logarithmic form as M dB/K. Thus the figure of merit (or G/T ratio) of a system with a gain of 60 dB and a noise temperature of 100 K is given by $M = 10 \log_{10} (10^6/10^2)$ or 40 dB/K. It will be noted that this ratio is not really appropriate for expression in *decibels*, since temperature is not linked to power in a well defined manner. However, the usage is widespread. It has recently been proposed to establish the symbol dB(K^{-1}) as a special notation for expressing values of M, as this is considered to be a better abbreviation for dB(W/W.K).

The G/T ratio is a very useful way of specifying the performance of earth terminal antennas, since it takes account of both the net gain (the gain allowing for mismatch and feeder losses, spillover, etc.) and the total noise temperature including the contributions of noise collected by the antenna, generated in the feeders, etc. Some of these factors vary with atmospheric conditions and the direction in which the antenna is pointing. Antenna performance requirements are therefore given in terms of effective figures of merit measured under specified conditions, which may include statistical considerations.

figures case In *alphabetic telegraphy*, a group of characters consisting mainly of figures and signs.

figures-shift signal In *alphabetic telegraphy*, a signal that causes the receiving apparatus to translate subsequent signals as secondary characters or functions included in the *figures case*.

fill A measure of the utilisation of the *pairs* in some section of a *local line network*, given by the ratio of pairs used to provide service to the total number of pairs, usually expressed as a percentage. This is also known as the *working fill*. The *assigned fill* refers to the percentage of pairs connected through to customers' (or potential customers') premises, including the pairs not providing service.

filled cable A cable in which the interstices between the *pairs* are filled with a jelly-like compound to prevent the ingress of moisture.

filter Generic term for a frequency-selective network; see *low-pass filter, high-pass filter* and *bandpass filter*. Details of specific types will be found in the companion *Dictionary of Electronics*.

final selector A *selector* having direct access to subscribers' lines from its outlets.

final signal unit See *signal unit*.

final traffic route The last-choice route from a *switching stage* in an *alternative routing* system.

finding The action whereby a *selector* or *functional unit* establishes a connection with one of a plurality of lines or devices that has requested service.

first-choice route See *primary route*.

first-party release A method of operation in which the release of a connection begins as soon as either party restores his telephone, data modem, etc. to its quiescent state.

fishbone antenna An *end-fire array* comprising a line of identical dipoles energised at their centres by a straight two-wire feeder.

five-unit code A binary *equal-length code* used in telegraphy, in which *character signals* (1) are composed of five-unit elements.

flag In a *packet-switching* network, a character (typically consisting of eight digits) used to mark the start of a *frame* (4).

flap attenuator A *slotted section* of *waveguide* in which a strip of absorbing material is inserted.

flare See *horn*.

flashing signal A signal used by an operator to gain the attention of another, or a signal sent by a subscriber held by an operator to gain the latter's attention.

flat-bed transmitter *Facsimile* apparatus in which the document to be transmitted is held flat and scanned line by line.

flat random noise See *white noise*.

flat-rate call A local call covered by the fixed charge levied under *flat-rate service*.

flat-rate service Telephone service in which subscribers pay a fixed charge irrespective of the number of local calls made during the billing period.

flat-top antenna An antenna of the inverted L or T type having all its horizontal elements in the same horizontal plane.

flexibility cabinet An overground weatherproof enclosure housing a *cross-connection point* and sometimes other apparatus such as a *line connector* or cable television equipment.

flip-flop A term whose use is internationally deprecated because it has a different meaning on each side of the Atlantic. In the US it has been used for a *bistable element*, whereas in the UK it has been used for a *monostable element*.

floating A method of operating secondary cells whereby they are kept in an approximately constant state of charge by connection to a constant-voltage power supply, usually a unit deriving power from the mains. In effect the power unit supplies current to the load, the batteries providing a reserve in case of mains failure.

floating-carrier modulation Compound *modulation* in which the *carrier* is amplitude-modulated in the normal sense but at the same time the carrier level is varied in accordance with the short-term mean amplitude of the modulating signal so that the *modulation factor* remains nearly constant. Also known as *controlled-carrier modulation*.

flush-mounted antenna   An *antenna* built into the surface of a vehicle, aircraft, etc. so that it does not affect the latter's shape. Also known as a *suppressed antenna*.

fold-over distortion   (1) Distortion resulting from the overlapping of the *sidebands* produced in the process of *sampling*. (2) In digital *amplitude modulation*, an effect that can occur in data systems using a relatively wide band of frequencies near to zero frequency when the lower sideband folds over about zero frequency. The effect can occur in simple on/off *voice-frequency* carrier systems if the *keying* is too abrupt, and the resulting distortion is sometimes called *keying loss*.

folded binary code   See *symmetrical binary code*.

folded dipole   An *antenna* consisting of two closely spaced parallel *half-wave dipoles* joined together at their outer ends. The antenna is fed at the centre of one of the dipoles and has an impedance of about 300 ohms, approximately four times that of a single unfolded dipole.

folded monopole or **folded unipole**   An antenna consisting of half a *folded dipole* with the unfed end connected to a conductive surface to which it is perpendicular.

follow-me diversion   A PABX facility enabling an extension user, by dialling a code, to divert calls incoming to his extension to another extension to which he is proceeding. At the second extension, by dialling a further code he can direct calls to his original extension to a third extension to which he is going, and so on. The diversion of calls arranged under this service may be cancelled, and normal service restored, by dialling a further code from the original extension.

follow-on call trap   A PBX function ensuring that an indication is given to the switchboard (instead of the bell being rung) when a call is received for an extension that has not yet been released from a previous connection. Similarly, if an outgoing call has been connected via the switchboard, the relevant extension is prevented from making another call until the original connection has been cleared.

footprint   An area on a surface illuminated by a contour-shaped beam within which the field strength everywhere exceeds a specified value.

forced release   A facility whereby a *circuit* or traffic-carrying device can be arbitrarily released, independently of any release action taken by the calling or called party.

foreign area (US)   Any *numbering-plan area* other than the one in which the given station is located.

foreign exchange line (US)   A subscriber's line connected to an *exchange* other than the one that would normally provide service at the relevant address, usually in accordance with the subscriber's wishes.

fortuitous distortion   Of a data or telegraph signal, random distortion that is independent of any *bias distortion* associated with the channel, and results from *interference* or similar causes.

forward busying   The process of successively changing the states of devices and links from *idle* to *busy* as a call is set up in the direction from the calling party to the called party. Also termed *forward seizure*.

forward clearing   The process of returning devices and links from *busy* to *idle* successively in the direction in which the call set-up took place.

forward echo   An *echo* propagating in the same direction as the original wave in a transmission line, and formed by energy reflected back from one irregularity and then onwards again by a second. Forward echoes can occur at all irregularities in a length of cable, and if they add systematically can impair its performance as a transmission medium. A *coaxial cable*, for example, may exhibit periodic minor irregularities as a result of the manufacturing process, and the echoes from these will add in phase at frequencies at which resonant effects occur.

In practical transmission systems, forward echoes caused by structural periodicity of the cables present no problems provided that the bulk of the signal energy lies in the region of the spectrum below 100 MHz. This means that standard FDM systems and first- and second-order PCM systems are relatively unaffected. Higher-rate systems, such as third-order PCM multiplexed signals operating at 560 megabits per second, may well be affected, however, the forward echoes giving rise to intersymbol interference. As a result, several methods of assessing the forward-echo performance of coaxial cables have been developed; see *excess-attenuation testing* and *through-pulse-echo testing*. See also *structural return loss*.

forward hold   The facility whereby circuits and/or switching equipment are placed and kept in the *busy* state as a result of a busy state in a previous *switching stage*.

forward recall signal   A *recall signal* sent by the caller or operator at the *outgoing* position to gain the attention of a distant operator.

forward scatter   A radio wave produced as a result of *scattering*, and propagating in the same general direction as the incident

107

wave.

forward seizure   See *forward busying*.

forward set-up   A method of operation in which a multi-link connection is established on a link-by-link basis in the direction from the caller to the called party. If the circuits are selected and switched substantially in parallel with the *signalling* of the *address information*, the process is called *forward parallel set-up*. If, however, the circuits are not interconnected until signalling activities have established that the call can mature (e.g. the number called is that of a non-barred subscriber whose equipment is free), the process is called *forward retrospective set-up*. In some versions of the latter process the relevant circuits may be selected and reserved in parallel with the signalling of the address information, but are not interconnected until it has been established that the call can mature.

forward signal   A *signal* (2) sent in the direction from the calling to the called party.

forward-transfer signal (US: *ring-forward signal*)   A *signal* (2) sent by an operator to request the assistance of another operator at a distant exchange.

four binary – three ternary code (4B3T)   A *line code* in which the incoming binary signal is divided into four-bit words, each of which is represented by a group of three ternary symbols, selected from a code table in such a way that the running *digital sum* of the signal is kept within prescribed bounds. *Table F.1* is a typical 4B3T code conversion table; the ternary symbols (signal levels) are shown simply as $-$, 0 and $+$. It will be seen that six of the possible 16 binary words are always represented by the same balanced ternary words, i.e. by words that do not affect the running digital sum of the output signal. The other ten words may each be represented by one of two ternary words having equal and opposite *disparity*. The coding process requires that the ternary word chosen to represent one of these ten words at a given moment shall be that which has the opposite sense of disparity from the signal's running digital sum—a value of zero being arbitrarily regarded as positive or negative for this purpose. As a result of the selection process the running digital sum is limited to extreme values of -3 and $+4$, these values occurring only during the transmission of certain code groups.

The principle of selecting code words to minimise the digital-sum variation can be extended to more than two alphabets, and the choice of which alphabet to use can be based on the actual value of the running digital sum instead of just its polarity; see for example *MS43*.

4B3T codes have a number of properties that make them

suitable for use in line coding. (a) The line *symbol rate* is reduced by a factor of three-quarters, leading to a corresponding reduction in the *bandwidth* required for satisfactory transmission. (b) The signals have no DC content and relatively little low-frequency energy. (c) The maximum number of consecutive zeros that can occur is limited to four, thus facilitating timing recovery. (d) Violation of the bounds of the running digital sum can be used to detect the occurrence of *digital errors*.

Table F.1

Binary words	Three-level output signal						
	Alphabet 1*			Alphabet 2*			
0000	+	0	−	+	0	−	
0001	−	+	0	−	+	0	Balanced
0010	0	−	+	0	−	+	(zero disparity)
0011	+	−	0	+	−	0	words
0100	0	+	−	0	+	−	
0101	−	0	+	−	0	+	
0110	0	0	+	0	0	−	
0111	0	+	0	0	−	0	
1000	+	0	0	−	0	0	
1001	+	+	−	−	−	+	Inverse pairs with
1010	+	−	+	−	+	−	equal and opposite
1011	−	+	+	+	−	−	disparity
1100	0	+	+	0	−	−	
1101	+	0	+	−	0	−	
1110	+	+	0	−	−	0	
1111	+	+	+	−	−	−	

*Alphabet 1 is used when the running digital sum at the end of the preceding word has a value of 0, −1 or −2: alphabet 2 is used if the sum is 1, 2 or 3.

four-frequency diplex telegraphy (US: *twinplex*) A system of radiotelegraphy in which two binary telegraph signals are transmitted simultaneously by *frequency shift keying*, each of the four possible signal combinations being represented by a specified separate frequency.

four-wire circuit Strictly, a *circuit* employing a *pair* of conductors for the go channel and another pair for the return channel. The term is now used generally to describe any circuit having separate go and return channels.

four-wire repeater A device for use in a *four-wire circuit* or a *four-wire type circuit* and consisting of two *amplifiers*, one for each direction of transmission.

four-wire terminating set Apparatus, consisting of a *hybrid coil* and *balancing network*, used to interconnect a *four-wire circuit* and a *two-wire circuit*.

four-wire type circuit A *circuit* working on the principle of separate go and return channels. (The term therefore applies to a single *pair* of conductors, provided that a different frequency band is used for each direction of transmission.)

frame (1) In *pulse code modulation*, a set of consecutive *digit time slots* in which the position of each slot can be identified by reference to a special signal known as the *frame alignment signal*. In the standard 24-channel primary PCM multiplex structure a frame consists of 193 digit time slots, i.e. 24 eight-digit channel time slots together with a one-digit time slot used for frame alignment and periodically for other purposes. (2) In a TDMA system, one complete cycle of *bursts* beginning with a *reference burst* from a designated *earth station* and followed by a *standard burst* from each of the stations in the system. (3) In automatic switching, a complete cycle during which all the devices in a group are inspected (by *scanning* (1) or *polling*) by a common control system. (4) In a *packet switching* network, a complete sequence of bits identified by an opening synchronisation character called a *flag*, and usually including an information field that can contain user's data, i.e. a *packet*.

frame alignment In *pulse code modulation*, the condition in which each *frame* (1) of the receiving equipment has the correct phase relationship with the received signal.

frame alignment recovery time In *pulse code modulation*, the interval of time between a valid *frame alignment signal* being available and *frame alignment* being established. This includes the time required for the specified number of validation checks.

frame alignment signal (US: *framing signal*) In *pulse code modulation*, a distinctive signal used for the purpose of *frame alignment*. A particular pattern of bits occupying *digit time slots* 2 to 8 of the first *channel time slot* in every other frame constitutes the frame alignment signal used in the standard CCITT 30-channel system.

frame alignment time slot In *pulse code modulation*, a *time slot* occupying a defined position in each *frame* (1) and used for the transmission of a *frame alignment signal*.

frame duration In switching, the time required to perform one cycle of *scanning* (1) or *polling*.

frame length In switching, the number of devices polled or scanned in one cycle.

frame slip In *pulse code modulation*, an amount of *slip* such that the added or deleted digit positions comprise a whole *frame*.

framing signal (1) See *frame alignment signal*. (2) In *facsimile*, a signal used to adjust the picture position in the direction of line progression.

110

Franklin array A *broadside array* composed of a number of end-fed vertical elements, each of which is folded several times so that the radiation from the various parts of it is in phase. Usually the array is backed by a curtain reflector.

Fraunhofer region Of an antenna, a deprecated term for the *far-field region*.

free The state of a *selector*, line, etc. when it is available for traffic.

free-code call (US) A call made by dialling the code for a service, such as information or repair, for which no charge is made.

free-line call (US) A call to a directory number made without charge to the caller.

free-line signal On a toll or trunk switchboard multiple, a visual indication of the next circuit to be taken into use.

free-space loss In radio-wave propagation, the loss between two identical isotropic antennas in free space, expressed as a power ratio, usually in *decibels*. This loss is not due to dissipation but to the fact that *power flux density* is inversely proportional to distance. It is given by the expression $20 \log 4\pi D/\lambda$, where D is the distance between the antennas and λ is the *wavelength* in the same units.

frequency band (1) A continuous range of frequencies defined by international agreement; see *band*. (2) A continuous range of frequencies allocated for a specific purpose, e.g. the 2-metre amateur radio band.

frequency band number See *band*.

frequency change signalling In telegraphy, an old general term describing the use of one or more specified frequencies to represent each significant condition of a telegraph signal. If the change from one signalling condition to another was achieved simply by replacing each given frequency by another, without maintaining continuity of *phase*, the process was described as *frequency exchange signalling*. If phase continuity was maintained, the process was termed *frequency shift signalling*.

frequency changing (also termed *frequency conversion)* A process in which the band of frequencies occupied by a signal is removed to another part of the spectrum, usually by mixing the signal with a single-frequency oscillation and filtering out the desired sum or difference signal. In the latter case the output signal is inverted; see also *frequency translation*.

frequency characteristic See *amplitude frequency characteristic*.

frequency conversion See *frequency changing*.

frequency coordination The internationally agreed consultative procedure designed to prevent the occurrence of harmful *interference* between new and existing terrestrial and space radiocommunication services sharing the same frequency bands. Under the Radio Regulations of the ITU, an administration wishing to bring a new station into use must first consult other administrations and countries whose services might be affected or whose transmitters might interfere with reception at the new station. As part of the consultative procedure, a chart of the geographical location of the new station is produced and the areas in which interference is possible are indicated thereon; see *coordination contour* and *coordination distance*.

frequency-derived channel   A *channel* obtained by the process of *frequency division*.

frequency deviation   In *angle modulation*, the peak difference between the instantaneous frequency of a modulated wave and its unmodulated value. In VHF broadcasting a frequency deviation of ± 75 kHz is used.

frequency discriminator   A circuit producing an output signal proportional to the departure of the phase or frequency of an input signal from a predetermined value.

frequency distortion   Deprecated term for *amplitude/frequency distortion*.

frequency diversity reception   The technique whereby two or more radio *carriers* having adjacent frequencies are used to transmit the same *modulating signal*. Since the carriers rarely fade simultaneously, the receiver is able to select the best signal at any particular instant.

frequency division   The technique of separating a number of transmission paths by the use of different frequency bands.

frequency-division multiple access   A technique whereby a number of *earth stations* are able to share the transmission capacity of a *transponder* in a communication satellite. The available bandwidth of the transponder is divided into a number of frequency bands (separated by *guard bands*), and each earth station is allocated one or more bands for its exclusive use. Care has to be taken not to overload the transponder because of intermodulation problems, and this method of multiple access is less efficient than *time-division multiple access*. It is also less flexible and hence is not so easily adapted to changing traffic patterns. See also *SPADE*.

frequency-division multiplex   A *multiplex system* in which the available transmission frequency range is divided into a number of narrower frequency bands, each available for a separate signal.

frequency-division switching   The connection of inlets to outlets by means of *frequency-division* techniques.

frequency modulation   Modulation in which the instantaneous frequency of a constant-amplitude carrier is varied from its unmodulated value by an amount proportional to the instantaneous value of a modulating wave.

frequency response See *amplitude/frequency characteristic*.

frequency reuse A method of increasing the traffic-carrying capacity of a *communication satellite* by using the allocated frequency bands more than once. The same frequencies can be used for the links to different geographical areas, provided that the antennas have sharply defined beams and any side lobes are suppressed. A further doubling of spectrum availability can be obtained by using opposite senses of polarisation for transmissions occupying the same frequencies in each beam; see *dual-polarisation transmission*.

frequency-shift keying (also known as *digital frequency modulation*) The process whereby the instantaneous frequency of the modulated wave is shifted between a set of predetermined discrete values in accordance with the significant conditions of the modulating digital signal. If the frequency of the *carrier* wave is varied smoothly between the discrete values, the process is termed *phase-continuous* frequency-shift keying. If, however, the discrete frequencies are each produced by a separate unlocked oscillator, the process is known as *phase-discontinuous* frequency-shift keying.

frequency-shift signalling (1) Signalling in which the various *signals* (2) are represented by specified changes in the frequency of a *carrier*. (2) In telegraphy, see *frequency change signalling*.

frequency standard A generator whose output frequency is very accurately controlled so that it may be used for precise reference purposes.

frequency swing In *angle modulation*, the difference between the maximum and minimum values of the instantaneous frequency of the modulated wave.

frequency translation A process in which the signals occupying a particular frequency band—e.g. a *group* (2)—are translated en bloc to another position in the spectrum so that the arithmetic difference between the frequencies of any two signals is unchanged.

Fresnel region Deprecated term for *radiating near-field region*.

Fresnel zone For a line-of-sight propagation path between two *microwave* antennas: a zone, usually on a plane, such that the sum of the distances from both antennas nowhere varies by more than half the operating wavelength. The concept is usually used to express the amount by which the *direct ray* clears possible obstructions such as mountain tops. Thus if the sum of the distances to a particular peak is one wavelength longer than the direct ray, a clearance of two Fresnel zones is said to exist.

front feed Of a *microwave* antenna, a *feed* that does not pass through the reflecting surface.

front-to-back ratio Of a *directional antenna*, the ratio, usually expressed in *decibels*, of the *radiation intensity* in the *main lobe* to the radiation intensity in the reverse direction.

frying Noise produced by small irregularities in the current flowing through a carbon microphone in the absence of any acoustic stimulation.

full availability See *availability*.

full cosine roll-off An *amplitude/frequency characteristic* of particular interest in digital transmission and defined by

$$A(\omega) = \frac{1}{2} \left(1 + \cos \frac{\pi\omega}{2\omega_1} \right)$$

See *Figure F.1(a)*. A transmission path or *filter* with such a characteristic has the following desirable properties: (a) the impulse response exhibits nulls (axis crossings) at points separated by the *Nyquist interval* (1) (of an ideal filter cutting off at ω_1) and also at the centre of these intervals—see *Figure F.1(b)*; (b) the half-amplitude response has a duration equal to the aforementioned Nyquist interval—see *Figure F.1(b)*; (c) the energy in the pulse tails falls off very rapidly.

From consideration of (a) and (b) it is apparent that, if the received signal is sliced at the half-amplitude level, full Nyquist-interval pulses can be formed without distortion since the responses to all other pulses at the half-amplitude instants will be zero. Property (c) ensures that the response is relatively insensitive to variations in the signalling rate. See also *intersymbol interference* and *Nyquist rate*.

full duplex operation Operation of a *circuit* so that each end can transmit and receive simultaneously.

full echo suppressor A type of *echo suppressor* usually located near one end only of a *four-wire circuit* and operating so that speech signals in either channel control the introduction of loss in the other channel. Full suppressors are suitable for use on circuits in the range 2500 to 4000 km in length. For longer distances the holdover time increases to the point where it is difficult for one party to interrupt the other, and a *half echo suppressor* is therefore used at each end of the circuit.

full route availability A routing arrangement in which any *inlet* can gain access to at least some of the *trunks* in all routes.

full wave dipole A *dipole antenna* whose *electrical length* is equal to one *wavelength* at the intended frequency of operation.

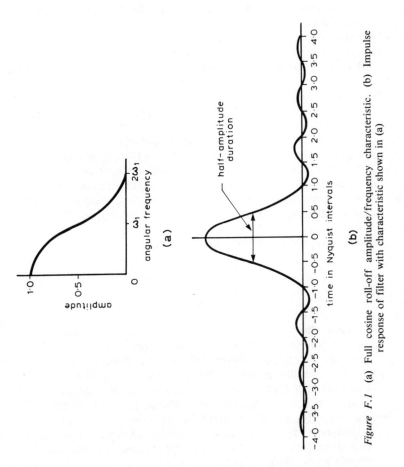

Figure F.1 (a) Full cosine roll-off amplitude/frequency characteristic. (b) Impulse response of filter with characteristic shown in (a)

115

fully automatic reperforator transmitter distributor (US) See *coupled reperforator and tape reader*.

fully dissociated signalling In *common-channel signalling*, a method of operation in which *signals* (2) can follow any satisfactory routes through the network without regard to those of the related traffic circuits.

fully provided route A route so dimensioned that it can carry the forecast peak traffic with a specified *grade of service* without the need for an *overflow route*.

function control See *functional command*.

function control signal In telegraphy or data transmission, a set of *signal elements* used to transmit commands such as carriage return, line feed, etc.

functional command In telegraphy or data transmission, a command that controls some operation of a recording or processing device other than the printing or recording of a letter, figure, etc. Also known as *function control*.

functional unit An entity of hardware, software, or a mixture of both, that is capable of performing one or more functions.

fundamental frequency Of a complex oscillation consisting of a set of harmonically related frequencies, the frequency whose value is the highest common factor of all the frequencies present in the wave.

fundamental mode See *dominant mode*.

G

gabled distribution A method of illuminating the *aperture* (3) of an antenna so that the *field strength* across a particular dimension increases from the edges to the centre.

gain (1) Of a device such as an *amplifier*: the ratio between the value of an output quantity, such as power or voltage, and the value of the input quantity giving rise to it. Power gain may be conveniently stated in *decibels*, but the input and output impedances must be specified if a voltage gain is so expressed. (2) For definitions of the concept with respect to *antennas*, see *absolute gain*, *relative gain* and *directive gain*.

galactic noise See *cosmic noise*.

gap character In data processing, a *character* (2) inserted in a *computer word* for technical reasons, but not representing data.

gate Generic term for a circuit element that can be turned on or off in response to one or more control signals. For example, a gate connected to a *highway* can be turned on for the duration of

116

a particular *time slot* so that the content of the slot can be examined.

gated AGC   A form of *automatic gain control* used in television receivers in which the control signal is related to the level of a particular part of the line waveform (usually the back porch or tip of the synchronising pulse) so that it is independent of changes in mean signal level caused by changes in picture content.

gateway exchange   An *exchange* providing for the interconnection of international circuits with a national network; see *Figure T.1* under *transmission plan*.

gating   The process in which a *gate* circuit is used to select those parts of a wave existing during predetermined time intervals.

gentex   Designation given to the switched telegraph service in Europe.

geostationary orbit   See *geostationary satellite*.

geostationary satellite   A satellite travelling in such a direction and at such a speed that it remains vertically above some point on the equator and hence appears to be stationary to observers on the surface of the earth. More concisely, a *geosynchronous satellite* in an *equatorial, circular, direct orbit*. Geostationary satellites have to be located at a height of about 35 800 km, where the resultant of a satellite's momentum and the earth's gravitational pull has the value needed to keep the craft in the desired circular path with respect to the centre of the earth. This path is commonly described as the *geostationary orbit*, although such usage is now deprecated, the term *geostationary satellite orbit* being preferred.

geosynchronous satellite   A satellite whose period of revolution about the earth is the same as the period of revolution of the earth about its own axis. The period of revolution of the satellite and the period of revolution of the earth are both defined with relation to the fixed stars; see *sidereal period of revolution* and *sidereal period of rotation*.

ghost   In *facsimile* or television, a displaced secondary image caused by a delayed signal received due to reflection or other indirect propagation.

glitch (US)   A short-term disturbance in the waveform of a received pulse.

global satellite communication system   The commercial system set up by INTELSAT whereby *geostationary satellites* positioned above the Atlantic, the Pacific and the Indian Ocean provide communication facilities between earth terminals located all over the world. The system comprises two elements: the space segment consisting of satellites owned by INTELSAT, and the ground segment consisting of the participating earth stations belonging to the countries in which they are located. In July 1980 the space segment consisted of seven INTELSAT IV and five INTELSAT IV A satellites, providing over 17 000 international voice circuits in addition to facilities for television and other services. The ground segment consisted of more than 250 earth terminals distributed in about 100 countries.

The first step in the establishment of the present system was taken in 1965 when the satellite *Early Bird* (later renamed INTELSAT I) was placed in a stationary orbit over the Atlantic. Early Bird had a capacity equivalent to 240 telephone channels, and was used principally to establish the acceptability of telephonic communication over channels subject to the transmission delay imposed by the long propagation path via a geostationary satellite. Brief notes on the later generations of satellites follow.

INTELSAT II. These satellites had approximately double the power of Early Bird. Three were launched in 1967, one positioned over the Atlantic and two over the Pacific.

INTELSAT III. Nearly fifty per cent heavier than their predecessors, the Mk III satellites had a transmission capacity of 1200 speech circuits, four TV channels or combinations thereof. Five were successfully placed in orbit during the period 1968–70, and one of these was positioned over the Indian Ocean to complete the global coverage of the system.

INTELSAT IV. Approximately five times the weight of a Mk III, each of these satellites has a nominal capacity of about 4000 telephone channels, plus two TV channels.

INTELSAT IV A. Similar in size and overall design to the Mk IV version, the latest satellites have a nominal capacity of 6000 voice circuits plus two TV channels. They are equipped with directional beam antennas, enabling *frequency reuse* to be employed.

INTELSAT V. The first Mk V satellite is expected to be launched in 1981. It should provide a saturation capacity of about 11 000 speech circuits using FDMA techniques and frequency reuse including *dual-polarisation transmission*.

Plans exist for Mk V A and VI satellites to follow on in the mid to late 1980s. The INTELSAT VI design is expected to provide up to 30 000 voice circuits plus two TV channels. Much of the increased voice-channel capacity will be achieved by the introduction at earth stations of *time-division multiple access* and *digital speech interpolation*.

goniometer An assembly of fixed coils disposed around a coil that can be turned through 360 degrees. By connecting suitable antennas to the field coils and a receiver to the movable coil, the direction of maximum response can be steered in azimuth.

goubau line   See *single-wire transmission line*.

grade of service   A measure of the service given by an *exchange* or group of *circuits* during the *busy hour*, usually expressed as the fraction of offered calls likely to fail at the first attempt owing to limitations of equipment.

graded-index optical fibre   An *optical fibre* in which the *refractive index* falls in value with radial distance from the centre in an approximately parabolic fashion. As a result off-axis rays are continually bent towards the centre of the fibre and there is an

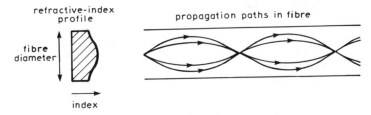

Figure G.1   Graded-index optical fibre

inherent self-focusing effect; see *Figure G.1*. Rays making the larger angles with the axis spend relatively more time in the lower-refractive-index regions where the velocity of propagation is higher, and are thus able to keep up with the more direct low-angle rays. In this way multimode dispersal is greatly reduced, so that this type of fibre effectively combines the advantages of *monomode optical fibre* (a large bandwidth) with a reasonably sized core.

graded multiple   See *grading*.

grading   (1) The generic term for the practice of arranging the interconnection of switching-stage *multiples* (2) in ways that enhance the traffic-carrying characteristics in a *limited availability* system. For example, the method of interconnection in which a group of *selectors* has access to *individual trunks* on early *choices* but shares access with other groups on later choices. (2) An interconnection scheme designed in accordance with the foregoing method. If all groups in a grading are treated in the same way the resulting arrangement is known as a *symmetrical grading*. If some groups are given special treatment, for example those having a larger traffic are given access to a larger number of individual trunks, then the resulting arrangement is known as an *unsymmetrical grading*.

grading group   A basic unit in the formulation of a *grading*, all

119

inlets of the group having access to the same set of *outlets* of the grading.

Gray code   A cyclic *binary code* in which sequential numbers are represented by code combinations, each of which differs from the preceding one in only one digit position. Also known as *reflected binary code*. In a data transmission system in which each level of a signal represents a specific code combination, the use of the Gray code can minimise the effect of errors in the transmission system. The most probable error is the interpretation of a received level as one of the adjacent levels, and hence the received binary group will contain only one incorrect digit.

gross information content   A measure of the total information in a message, including any *redundancy* (1), and expressed by the number of *shannons* (or *hartleys*) required to transmit it with a specified degree of accuracy over a noise-free channel. See also *information content*.

ground (US)   See *earth*.

ground absorption   In radio-wave propagation, *absorption* (1) due to the resistivity of the earth.

ground-based duct   See *tropospheric duct*.

ground bed   A substantial body of conducting material buried in the ground and forming part of a *cathodic protection* system. The ground bed is connected to the positive pole of a source of direct current, the negative pole being connected to the structure to be protected.

ground mat   A system of conductors laid on the ground to provide a highly conductive surface in the vicinity of an antenna.

ground-plane antenna   A *unipole antenna* for which the conducting surface consists of an assembly of radially disposed conductors or a metal disc.

ground wave   A radio wave that travels between transmitting and receiving *antennas* situated above the surface of the earth but within the *troposphere*. A ground wave may therefore be a *direct wave*, a *surface wave* or a ground-reflected wave.

group   (1) An assembly of 12 *telephone channels* forming a 48 kHz frequency band of a *carrier transmission* system. (2) A standardised 48 kHz frequency band of a carrier transmission system. A group band may be used for data transmission, for example. (3) An abbreviation for a *group link* together with the terminal equipment at its ends.

group acknowledgement signal   A *signal* (2) sent back to acknowledge the receipt of a group of signals.

group call   See *extension group hunting*.

group delay (US: *envelope delay*)   Between two points of a system or network, the time of propagation of a particular point on the envelope of a wave. In the absence of *delay distortion* this will be the same as the *phase delay* at any frequency in the band occupied by the wave.

group delay characteristic A plot of the slope of the *phase/frequency characteristic* over the range of frequencies of interest, i.e. a graph of $d\phi/d\omega$, where ϕ is the phase shift in radians at a particular frequency and ω is the angular frequency in radians per second.

group distribution frame In FDM carrier systems, a frame providing for the interconnection of apparatus transmitting signals with frequencies in the *basic group* range of 60–108 kHz.

group link See *link*.

group reference pilot See *reference pilot*.

group retardation In radio-wave propagation, a reduction in the *group velocity* of a wave train, caused by the ionised medium through which it propagates.

group section See *link*.

group selector A *selector* having access to a number of groups of *trunks*. Selection of the desired group is directly or indirectly controlled by the dialled digit(s), but hunting for a free trunk within a group is automatic.

group switching centre UK designation for an exchange serving as the first-level *trunk exchange* for a number of *local exchanges*; see *Figure T.4* under *trunk transit network*, and also *classification of exchanges*.

group translating equipment In carrier telephony, apparatus that frequency-translates five basic 12-channel 48 kHz groups and assembles them into a basic *supergroup* in the range 312 kHz to 552 kHz, or carries out the reverse process.

group velocity (US: *envelope velocity*) The velocity of propagation of a point on the envelope of a wave, provided that the latter moves without any significant change of shape.

guard band A band of frequencies left vacant between two adjacent *channels* to prevent mutual *interference*.

guard time The interval of time provided between *bursts* in a TDMA system in order to prevent them from overlapping owing to short-term variations in the earth-station clock and/or changes in transmission time caused by movement of the satellite.

guarding (1) In general, the function of preventing false operation of a device. (2) In *voice-frequency signalling*, the process whereby signalling receivers are protected from false operation by speech or other spurious signals having components within the frequency band, usually by detecting the simultaneous presence of other components outside the band.

guide See *waveguide*.

guide wavelength For a given frequency and *mode* (2) of propagation, the distance along the axis of the *waveguide* between two similar points at which the *phase* of the signal differs by 2π radians.

guide wire See *single-wire transmission line*.

guided wave An *electromagnetic wave* travelling along a *waveguide*.

guy (US) A member providing tensional support to an overhead structure.

guy anchor A buried beam, log, mass of concrete, etc. providing an anchorage for a *guy wire*.

guy wire A stranded steel cable used to connect an anchor to a pole, radio tower, etc. to provide structural support.

gyrator A *waveguide* component that introduces a *phase* shift of zero radians in one direction of propagation and π radians in the other.

gyro frequency The lowest frequency at which charged particles spiral under the influence of a constant magnetic field. In the context of ionospheric propagation, the term describes the rotational frequency of free electrons caused by the earth's magnetic field. The gyro frequency corresponding with the component of that field along the direction of propagation is called the *longitudinal gyro frequency*, whereas that corresponding with the component at right angles to the direction of propagation is termed the *transverse gyro frequency*.

H

H antenna An antenna resembling a letter H and consisting of a dipole with a similar reflecting element mounted one-quarter of a wavelength away.

H bend A length of *waveguide* with a smooth change in the direction of its line of centres, such that the *direction of polarisation* of the electric field is perpendicular to the plane in which the centres lie. Also known as *H-plane bend*.

H mode Designation formerly used in the UK for *TE mode*.

H_{mn} mode Designation formerly used in the UK for TE_{mn} mode; see *TE mode*.

H-plane bend See *H bend*.

H-plane lens A structure for converging (or diverging) radio waves and consisting of a number of thin parallel conducting plates arranged so that they are parallel to the magnetic vector.

H-plane sectoral horn   A *sectoral horn* flared so that the electric field of the *dominant mode* of the waveguide feeding the horn is parallel to the parallel sides of the horn.

H-plane T junction   See *shunt T*.

half duplex operation   The use of a *circuit* capable of simultaneous bothway transmission for transmision in only one direction at a time, owing, for example, to limitations in the terminal equipment.

half echo suppressor (US: *split-type echo suppressor*)   A type of *echo suppressor* that operates so that speech signals in the go channel control the insertion of loss in the return channel, but the action is not reciprocal. A suppressor of this type therefore has to be included at each end of a long-distance *four-wire circuit*, e.g. one over 4000 km in length. See also *full echo suppressor*.

half-tone picture   In *facsimile*, a picture having a range of tones lying between picture black and picture white.

half-wave dipole   A *dipole antenna* having an *electrical length* equal to half the *wavelength* of operation.

half-wave polariser   A device for changing the *polarisation* (1) of a wave by applying, in a given plane, a phase delay of 180° with respect to the orthogonal plane.

Hamming codes   *Error-correcting codes* complying with the principles enumerated by R. W. Hamming. In the basic code the message is divided into blocks of information digits, and each block is associated with k *parity check* digits to form code words of $m + k$ digits. Each check digit is associated with a given group of information digits in the word, in such a way that if a single error occurs it is possible to determine its position in the word by means of systematic parity checking.

Hamming distance   In coding theory, a measure of the difference between any two valid words in a given code, expressed as the number of digit positions in which they differ. Also known as the *minimum distance*. The concept is useful in connection with the error detecting and correcting capabilities of a code. Clearly, if the minimum distance in a particular code is two, a single digital error cannot transform the mutilated word into another valid code word, and the error can be detected. In this case it cannot be corrected (except by retransmission), since the mutilated word could have been produced by an error in either of two valid words. If the minimum distance is increased to three, however, it is possible to both detect and correct a single error in a word, since the mutilated form will resemble the original word more closely than it does any other valid word. In general, if the minimum distance is m it is possible to detect $(m - 1)$ errors in a code word and to correct half this number. By extension the term is applied to the number of digit positions in which two code words of the same length differ, regardless of the radix. Hence the Hamming distance between 123456789 and 123456123 is three.

Hamming weight In coding theory, the number of zeros in a code word.

hand receiver An earphone supplied as an extra with a telephone to enable a second person to listen in.

handset Of a telephone, a rigid combination of microphone and earphone designed to be held in the hand. In some designs a *keypad* is mounted in the handset.

handshaking Verification by a calling terminal that it has established a satisfactory connection with a wanted terminal (or terminals) so that the transmision of data or other signals can begin.

hang-up signal See *clear-back signal.*

hangover (US) See *tailing.*

hangover time See *echo suppressor.*

hard limiter (US) See *limiter.*

hardware A term used in the context of computers to describe physical equipment, in contrast with *software.*

Hargelbarger code A type of recurrent code designed to enable burst errors to be corrected provided that there are relatively long error-free intervals between the bursts. The principle of operation is to insert *parity check* bits spread out in time so that an error burst is not likely to affect more than one of the groups whose parity is checked.

harmful interference Internationally defined as *interference* that endangers the functioning of radionavigation systems or other safety services, or seriously degrades a radiocommunication service operating in accordance with the Radio Regulations.

harmonic A sinusoidal component of an alternating waveform having a frequency that is a whole multiple of the *fundamental frequency.*

harmonic distortion *Distortion* caused by non-linearity, for example by an overloaded *amplifier,* and consisting of the production in the output signal of additional sinusoidal components having frequencies that are integral multiples of the sinusoidal components of the input signal.

harmonic telephone ringer A subscriber's *telephone ringer* designed to respond only to alternating currents in a narrow frequency band. Several ringers of this type can be used for *selective ringing* if each is adjusted to respond to a different frequency.

hartley The unit of information in a denary scale, i.e. the amount of information that can be derived from the knowledge of the occurrence of one event out of ten possible and equiprobable events. See also *shannon* and *information content*.

Hartley–Shannon law A statement defining the theoretical maximum rate at which binary digits can be transmitted over a bandlimited channel in the presence of *white noise*. The law is usually expressed in the form

$$C = W \log_2 \left(1 + \frac{S}{N} \right)$$

where C is the channel capacity in bits per second, W is the bandwidth in hertz and S/N is the signal-to-noise ratio. It will be seen that in the limiting case for a signal-to-noise ratio of unity this reduces to $C = W$, i.e. the capacity in bit/s is equal to the bandwidth in Hz. For a good-quality speech channel with a signal-to-noise ratio of 30 dB and a bandwidth of 3 kHz, a theoretical capacity of approximately 30 000 bit/s is indicated. This is an ideal value that cannot be obtained in practice owing to the need to secure reliable transmission in the presence of noise, which is likely to be impulsive rather than white in character.

head end Of a cabled distribution system, equipment that processes signals received from antennas and/or other sources prior to their distribution over the network.

head-on collision A condition that can occur on a bothway data circuit used for *common-channel signalling* when the exchanges at either end seize the circuit at approximately the same moment. The effect of head-on collision can be minimised by giving one of the two exchanges priority, the other exchange withdrawing from the circuit and making a repeat attempt to set up the call on another circuit.

headset A lightweight microphone and telephone receiver assembled on a headband and worn by switchboard operators so as to leave the hands free.

heat coil A thermally operated device connected between a line and exchange apparatus to prevent damage by currents dangerous to the apparatus but of too low a value to operate other protectors or fuses.

Heaviside layer See *E layer*.

height gain A measure of the increase in *field strength* with height for a particular mode of radio-wave propagation, expressed as the ratio of the field strength at a given height to that at the earth's surface.

helical antenna An antenna consisting of a conductor wound into a helix. Characteristics such as the *directivity pattern* and *polarisation* (2) of such an antenna are controlled by the diameter, pitch and number of turns of the helix in relation to the wavelength of operation.

helix   In *facsimile*, a conductor formed into a helix and supported so that it can be continuously rotated to form one electrode of a *continuous recorder*. Also known as a *scroll*.

hell system or **hellschreiber system**   An early form of *alphabetic telegraphy* in which each character is represented by up to forty-nine signal elements, which control an inked spiral so that the required character is formed on a moving paper tape.

hertzian radiator   See *doublet (electrical) radiator*.

hertzian waves   Electromagnetic waves with frequencies lower than those of the infra-red region of the spectrum.

heterochronous   A qualifying term applied to digital signals whose corresponding transitions do not necessarily occur at the same rate. For example, they may be controlled by separate *clocks* or have different nominal *digit rates*.

heterodyne   A process in which two sinusoidal waves interact to produce two new waves having frequencies equal to the sum, and to the difference, of the frequencies of the original waves.

heterogeneous multiplex   A multiplex structure in which the channels do not all have the same *data signalling rate*.

heterogeneous switching network   See *switching network*.

hierarchic network   See *mutually synchronised network*.

high-density bipolar code   An extension of the bipolar code (see *alternate mark inversion*) in which long strings of zeros are replaced by code groups containing timing information, the substitutions being recognisable because they contain marks violating the AMI rule. See also *compatible high-density bipolar code*.

high-frequency repeater distribution frame   A frame providing flexibility in the interconnection of apparatus and external cables on which groups are transmitted.

high-level language   See *programming*.

high-pass filter   A frequency-selective network offering very little *attenuation* to waves with frequencies above a defined cut-off value, but attenuating all lower-frequency waves.

high-usage route or **high-usage trunk group** (US)   In a network employing *alternative routing*, an early-choice group of circuits intended to carry only a portion of the traffic offered, the overflow being diverted on to an alternative route.

higher-order mode   In *waveguide* propagation, any mode of propagation other than the *dominant mode*.

highway (US: *bus*)   A path or set of parallel paths over which digital signals from a number of channels pass, with separation

126

achieved by *time division*. The term is confined to paths within equipment or an exchange.

hiss Audio-frequency *noise* having a continuous spectrum and caused by the combined effect of *shot noise*, thermal agitation, etc.

hits (US) General term for short-term disturbances in a transmission channel caused by storms, accidents, maintenance work, etc.

hoghorn A *microwave* antenna element providing a smooth transition from a *waveguide* to a *cheese antenna* with an asymmetrical feed.

hold To maintain a *selector, circuit*, etc. in the busy or set state.

hold current The minimum current needed to keep a *selector, relay* or similar device in the operated position.

hold for enquiry A PABX facility enabling an extension user already engaged on an incoming exchange line or inter-PBX call to set up a call and speak to a third person with security from, and without losing, the original connection. The service may be invoked by pressing an auxiliary button—or by dialling a special code—and then dialling the required number. The 'enquiry' call may be to another extension, to another PBX or to another installation via the public network, and the caller can release it at any time and return to the original call.

holding time Term used in the context of teletraffic studies to describe the total time that a circuit or device is held in connection with a given call.

holding-time distribution An expression giving the probable distribution of *holding times*.

holdover time See *echo suppressor*.

home area (US) The *numbering-plan area* in which a given station is located.

home position The position taken up by the wipers of a sequential switch such as a *uniselector* following the action of *homing*.

homing In automatic switching, the automatic return of a sequential selector to a predetermined unoperated position following its release.

homochronous Qualifying term applied to digital signals whose corresponding *significant instants* have a constant, but uncontrolled, phase relationship. The signals would be *synchronous* if their phase relationship could be fixed at a desired value.

homogeneous grading A grading formed by *skipping* and *slipping* so that the outlets of the same number of *grading groups* are connected to each outgoing trunk.

homogeneous multiplex A multiplex structure in which all the

127

channels have the same *data signalling rate*.

homogeneous switching network   See *switching network*.

hop   In radio-wave propagation, a transmission path from one point on the earth to another via the *ionosphere* and without intermediate reflection from the surface of the earth.

horizontal polarisation   *Linear polarisation* in which the direction of the electric field is horizontal or, by extension, parallel with some other chosen plane of reference.

horn (also known as a *flare*)   A length of *waveguide* the cross-sectional area of which increases progressively towards its open end. A horn may be used as an elementary radiator but may also be used as part of a larger antenna, i.e. it may illuminate a paraboloidal reflector as in a horn reflector antenna. See also *sectoral horn*.

housekeeping digits   See *service digits* (2).

howler   A device for producing a loud tone that may be applied to a subscriber's line or PBX extension to indicate that the handset is off hook.

hum   Unwanted low-frequency currents interfering with a desired signal and usually having their origin in the alternating power-supply mains.

hundred call seconds   A unit of *traffic intensity* equal to the average number of calls per hour assuming a mean holding time of 100 seconds. Hence thirty-six HCS are equivalent to one *erlang*. Also known as *cent call seconds* or *unit call*.

hunting   The action of searching for a circuit or device that meets stipulated conditions. The term thus describes the act of searching for an available trunk in order to establish a connection. It also applies to the action of seeking a busy circuit for traffic record purposes. In electromechanical systems hunting is usually performed sequentially over the available inlets or outlets, starting from a defined *home position*. If the process is controlled in such a way that each available inlet or outlet is equally likely to be seized, it is termed *random hunting*.

hybrid balance (US)   See *balance return loss*.

hybrid coil (also known as *hybrid transformer*)   A differential transformer with three windings used in a *four-wire terminating set* to couple the two-wire and four-wire circuits together; see *Figure H.1*. The windings on the transformer are so arranged that speech currents are transferred from L1 to L2 and from L3 to L1 with a loss of little more than 3 dB. Provided that the balancing network BN closely matches the impedance of the two-wire line, the loss between L3 and L2 and between L1 and BN will be very high.

hybrid coupler or **hybrid junction**   A four-part reciprocal

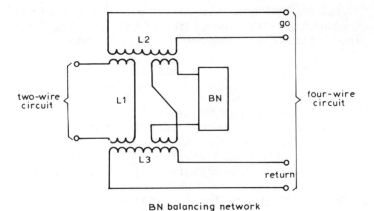

Figure H.1   Hybrid coil

microwave junction in which, under matched conditions, the power fed into any one port is divided equally between two other ports, no power appearing at the fourth port and none being returned to the first. The device is thus a directional coupler with a coupling factor of 3 dB.

hybrid loss   The *attenuation* suffered by a signal passing through a *hybrid coil*. Because the signal current is divided into two, the loss is usually a little over 3 dB.

hybrid mode   A waveguide transmission *mode* (2) in which both the electric and magnetic fields have longitudinal components.

hybrid ring (US: *rat race*)   A *hybrid junction* in the form of a length of waveguide bent into a complete circle with four waveguide ports appropriately spaced around it.

hybrid T   A *hybrid junction* formed from a *series T* and a *shunt T*, with the side arms both located at the same cross-section of the main waveguide. Also known as *magic T*.

hybrid transformer   See *hybrid coil*.

hybrid wave   In radio-wave propagation, general term for a wave in which both the electric and magnetic field vectors have longitudinal components.

hypergroup   A term used in the UK to describe an assembly of 900 channels formed directly from 15 *supergroups* without resorting to *mastergroups*.

hypothetical reference connection   An imaginary international connection specified by the CCITT to enable administrations to study the possible effects on overall transmission quality of changes in the planning parameters of their national networks. Such a model can also be used to test national planning rules against any performance criteria recommended by the CCITT for national systems. Various types of reference connection are specified according to length and the kind of service provided.

I

ISM apparatus Designation used in connection with radio interference studies to describe industrial, scientific and medical apparatus producing radio-frequency energy.

identification The process carried out by a common control system whereby it determines the identity of an individual line, device, subscriber, etc. requiring service.

identifier Apparatus that may be allotted to a switching network to find the location of terminal equipment requiring service.

idle The state of a *selector*, line, etc. when it is not in use. It may be free or busied out.

idle character A control character sent over a data network when there is no information to be transmitted.

idle RQ In data transmission, a method of *error control* using *decision feedback* and so arranged that after transmitting a block of data the sending terminal remains in the idle state until an acknowledgement signal is received over the return channel. The next block is then transmitted or the same block is retransmitted, depending on the content of the acknowledgement signal. This method of operation is not as efficient as *continuous RQ* owing to the gaps between the blocks. The length of these gaps depends on system parameters such as the transmission speed in the return channel, modem turn-round times and the loop propagation time of the line.

idle signal unit In *common-channel signalling*, a *signal unit* sent over a *signalling link* at times when no signal messages are available for transmission. The functions of the idle signal unit and *acknowledgement signal unit* are often combined.

idler frequency See *parametric amplifier*.

idling performance Of a quantiser, the behaviour of the device in the absence of any input signal.

idling region Of a quantiser, the region of the device's response characteristic corresponding with near-zero input signal levels.

image antenna An imaginary electrical counterpart of a real antenna, assumed for the purpose of calculation to exist beneath the surface of the earth (or a ground plane serving as the earth) and symmetrically located with respect to the real antenna.

image frequency In *superheterodyne reception*, a frequency differing from that of the *local oscillator* by the value of the receiver's intermediate frequency, but being higher than the local oscillator if the wanted signal is lower or vice versa. A strong signal, at or near the image frequency, that is able to pass through the earlier tuned circuits and reach the input to the frequency changer can thus give rise to an unwanted *image response* or *second-channel response*.

image rejection ratio   Of a superheterodyne receiver, a measure of the ability of the receiver to reject unwanted *image frequency* signals. It is usually expressed as the ratio in *decibels* between the level of a signal at the wanted frequency and the level of a signal at the image frequency producing the same power at the receiver output.

image response   See *image frequency*.

immediate ringing   In certain automatic systems, the application of a pulse of ringing current to a subscriber's line or PABX extension immediately a call is set up. After the initial pulse, normal *interrupted ringing* is applied. Also sometimes called *instant ring*.

impairment scale   A scale used in the subjective assessment of degradations caused to a television picture by imperfections in transmission links or equipment. Usually such a scale has five points ranging from 'imperceptible' to 'very annoying'. The results of a large number of laboratory tests using panels of observers can be used to relate the effects of various kinds of distortion to the degree of annoyance caused to viewers. This information may then be used to specify performance parameters for equipment etc. in terms of measured amounts of the various types of distortion. See *K-rating system*.

impedance simulating network   See *balancing network*.

impulse   See *pulse*. The term impulse is preferred by some authorities for the description of pulses whose duration is extremely short in comparison with the time scale of interest; see *impulsive interference* and *unit impulse*.

impulse transmission   A form of digital transmission in which impulses of either or both polarities are transmitted to indicate the occurrences of *transitions* in the input signal. This type of transmission can be used to minimise the effect of low-frequency *interference*, the impulses being formed by suppressing the low-frequency components in the input signal.

impulsing relay   In automatic switching, a *relay* used to repeat the pulses transmitted from a dial.

impulsive interference or **impulsive noise**   *Interference* or *noise* characterised by short-duration disturbances separated by quiescent intervals. The interference with radio reception caused by a car ignition system is classed as impulsive interference.

in-band signalling The transmission of *signals* (2) relating to a call, within the frequency band and over the channel or circuit used for the call.

in-slot signalling The use of one digit in a *channel time slot* for the signals associated with the traffic carried by that channel. The digit time slot may be permanently allocated for signalling or may be made available periodically by means of a *multiframe*.

incidental modulation Unwanted *modulation* of a form other than that which is the object of a given modulation process, e.g. unwanted *amplitude modulation* produced by a phase or frequency modulator.

inclined orbit Of a *communication satellite*, an orbit that is neither equatorial nor polar.

inclined V antenna A directional *travelling-wave antenna* consisting of two straight conductors set at an angle to one another so that they form a V in a plane inclined to the horizontal. The antenna is fed at its highest point—the apex—and each arm is connected to earth at its lower end through the correct impedance.

incoming A qualifying term applied to circuits at some point in a network to indicate that the direction of a call set-up is towards that point from some other point. Hence 'incoming trunk' describes a *one-way trunk* at a central office other than that originating the traffic.

incoming call storage and retrieval A PABX facility enabling an extension user to store or park an incoming call for a specified period after having asked the caller to hold the line. The call is stored by pressing an auxiliary button and dialling a special code. It can be retrieved, within the designated period, by dialling another code from any extension. If the call is not retrieved within the specified period it is released, a recorded announcement being given to the caller.

incoming traffic Traffic passing through a given network and having its origin in some other network, regardless of its destination.

independent-sideband transmission The transmission of two *sidebands*, each of which corresponds to one or more modulating signals independent of that (those) used to modulate the other sideband. The *carrier* is either partially or wholly suppressed.

index of cooperation In *facsimile*, the *factor of cooperation* divided by π. The term is generally applied to drum-type apparatus in which the total line length is π times the diameter (D) of the drum, so the index is equal to the product of the diameter and the *scanning density* (F). An alternative way of expressing this is D/P, where P is the *scanning pitch*.

indirect back scatter A back-scattered radio signal propagated via the *ionosphere* from the region in which *scattering* is taking place. Also known as *long-distance back scatter*.

indirect control system In automatic switching, a system in which *registers* (2) or similar functional units store and process information required to establish connections, a device being associated with a given call only for that time during which it exercises its control function.

individual answering A switchboard feature such that an individual *call indicator* is provided for each connected circuit, these indicators being *multipled* to every position capable of answering calls. See also *common answering* and *selective answering*.

individual line A line providing exclusive service for one subscriber, even though it may be terminated by a *call connect system* giving access to a number of extensions.

individual trunk A connecting circuit serving only one *grading group*.

induced interference *Interference* arising in a communication circuit as a result of coupling with the field produced by an interference source.

induction coil A transformer in a telephone that serves to match the microphone and receiver to the line and reduces *sidetone*.

inductive coordination Consultative arrangement between electricity supply authorities and telecommunications authorities designed to prevent *induced interference*.

inductive field region Of an antenna, see *reactive near-field region*.

infinitesimal dipole See *doublet (electrical) radiator*.

information In telecommunications, essentially any facts, data, etc. that, when transferred from a source or over a link, add to the knowledge of the recipient. This definition emphasises the unpredictability of information, since this quality forms the basis on which it is treated quantitatively in information theory. (Clearly if the content of a message is known prior to its receipt, no information is conveyed to the recipient.) In a more general sense, information has been defined as the meaning assigned to data by established conventions.

information bits In data transmission, those bits generated by the data source, excluding any bits used for *error control*.

information content Of a *symbol* emitted by a source, the quantity of information conveyed by the symbol in *hartleys* or *shannons*, as given by the negative of the logarithm of the probability that this particular symbol will be emitted. The base used for the logarithm determines the unit in which the information content is expressed, logarithms to the base two corresponding to the shannon and logarithms to the base ten to the hartley. If binary transmission is assumed, with equiprobability of either symbol being emitted, the probability of a particular value occurring is one half or 2^{-1} and hence each symbol conveys one shannon of information. Similarly if denary transmission is assumed, with equiprobability of any symbol having one of the ten possible values, the probability of a particular value occurring is one-tenth or 10^{-1} and hence each symbol conveys one hartley of information. Since $\log_2 10 = 3.323$, it follows that one hartley equals 3.323 shannons. It should be noted that in practice the probability of a particular value of a symbol being emitted may depend on the value(s) of one or more of the preceding symbols. Often the average information content per symbol is quoted. The term *self information* is sometimes used in place of information content.

information feedback system A data transmission system using *message feedback* and retransmission of any erroneous groups. The disadvantages of this type of system are the need to use *duplex* transmission facilities and the possibility of errors occurring in the return channel.

information rate The number of symbols emitted by a source per second times the average *information content* per symbol.

information symbol A graphic symbol used in a telephone directory to describe special features of the telephone service, e.g. a symbol used to indicate that a subscriber has an answering device attached to his telephone.

information transfer The overall result of the transmission of data from a source (DTE) to a sink (DTE).

infra-red radiation Electromagnetic radiation in the wavelength range from 780 to 10^5 nanometres, i.e. the range extending from visible red light to the shortest *microwaves*.

infrasonic frequency A frequency below that of sound waves audible to the human ear, usually taken as a frequency below 15 Hz. Also termed *sub-audio frequency*. The term *subsonic frequency* is now deprecated because of the use of subsonic in connection with aircraft speeds.

inhibit To prevent a process from taking place. Thus an inhibit input standing at its 1-state prevents a *logic element* from carrying out its defined function. In binary logic a negated inhibit input is obviously equivalent to an *enable input*, and the latter terminology is preferred in many cases.

initial address message In *common-channel signalling*, the first signal message transmitted in a call set-up process. The IAM contains all the *address information*, or sufficient to enable the routing of the call to be commenced.

initial signal unit See *signal unit*.

inlet Of a switching stage, the terminals through which incoming traffic enters the stage.

input (1) The signal, current, voltage, data, etc. applied to a device or circuit. (2) The terminals or port where these quantities are applied.

input-output equipment In data transmission, any user equipment permitting data to be fed into, or extracted from, the system.

insertion gain [loss] The gain [loss] in *decibels* caused by the insertion of a *transducer* into a system, and given by the ratio of the power delivered to that part of the system following the transducer to the power delivered to the same part prior to insertion of the transducer. The ratio would be inverted in the case of loss. Usually matched terminations are assumed. In the case of a multicomponent signal it is usually necessary to specify the particular component and any weighting used, for example for *noise*.

insertion test signal A signal with a closely specified waveform inserted on a vacant line during the field blanking interval of a television signal to enable the performance of transmission links and equipment to be continuously monitored. Usually the signal consists of a 2T $\sin^2$ pulse, a bar and a staircase waveform. See also *waveform testing*.

instant ring See *immediate ringing*.

instantaneous companding *Companding* in which the instantaneous value of the signal controls the degree of amplification used in the compression and expansion processes.

instantaneous frequency Of an oscillatory quantity such as an angle-modulated wave, the rate of change of phase in radians per second divided by 2π.

integrated digital network A network employing both digital transmission and digital switching.

integrated numbering plan See *numbering plan*.

integrated numbering-plan area An area of the world identified by a *world zone number* which also serves as the *country code*. An example of such an area is North America, where the digit 1 is the country code for the US, Canada, and the other countries in the zone.

integrated-service digital network An *integrated digital network* used for more than one service, e.g. telephony and data.

intelligibility A measure of the ability of a communication system to convey *information* by means of speech. Intelligibility is expressed as the percentage of simple ideas correctly received

135

over the system. See also *articulation*.

intensity of traffic See *traffic flow*.

interchannel interference In a *frequency-division multiplex system, interference* in a given channel caused by signals in one or more of the other channels.

interconnecting number In a *homogeneous grading*, the number of grading groups connected together.

interdigit pause See *intertrain pause*.

interface A distinguishable boundary between two related systems, defined for the purpose of specifying the type and form of signals passing between them. A typical example of a hardware interface is the connection between a *data-circuit terminating equipment* and a *data terminal equipment*.

interference (1) The generic term for any form of unwanted energy appearing in a communication *channel* at a level sufficient to degrade the performance of the channel to a significant extent. (2) The disturbance of a signal resulting from such unwanted energy.

Interference thus includes various types of noise: *crosstalk, spurious emission*, voltages induced from high-voltage power lines, and signals from transmitters operating on incorrect or unauthorised frequencies. Interference is classified according to its effect (see *harmful interference, permissible interference* and *acceptable interference*) and according to its type.

interference fading In radio reception, *fading* caused by the interaction of two or more waves of similar amplitude but differing in phase.

interference field strength The *field strength* of a disturbing source, measured in accordance with the procedure laid down in the publications of CISPR.

interference guard band See *guard band*.

interference pattern In *facsimile*, a defect caused by some form of recurrent *interference* and manifesting itself as a superimposed pattern of lines or density changes on the reproduced picture.

Interim Eutelsat The provisional organisation set up by the telecommunications administrations and operating agencies of Europe to manage the developing satellite systems such as ECS and MARECS. The constitution of Interim Eutelsat allows all 26 members of CEPT to become signatory parties. Separate arrangements relate to the ECS and MARECS space segments, each of which is managed by an independent Interim Eutelsat Council. Until it becomes a definitive body the organisation cannot enter into contracts or agreements, and the French PTT has therefore been empowered to act on its behalf for matters concerning the ECS project. The UK has a similar mandate for the MARECS project.

interlock code In a public data network, information identifying a particular *closed user group*.

intermediate distribution frame A *distribution frame* providing for the termination and cross-connection of units of *exchange equipment*.

intermediate feed antenna A vertical *antenna* having one end close to the ground and being fed at a point whose position with respect to the ground is chosen to give the antenna desired characteristics.

intermediate frequency In *superheterodyne reception*, the frequency to which the received carrier is changed by the frequency changer.

intermodulation A process occurring in a non-linear device or system whereby the components of a complex wave modulate each other to produce new waves having frequencies equal to the sums and differences of the frequencies of the various components or harmonics of the input wave. Intermodulation is a major cause of distortion in non-linear devices, e.g. an overloaded audio amplifier, and its effects are usually treated separately from the *harmonic distortion* that also occurs in such cases. In wideband FDM transmission systems the result of intermodulation is usually termed *intermodulation noise*.

intermodulation-noise dispersal A technique used to reduce the limiting effect of *intermodulation* on the capacity of a satellite operating in the FDMA mode. The principle of operation is to spread the intermodulation products over the bandwidth of a transponder by frequency-modulating the vision carrier of any television signal with a low-frequency triangular wave. The same process is applied to carriers modulated by frequency-division multiplexed assemblies of telephone channels when the traffic falls to a low level and a strong carrier-frequency component is present. The process is sometimes known as *carrier-energy dispersal*.

internal blocking (US: *matching loss*) In a link system, the condition in which a connection cannot be set up between a given inlet and any suitable free outlet, owing to the unavailability of a free path.

internal congestion See *link congestion*.

internal traffic Traffic originating and terminating in a given network.

International Electrotechnical Commission (IEC) Founded in 1906, the IEC has been responsible for much standardisation in the electrical field including the formulation of the MKSA system of units. When the International Standards Organisation

137

was set up in 1947 the IEC was loosely affiliated to it and assumed responsibility for international standards in the electrotechnical field. Membership is by way of national standards organisations, as for the ISO, and the work is conducted by technical committees backed by sub-committees and working groups. Some of the IEC's work relates to telecommunications—e.g. in the fields of wires, cables, waveguides and CATV systems—and there is clearly some overlap with the CCIR and CCITT. In the main, demarcation difficulties are avoided by the IEC concentrating on standards for materials, components and methods of measurements, leaving it to the CCIs to deal with operating and service matters. Cross-representation at meetings also aids the necessary coordination. In the specific areas of graphical symbols and terminology the IEC cooperates directly with the CCIs in joint committees with representation drawn from all three organisations.

International Frequency Registration Board (IFRB) Established in 1947, the IFRB is one of the permanent organs of the ITU. It is responsible for maintaining a master list of radio frequencies used throughout the world, and seeks to ensure that no new frequency is taken into use by any country if interference with existing radio services would result. The Board consists of five radio experts elected by the Plenipotentiary Conference on a wide geographical basis. It acts as a corporate body independent of country or regional interests and is assisted by a specialised secretariat. Its principal task is the examination of countries' proposals for the assignment and use of radio frequencies, in order to decide whether they are in accordance with the Convention and Radio Regulations and whether they are likely to cause interference with other radio services. Approved frequency assignments are recorded in the 'Master International Frequency Register' and thus obtain formal recognition and protection. Information from the master list is published periodically in the International Frequency List, which gives particulars such as type of emission, power output, etc. for some half-million frequency assignments.

International Morse Code See *Morse code*.

international number All the digits that have to be dialled after the *international prefix* to obtain access to a subscriber in another country. An international number thus consists of a *country code* followed by the national (significant) number; see *national number*.

international prefix The combination of digits that has to be dialled to gain access to the automatic outgoing international equipment. In the UK the digits 010 are used. Some countries use more than one international prefix either to cater for different classes of call or to permit the use of shorter codes on calls to certain regionally associated countries; see *country code*.

International Radio Consultative Committee (CCIR) Founded in 1927, the CCIR is one of the permanent organs of the ITU. It is responsible for technical questions specifically related to radio communication, in the same way that the CCITT is responsible for questions related to telephony and telegraphy. Membership is on the same basis as for the CCITT, except that the governmental telecommunications authorities of participating countries play a more active role in view of the CCIR's involvement with regulations relating to the use of the radio-frequency spectrum. As in the CCITT, study groups deal with technical questions in selected areas and draft reports, resolutions, recommendations, etc. for approval at plenary assemblies. CCIR Recommendations are not mandatory but are generally adopted by telecommunication authorities.

International Special Committee on Radio Interference See *CISPR*.

International Standards Organisation (ISO) Set up in 1947 as a specialised agency of the United Nations, the ISO is concerned with international standardisation across a broad field of industrial products. Membership is by way of national standards organisations (e.g. the BSI in the UK) and over 60 nations are currently members. The ISO works through about 100 technical committees and publishes international standards, which are usually used as the basis of national standards by participating nations. By agreement, work in the electrotechnical field is regarded as proper to the IEC, but there is some overlap of interest. ISO standards for materials etc. are obviously relevant to the manufacture of telecommunication equipment, and its work in the field of data processing is of interest to the CCITT. Cross-representation at meetings is used to try to achieve effective coordination.

International Telecommunications Satellite Organisation (INTELSAT) An organisation of governments and their designated telecommunications entities (whether public or private) set up to design, develop, construct, operate and maintain the space segment of the *global satellite communication system*. Currently over 90 countries are members of INTELSAT, each telecommunications entity holding a quota of investment shares based on its use of the system.

International Telecommunications Union (ITU) An organisation of over 150 nations founded in 1865 with the purpose of extending and maintaining international cooperation in telecommunications. The ITU seeks to promote the development of technical facilities with the aim of improving the efficiency of world telecommunications services. Recognised as a specialised agency by the United Nations in 1947, the ITU is charged to take due account of the needs of new and developing nations. It has a permanent secretariat based at its headquarters in Geneva and three permanent organs:

- *International Frequency Registration Board (IFRB),*
- *International Radio Consultative Committee (CCIR),*
- *International Telegraph and Telephone Consultative Committee (CCITT).*

The ITU's Convention and Telephone, Telegraph and Radio Regulations have the status of formal treaties between the participating countries and are binding on those signatories who have acceded to them. The method of operation is via plenipotentiary and administrative conferences and by way of meetings and plenary assemblies of its various organs. ITU publications include statistics, technical handbooks, frequency lists and a monthly journal.

Formal participation in ITU activities is through member nations' governments (the Home Office in the UK and the FCC in the USA), but other organisations concerned with telecommunications such as British Telecommunications and the Bell Telephone Company can become Recognised Private Operating Agencies (RPOAs). Such bodies take a direct part in the activities of study groups and special committees of the CCITT and the CCIR, and advise and assist their respective formal members in other ITU activities.

International Telegraph and Telephone Consultative Committee (CCITT) Formed in 1956 by a merger of separate telephone and telegraph committees, the CCITT is one of the permanent organs of the ITU. Member countries participate via their telecommunication authorities, recognised operating agencies (such as British Telecommunications and Cable and Wireless in the UK, and the Bell Telephone Company in the USA), and industrial and scientific organisations. The CCITT's function is to study technical, operating and tariff questions relating to telephony and telegraphy and to issue recommendations on them. CCITT Recommendations are not binding, but are usually adopted by telecommunication authorities in order to facilitate the interworking of national networks. The CCITT operates through a number of study groups, each of which is responsible for questions in a prescribed area such as telegraphy, data transmission, digital networks, etc. Plenary assemblies are held every three or four years in order to receive reports from the

study groups and to approve draft resolutions, recommendations, handbooks, etc. for publication.

The responsibilities of the CCITT and the CCIR tend to
overlap in certain areas, e.g. the long-distance transmission of
television programmes, and some joint study groups have
therefore been established. The two organisations also cooperate
in a number of plan committees responsible for drawing up
overall telecommunications plans for the whole world and for
specific regions such as Africa and Latin America.

International Teletraffic Congress (ITC) An organisation formed
mainly of representatives of telecommunications authorities and
industry. The ITC serves as a major teletraffic forum and
collaborates with the CCITT in this field. A congress is held
approximately every three years.

international transit exchange An *exchange* that switches traffic
between countries other than the one in which it is located.

inter-port isolation Of a multi-port antenna, the ratio (usually
expressed in *decibels*) of the power applied at an input port to the
unwanted power appearing at another port.

inter-position transfer A switchboard feature enabling an
operator to transfer a call to other positions or to accept calls so
transferred.

interrupted carrier-wave transmission A form of radio
transmission in which the *carrier* wave is interrupted at a
constant audio-frequency rate.

interrupted dial tone A non-standard *dial tone* returned to a
PABX extension user attempting to make an outgoing call while
incoming calls to his number are subject to a diversion service.

interrupted isochronous transmission See *burst isochronous
transmission.*

interrupted ringing Standard *power ringing* that is automatically
interrupted in a periodic manner.

interstation muting or **interstation noise suppression** See *muting.*

interswitchboard line See *tie-line.*

intersymbol interference In digital transmission, the effect arising
when some of the energy relating to a signal element in a given
signalling interval spills over into the adjacent interval(s). Such
interference is caused by the dispersion in time of the energy in
the pulse signal as a result of inadequacies of the transmission
channel such as insufficient *bandwidth* or poor *equalisation*. Its
effect on the *eye pattern* at the input to the decision circuit of a
regenerator is to reduce the area of the eye opening, thereby
increasing the possibility of errors due to noise. Nyquist showed
that there are three requirements for the suppression of
intersymbol interference in a band-limited channel, as follows.

(a) The impulse response of the channel must have equally spaced nulls or axis crossings. (b) There must be equal time intervals between transition values, i.e. in the case of binary pulse transmission the values corresponding to half the difference between the 0 and 1 values. (c) The area under the received wave during the signal time unit should be preserved, since in this case the response to each impulse will have zero area for every other signalling interval than its own. See also *Nyquist rate*.

intertoll trunk (US) A circuit connecting *toll offices* in different *exchanges*.

intertrain pause In dialling, the time interval between the end of one train of pulses representing a digit and the start of the next. Also known as *interdigit pause*.

intrinsic impedance Of an *antenna*, the theoretical input impedance of the antenna in the ideal case, i.e. if all elements are assumed to be lossless, uniform and of exact dimension and if the earth or ground plane is assumed to be a perfect conductor.

intrusion The act of intervening in an established call in order to speak to the parties thereto. For example, intervention by a PBX operator for the purpose of offering an incoming international call.

intrusion inhibition A PABX service which may be applied to selected extensions to protect them against *instrusion* by the operator and/or other extensions. Protection may be arranged by giving an extension a predetermined *class of service*, in which case all outgoing calls are protected automatically. A call connected via the operator can be protected if the operator takes appropriate action after connecting the call. Each individual call from a selected extension can be protected if the user dials a suffix code after the wanted party has answered.

intrusion tone An audible signal used to indicate to the parties engaged on a call that *intrusion* has taken place. Also known as *beep tone, warn pulse* and *warn tone*.

inverted-L antenna An antenna consisting of an elevated horizontal conductor, which may be a *multi-wire element,* insulated at one end and connected to a down lead at the other.

inverted-V antenna A directional *travelling-wave antenna* consisting of two straight conductors arranged at an angle to one another so that they form an inverted V. The antenna is fed at the apex and each arm is connected to earth through the correct impedance.

inverter (1) Equipment for converting a direct current into an alternating current or a higher-voltage direct current. (2) A *logic element* used to change the polarity of a logic signal.

ionogram A record of an *ionospheric sounding*, usually consisting of a plot of the *virtual height* as a function of frequency.

ionosonde A radar system used for *ionospheric sounding*.

ionosphere That part of the earth's atmosphere, above a height of about 50 km, in which the propagation of radio waves is affected by the presence of free ions and electrons. For reference purposes the ionosphere is divided into three regions having spherical boundaries concentric with the surface of the earth. The *D region* extends from the lowest boundary (50 km) up to a height of about 90 km, the *E region* extends on up to a height of about 150 km and the *F region* lies beyond that boundary.

ionospheric absorption *Absorption* occurring as a result of interaction between a radio wave and gas molecules in the *ionosphere*. See also *non-deviative absorption* and *deviative absorption*.

ionospheric crossmodulation An effect due to non-linear absorption whereby the *modulation* on a strong carrier is impressed upon another carrier passing through the same region of the *ionosphere*. Also known as the *Luxembourg effect*.

ionospheric focusing [defocusing] In radio-wave propagation, enhancement [reduction] of the *field strength* at a receiving site owing to the focusing [defocusing] caused by small-scale or large-scale curvature of the surfaces of ionospheric layers.

ionospheric forecast or **ionospheric prediction** A forecast of conditions in the *ionosphere*, used in connection with radio communication services.

ionospheric recorder Apparatus used to examine and record ionospheric properties affecting the propagation of radio waves. A *vertical-incidence recorder* is used, for example, to measure the *virtual heights* of ionospheric layers vertically above its location. An *oblique-incidence recorder* is usually located a long distance from the transmitter and is used for recording ionospheric properties affecting propagation between the transmitter and the receiving site.

ionospheric scatter Propagation of radio waves as a result of *scattering* occurring in the lower part of the E-region. Communication over longer distances than those obtainable with *tropospheric scatter links* is possible as a result of the increased height at which scattering takes place.

ionospheric sounding The measurement of ionospheric properties by means of special radio transmissions. Usually the *virtual heights* of the various ionospheric layers are determined by measuring the time taken for pulses of radio-frequency energy to travel up to a layer and back down again after reflection. By

143

varying the frequency of the carrier periodically over a range of values, the virtual heights of the various layers for different frequencies can be computed or displayed.

ionospheric storm A severe and prolonged ionospheric disturbance.

ionospheric wave A wave that is reflected or refracted towards the earth by the *ionosphere*.

iris In a *waveguide*, a thin metal plate perpendicular to the axis of the waveguide and partly blocking it.

isochronous modulation [**restitution**] Telegraph *modulation* [*restitution*] in which all *significant intervals* are nominally equal to the *unit interval* or to a whole multiple thereof.

isochronous signal A digital signal in which the time interval separating any two signal *transitions* is nominally equal to the *unit interval* or to a whole multiple thereof.

isolation A measure of the amount of unwanted power transfer between circuits, devices or different parts of a system. In the case of a directional coupler it is the loss, in *decibels*, between two ports in the unwanted direction of propagation with all the ports correctly terminated. Similarly the *isolation ratio* of two antennas is the ratio, in decibels, of the power input to one antenna to the power received by the other.

isolator A passive *waveguide* component in which the transmission loss in one direction is much greater than that in the opposite direction.

isotropic gain See *absolute gain*.

isotropic radiator A hypothetical lossless *antenna* radiating uniformly in all directions and forming a reference for expressing the performance of real antennas.

J

JK bistable A logic storage element having two inputs designated J and K and two outputs whose states are always complementary. Each occurrence of the condition J = K = 1 causes a single complementary change at the outputs.

jack A fixed socket into which a plug may be inserted to make connection with one or more circuits.

jamming Deliberate interference with a radio-communication service by the transmission of a powerful disturbing signal.

jitter Generic term for sudden, small, irregular departures from the ideal value of a parameter such as the *phase, amplitude* or *pulse duration* of a signal. In the case of digital transmission systems the term usually refers to variations in the timing of the signal. In long systems jitter tends to accumulate, particularly if systematic pulse patterns are present in the signal. This effect can be reduced; see *data scrambler*. See also *dejitteriser, justification jitter* and *waiting-time jitter*.

Johnson noise   See *thermal noise*.

judder   In *facsimile*, irregular movement of the mechanisms in a transmitter or receiver resulting in wavy or broken reproduction of lines that are straight on the original document. The effect can be resolved into *longitudinal judder* (defects in the direction of the *scanning lines* caused by variations in the *scanning speed*) and *transverse judder* (variations in the *scanning pitch* causing both underlap and overlap).

jump   In a digital network, a deliberate adjustment in the rate of a digital signal, consisting of the addition or subtraction of a set of consecutive digit positions, e.g. a complete *frame* (1). This type of adjustment occurs comparatively rarely and should not be confused with *justification*. The term *slip* has been widely used in this context, but is more appropriately applied to an involuntary occurrence such as a loss of synchronism.

jumper   A short length of cable used to effect a connection on a *distribution frame*.

junction circuit   A circuit directly connecting two exchanges sited relatively close to one another. In the UK the distinction between *trunk circuits* and junction circuits is that the latter are usually less than 15 miles long.

junction pole   Of an *open-wire* line, a pole at the end of a *transposition section* or between two such sections.

junction transposition (US: *S-pole transposition*)   A *transposition* located at a *junction pole*.

junctor   A link circuit between switching frames in a crossbar exchange. The term is also used in the context of modern processor-controlled exchanges to describe sub-systems serving to link parts of a switching network together, and usually performing other functions as well. Thus a unit serving as a *transmission bridge* and used in the completion of local calls is termed a *local junctor*. A *trunk junctor*, on the other hand, may have to provide an interface with various types of signalling systems, and its functions may be split between incoming and outgoing units.

justifiable digit time slot (US: *stuffable digit time slot*)   A *digit time slot* provided in an output multiplex signal to accommodate a *justifying digit* or an information digit from a tributary signal.

justification (US: *pulse stuffing*)   The generic term for the process that enables *plesiochronous* digital signals to be combined and satisfactorily transmitted over a common path by *digital* *multiplexing*. Essentially, the requirement is to adjust slightly the digit rate of each tributary signal so that it can accord with the rate determined by the multiplex equipment. There are two basic approaches to this problem.

In *positive justification* the digit rate of each channel in the output multiplexed signal is made slightly higher than the maximum allowable tributary rate so that time slots will always be available for information digits from the tributaries. Each channel in the multiplexed signal includes a number of dedicated time slots (*justifiable digit time slots*), each of which can be used for an information digit from the corresponding tributary or can be filled (stuffed) with a non-information digit, as necessary. Two-condition control signals are transmitted by means of *justification service digits* to advise the demultiplex equipment on the status of the digits in the justifiable digit time slots. Information digits are then added back to the relevant demultiplexed tributary signals, non-information digits being ignored.

In *negative justification* the digit rate of each channel in the output multiplexed signal is made slightly lower than the minimum allowable tributary rate so that time slots will not be available for all the information bits from the tributaries. Surplus bits are therefore extracted from the input signals in a controlled manner and transmitted separately to the demultiplex equipment together with the necessary control signals.

The two basic approaches may be combined to yield *positive-negative justification*, in which either digits are deleted or non-information digits are inserted at each justification opportunity.

An extension of this technique that is recommended by the CCITT for second-order multiplex equipment combining four 2048 kbit/s tributary signals into a single 8448 kbit/s bit stream is called *positive-zero-negative justification*. In this method the digit rate of each channel in the output multiplex signal is nominally the same as the tributary rate, so that no justification action need be taken unless the actual rates differ. The system has the advantage that it is readily adapted to handle a mixture of plesiochronous and synchronous signals, an important consideration in the development of synchronous digital networks.

justification control signal   A signal used to transmit information on the status of the digit in a *justifiable digit time slot*. An error in this signal can be serious, since it can cause loss of *frame alignment* in dependent multiplexes. The signal is therefore usually composed of three identical digits to enable a majority decision to be taken by the demultiplex equipment. The three digits are also distributed in the frame of the output multiplex signal to provide protection from burst errors.

justification jitter   Irregularity in the timing of a digital signal, due to the deletion or insertion of time slots in the process of *justification*. The jitter produced varies with the method of justification, but it is generally useful to distinguish between regular components produced by the discrete timing changes of one digit period and low-frequency components arising from the fact that justification is normally carried out at an arbitrary point in each frame; see *waiting-time jitter*.

justification rate (US: *stuffing rate*)   Of a tributary signal in digital multiplexing, the average rate at which digits are inserted or removed in the *justification* process. The *nominal justification rate* refers to the value when both the tributary signal and the multiplex equipment have their nominal rates. The *maximum justification rate* defines the ability of a system to handle rate variations in the input signal, a typical value being 10 kbit/s for a 2.048 Mbit/s signal.

justification ratio (US: *stuffing ratio*)   A measure of the usage of the *justification* capacity of a system, given by dividing the actual *justification rate* by the maximum justification rate.

justification service digit (US: *stuffing service digit*)   A digit forming part of a *justification control signal*.

justifying digit (US: *stuffing digit*)   A non-information digit inserted in a *justifiable digit time slot* when the slot is not required for an information digit from a tributary digital signal.

K

KP signal   See *start-of-pulsing signal*.

K-rating   A numerical factor determined by waveform testing in accordance with the *K-rating system* and expressing the transmission performance of television links or equipment insofar as linear waveform distortions are concerned.

K-rating system   A system for specifying and measuring the performance of television equipment and links in terms of a single rating factor K, whose value is determined by waveform response tests using pulse-and-bar and square-wave test signals. The system seeks to place limits on the various waveform features in such a way that the degree of subjective impairment caused to a transmitted picture will be the same regardless of how the test waveform reaches the limits. The various limits were devised using as a reference the distortion caused by a single

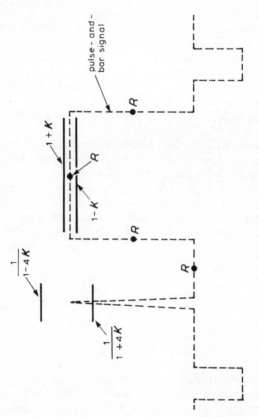

Figure K.1 Limits for bar response and pulse-to-bar ratio, drawn for K = 5 per cent (Note: oscilloscope controls adjusted so that trace passes through points marked R)

148

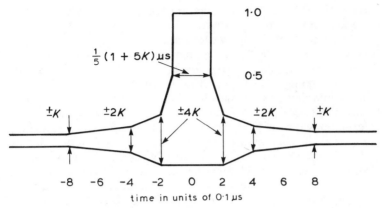

Figure K.2 Limits for 2T-pulse response, drawn for K = 5 per cent

long-term echo separated from the main signal by at least eight times the half-period of the upper cut-off frequency of the TV system. The relative amplitude of the long-term echo gives the percentage K rating. *Figures K.1 and K.2* show the limits applied to the pulse-and-bar signal and the 2T pulse respectively. From the latter it is apparent that the disturbing effect of a single long-term ($t > 0.8 \, \mu$s) echo of amplitude K is the same as that of four times as large a short-term echo ($t = 0.2 \, \mu$s). As explained under *waveform testing*, transparent masks engraved with limits for different values of K are used for routine tests.

Kendall effect   A form of *non-linearity distortion* in which a modulated carrier is partially demodulated. If the resulting *baseband* signal overlaps the wanted carrier *sidebands* it constitutes a form of interference that cannot be filtered out. The effect is of little concern in speech or data transmission, but can affect some types of *facsimile* where small distortions are visible.

Kennelly-Heaviside layer   See *E layer*.

key   A switching device having one or more sets of contacts that can be operated manually by means of a small handle or pushbutton.

key and lamp units   Items of apparatus that can be associated with telephones in a customer's office to provide flexible arrangements for dealing with incoming and outgoing calls on a number of *exchange* lines, extensions or private circuits.

key-clicks   Interference with radio reception as a result of out-of-band radiation from a radio-telegraph transmitter operating on an adjacent channel. The radiation is a transient phenomenon occurring when the transmitter is keyed, and is heard as a succession of clicks or chirps.

149

keyboard Of telegraph or data apparatus, an assembly of *keys* similar to those on a typewriter.

keyboard perforator See *perforator*.

keyboard transmitter A telegraph transmitter controlled by a *keyboard* so that selection of a character causes the corresponding coding symbol to be sent to line.

keyed automatic gain control (US) A form of AGC used in television receivers whereby the control voltage is derived by examining the signal level momentarily during each line-blanking interval. In this way the control voltage is unaffected by picture information or noise occurring during the active line period.

keying Generic term for the process of changing some characteristic of a direct current or other carrier between a set of discrete values in order to convey information.

keying chirps See *key clicks*.

keying filter A network used to attenuate the higher-frequency components in the keying signal waveshape of a radio-telegraph transmitter, thereby reducing *sideband* spread and the possibility of causing interference by *key-clicks*.

keying loss See *fold-over distortion* (2).

keyless ringing A manual switchboard facility whereby ringing is applied automatically as a result of the insertion of the calling plug into the jack of the called line.

keymaster telephone Designation used in the UK for a type of telephone that can be associated with one or two exchange lines to provide a range of facilities useful for small businesses or large homes. The name derives from the use of a number of pushbutton keys on each instrument in addition to the normal rotary dial.

keypad A rectangular array of pushbutton *keys* that can be used for signalling purposes instead of a rotary dial.

keyshelf That part of a manual switchboard on which the keys used by an operator are mounted.

kick-sorter A multichannel pulse-height separator used to count the number of received pulses falling within a number of specified amplitude ranges.

L

L-antenna See *inverted-L antenna*.

label-addressed signalling See *common-channel signalling*.

labelled message In *common-channel signalling*, a message containing a label that identifies the particular call, circuit, management action, etc. to which the information in the message relates.

language code An address digit that may be used on an international call to enable an originating operator to obtain assistance in a desired language.

language compiler See *programming*.

laser General term for devices that convert electrical power into radiant energy in the visible or infra-red regions of the spectrum by making use of *stimulated emission of radiation*. (Laser is an acronym for 'light amplification by stimulated emission of radiation'.) Because lasers emit narrow beams of light having a comparatively small spectral bandwidth they form useful light sources for optical transmission systems. At the present time units with a spectral width of from 1 to 2 nm at wavelengths of around 820 nm are in use in operating systems. Considerable research effort is also being devoted to the development of solid-state crystal lasers able to operate at wavelengths of around 1060 and 1270 nanometres, where current *optical fibres* have lower values of *attenuation*.

last-party release A method of operation in which the release of a connection does not begin until both parties have restored their telephones, data modems, etc. to the quiescent state.

latching The process of holding a device such as a *crosspoint* or *relay* in its operated condition independently of the normal means of operation. Latching may be achieved mechanically or magnetically.

layer In radio-wave propagation, a stratum in the *ionosphere* in which the variation of free electron density with height attains a maximum value or has some other specified characteristic; see *ledge*.

layer height The vertical distance from the surface of the earth of a given characteristic of an ionospheric *layer*, usually the height of the level of maximum ionisation.

leaky wave antenna An antenna whose radiation results from the continuous or quasi-continuous leakage of energy from a specially adapted length of *waveguide* in which a fast wave propagates. The leaky structure may consist of a length of waveguide with a continuous slot or a row of holes along one face.

leased circuit A *circuit* provided for the exclusive and permanent use of a subscriber.

leave-word call (US) A person-to-person call held for subsequent completion because the wanted party was unavailable.

lecher wires Two parallel wires several wavelengths long and a small fraction of a wavelength apart on which *standing waves* are set up, usually for the purpose of *wavelength* measurement.

lecture call A PABX feature enabling the operator, or automatic equipment activated by an extension user, to establish a unidirectional speech path from the extension to two or more other parties.

ledge An ionospheric *layer* in which the gradient of free electron density with respect to height first decreases and then increases, but without becoming negative.

left-hand polarised wave See *counter-clockwise polarised wave*.

lens Of an *antenna*, a structure of dielectric material or metal, transparent to radio waves but introducing a phase delay over the cross-section of an *aperture* (3) so as to effect a convergence (or a divergence) of the incident waves over a specified frequency band.

lens antenna A *microwave* antenna consisting of a *lens* and suitable feed.

letters case In alphabetic telegraphy, a group of characters consisting mainly of letters.

letters-shift signal In alphabetic telegraphy, a signal that causes the receiving apparatus to translate subsequent signals as primary characters or functions included in the *letters case*.

level (1) Of a quantity such as power or voltage, the magnitude of the quantity expressed in physical units or transmission units (usually *decibels*). See also *absolute power* [*voltage*] *level*, *relative level* and *signal level*. (2) One of the rows of contacts forming part of a *two-motion selector* bank.

level-measuring set Apparatus for measuring test-signal levels in lines and consisting of a receiving circuit calibrated in *decibels* relative to 1 mW in specified impedances.

level multiple In a *step-by-step automatic system*, the *multiple* (2) provided to carry the traffic outgoing from a given level of a *selector* bank.

level recorder Apparatus that makes a record on a chart of the level of an electrical quantity or signal as a function of time.

light conduit See *light guide*.

light-emitting diode General term for a semiconductor junction diode able to emit radiant energy in the visible region of the spectrum as a result of the recombination of electrons and holes. Light-emitting diodes can be used as light sources in *optical fibre* transmission systems, although the comparatively wide spectral width of the radiation coupled with the relatively low output makes them less attractive than *lasers*. Nevertheless special forms of device have been developed and are in use; see *Burrus diode*.

light guide (US: *light conduit*) An assembly of *optical fibres* used for the transmission of light flux rather than optical signals.

limited availability See *availability*.

limited scanning In *facsimile*, scanning in which the number of *scanning lines* used is reduced to an integral fraction of the normal in order to shorten the transmission time, mainly at the expense of poorer transverse resolution.

limiter General term for any device that acts on a signal to produce a desired form of *limiting*. A *hard limiter* is one that prevents the instantaneous amplitude of the output signal from exceeding a predetermined threshold value. If the threshold is set so that only the tips of the signal are affected it is also called a *peak clipper* or *peak limiter*. Limiters may act on positive or negative signal values, or both. Typically a limiter may be used to remove any incidental *amplitude modulation* from a frequency modulated signal.

limiting General term for the process whereby the *amplitude* of a signal is restricted in some manner once it reaches a predetermined threshold level; see *limiter*. Unfortunately the term is applied both to the linear process in which the mean amplitude is reduced to avoid overloading subsequent equipment and to the non-linear process in which the instantaneous amplitude of the signal is never permitted to exceed the threshold value. The latter process is also termed *clipping* or *hard limiting*.

lincompex A method of transmission using true *companding* action to reduce the effects of fading and noise on long-distance radio telephone services operating in the high-frequency *band*. The principles of operation are essentially as follows. Speech at the sending end is compressed at about the syllabic rate to yield a nearly constant-amplitude signal. Information on the degree of compression applied is derived from the compressors and is used to frequency-modulate a 2900 Hz tone. This tone is transmitted together with the constant-amplitude speech signal over a standard 3 kHz radio channel. At the receiving end the signals are separated, the tone signal being demodulated and used to control the instantaneous gain of expanders through which the other signal passes. In this way the original amplitude variations of the speech signal are restored. Because the level of the output signal is directly related to that of the input signal the overall loss of the system is held sensibly constant and stability can be maintained without the aid of *singing suppressors*. This leads to a considerable improvement in performance, and the parameters of these systems have been standardised by the CCIR.

line (1) Metallic conductors used for transmission purposes. (2) The path traced by a *scanning spot* in television or facsimile equipment.

line busy tone (US) See *busy tone*.

line circuit *Exchange* apparatus that receives and responds to control signals and supervises the conditions of a subscriber's line.

line code In digital transmission, a series of rules giving the equivalence between a set of digits generated by PCM or data equipment and the digits used to represent them for transmission to line. Line codes are selected so that parameters of the resultant signal, such as its frequency spectrum, suit the transmission facility. See *four binary – three ternary code* and *MS43*.

line concentrator (1) A *switching stage* in a *local exchange* that serves to concentrate the traffic from a number of subscribers' lines on to a smaller number of outlets to subsequent switching stages. (2) A *pair gain system* in a local line network; see *loop switching system*.

line connector UK designation for an electromechanical *pair gain system* consisting essentially of two switching units (or concentrators), one located at an *exchange*, the other at some point in the *local line network*. The units are linked by a smaller number of pairs (e.g. four) than the number of subscribers (e.g. 22) served by the remote unit. See also *loop switching system*.

line diversion A PBX switchboard feature enabling selected lines to be diverted to alternative terminations. If a line is busy when the relevant key is operated or restored, switching is delayed until the connection is released.

line extender UK term for a *range extender*.

line-extender audio A stable bidirectional two-wire audio amplifier that can be fitted at a *local exchange* to improve the transmission performance of a long local line.

line-extender signalling An electronic device fitted at a *local exchange* to boost the voltage sent to line, thereby enabling satisfactory *signalling* over a line exceeding the normal loop resistance limit.

line feed In telegraphy or data transmission, movement of the paper on a page printing machine so that the printing mechanism is positioned for printing the next line.

line fill Of a local line provided with means for serving two or more subscribers, the ratio of the number of subscribers connected to the number that could be connected.

line finder In an electromechanical switching system, a *selector* used to establish a connection with a line requiring service.

line identification A PBX facility whereby an operator answering or making a call can control a display giving the identity of the connecting line or calling extension.

line lengthener A device for changing the *electrical length* of a transmission line without altering its physical length.

line lock-out   A facility provided to prevent a line having a permanent loop condition or an excessive release time from unduly holding exchange equipment or causing *repeated call* conditions to arise.

line noise   *Noise* originating in a transmission line.

line-of-sight radio link   A terrestrial radio link in which there is sensibly an unobstructed straight-line path between the transmitting and receiving antennas. All *microwave* radio relay links are of this type, although the paths followed by the beams are not in fact straight lines owing to the effect of atmospheric refraction (see *radio horizon*). For planning purposes it is convenient to allow for this effect by adjusting the radius of the earth to a value that enables the propagation path to be drawn as a straight line; see *effective radius of the earth*. To allow for abnormal conditions of propagation, which can exist for a small proportion of the time, real links are usually planned using an earth radius factor of 0.7, rather than the 1.33 value used with standard propagation conditions.

line signal   A *signal* (2) transmitted by a *line signalling* system. Line signals have a simpler function than those used for routing purposes and hence can be provided by means of simple tones; see, for example, *tone-on-idle signalling*. Inter-register signals conveying routing information are usually provided by a more complicated signalling system, and these signals only need to be transmitted during the call set-up period.

line signalling   A method of signalling in which signals are passed between equipments that terminate and continuously monitor the line. Some signalling systems (e.g. CCITT/R2) use line signalling for the transmission of supervisory signals and *register signalling* for the transmission of call set-up signals.

line simulator   See *artificial line*.

line stretcher   A mechanical component for varying the *electrical length* of a transmission line or waveguide by changing its physical length.

line switch   In an *exchange*, a switching device associated with a subscriber's line and used to connect it to other switching apparatus when a call is originated.

line temperature-compensating equaliser   A network used to compensate for changes in the attenuation/frequency characteristic of a line resulting from changes in temperature.

linear analogue control   See *analogue control*.

linear array   An *antenna array* in which the centres of the radiating elements are in a straight line.

linear detection   *Demodulation* in which the output signal is substantially proportional to the input signal over the useful range of the device.

linear polarisation In radio-wave propagation, *polarisation* in which the direction of propagation and the direction of the electric field are always in one plane. Since the *electric field vector* will oscillate in amplitude with time, its extremity will trace a straight line in any fixed plane normal to the direction of propagation. See also *orthogonal polarisation*.

linear waveform distortion Unwanted changes in a waveform caused by a device or system that does not produce any *amplitude/amplitude distortion* but has an imperfect amplitude/frequency and/or phase/frequency response. The term is widely used to describe the distortion caused to special waveforms designed to test the performance of television links and equipment; see *waveform testing, pulse-and-bar signal* and *K-rating*.

linewidth Of an optical source, the range of wavelengths emitted by the device, usually given as the half-amplitude width in nanometres. For a *light-emitting diode* operating at a mean wavelength around 850 nm a linewidth around 40 nm is typical. This compares with a figure of about 2 nm for a Ga(Al)As *laser*.

link (1) In a *link-connected switching stage*, an internal connection between two *partial switching stages*. (2) In general, a communication facility of specified characteristics between two points.

The terms 'section' and 'link' are used in a number of international definitions of complete transmission facilities. Thus a *group section* consists of the whole means of transmission using a standard 48 kHz frequency band between two consecutive *group distribution frames*. A *group link* consists of the whole means of transmission using a standard 48 kHz frequency band between two assemblies of terminal equipment such as *channel translating units, modems*, etc., and it can include tandem-connected group sections. It is usually taken to be bidirectional unless otherwise stated. The definitions for *supergroup* and *mastergroup* sections and links closely parallel the foregoing, except for the obvious substitution of the appropriate bandwidths, etc.

link-by-link signalling In a multi-link connection, a method of *signalling* in which signals arriving at each intermediate *switching centre* are stored and examined before being transmitted to the next switching centre.

link cable In a local cable network, a cable between two *cross-connection points* providing flexibility and relief.

link congestion *Congestion* occurring in a link system owing to overloading of the internal interconnection. Also termed *internal* *congestion.*

link-connected switching stage   A *switching stage* consisting of a number of sub-units that act jointly and are interconnected by internal links. Switching systems utilising stages of this kind—usually with some form of common control—are called *link systems.*

listener echo   See *echo.*

listening-in   The act of listening to a telephone conversation by someone who is not a party to the call.

load (US)   In traffic engineering, see *traffic volume.*

load capacity   In *pulse code modulation*, the level of an input sinusoidal signal the positive and negative peaks of which coincide with the *virtual decision value* of the encoder. Also described as the *overload point*, the level is usually expressed in dBm0 (see *signal level*).

loaded folded dipole   An *antenna* consisting of a *folded dipole* with additional conductors or circuit elements that change the current distribution or input impedance, thereby improving its broad-band performance.

loading   A method of improving the transmission characteristics of a line throughout the telephone frequency band by the addition of series inductance. The inductance may be added by connecting small coils in series with each leg of the line at regular intervals. This technique is known as *lumped loading* or *coil loading*, and typically coils having an inductance of 88 millihenries are inserted every 1.83 km (2000 yards). Such a line behaves in a similar manner to a *low-pass filter* having a cut-off frequency of around 4000 Hz. A higher cut-off frequency results if the added inductance is obtained by applying a continuous layer or wrapping of magnetic material to each conductor of the line. This technique is known as *continuous loading* and was used with some of the earlier submarine cables.

lobe   In the *directivity pattern* of an antenna or array, an area of the pattern bounded by directions of minimum radiation.

local automatic message accounting   See *automatic message accounting.*

local battery system   Description applied to old telephone systems in which a battery at the subscriber's premises supplied the energy used for speaking.

local carrier reception   A technique used in reception of *single-sideband transmissions*, whereby an oscillator in the receiver supplies the carrier used for demodulation of the incoming signal. The frequency of the oscillator must not differ by more than a few hertz from that of the original carrier if unacceptable distortion is to be avoided. Usually the frequency of the local carrier is controlled by a quartz crystal or by a *pilot carrier*.

local exchange or **local office** (US) An exchange in which *subscribers' lines* are terminated. See also *end office* and *classification of exchanges*.

local line network (US: *loop network* or *loop plant*) All the cables, ducts, joint boxes, *flexibility cabinets*, poles and ancillary equipment provided to enable subscribers to be given service by their *local exchange*. Local line practice varies in different countries but follows the same broad principles. In the UK the average length of a subscriber's line is about 2 km, and the local network divides naturally into two parts, designated main and

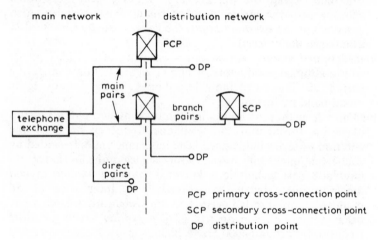

Figure L.1 Local line network

distribution respectively; see *Figure L.1*. The *main network* consists of the large cables joining the exchange to the flexibility cabinets. These cables are pressurised with dry air from the exchange, and are almost always accommodated in ducts. The flexibility provided by the cross-connection cabinets makes it possible to install main cables in economical instalments to meet forecast growth. The *distribution network* extends from the flexibility cabinets to the distribution points where the subscriber's lines are connected. Some distribution cables may be in ducts, but many are directly buried in the ground. They range in size from 2 to 100 *pairs*, and are generally filled with petroleum jelly.

local oscillator In a superheterodyne receiver, an oscillator whose output is mixed with the incoming signal to produce sum and difference frequencies, one of them being equal to the *intermediate frequency* of the receiver.

158

local record In telegraphy, a display of a transmitted message provided by means of a receiver associated with the sending apparatus.

local service area The area containing stations that a customer can call at rates in accordance with the local tariff.

local telephone circuit The combination formed by a subscriber's instrument, line and *feeding bridge*.

lockout In a connection including two voice-operated devices such as loudspeaking telephones, a condition in which neither subscriber can get through, owing to excessive local circuit *noise* or continuous speech from one or both parties.

logatom An isolated meaningless syllable, often consisting of a vowel sound preceded or followed by a consonant and used in connection with speech testing of telephones; see *articulation*.

logic convention A means of specifying the relationship between *logic states* and *logic levels* on a diagram drawn without the use of the polarity indicator symbol. On a diagram drawn in *positive* logic the 1-state everywhere corresponds with the more positive value of the quantity (usually voltage) used to represent the logic states in the hardware. With the *negative* logic convention the 1-state corresponds with the less positive value of the variable quantity. If the polarity indicator symbol is used, its absence or presence at every input and output of each symbol indicates the logic relationship in force at each point. (The presence of the symbol indicates that negative logic is in force at the designated point, its absence that positive logic applies.)

logic element General term for a device whose behaviour can be specified in terms of the *logic levels* existing at its inputs and outputs; for example, a *NAND gate*.

logic level A value (or usually a restricted range of values) of a physical quantity, used to represent the *logic state* of a signal in equipment. In binary logic there are two logic levels corresponding with the two *logic states*. Some logic elements are called *tri-state* devices because they have outputs that can take on a high-impedance condition as well as the two defined logic levels. The terminology is an unfortunate choice, because the high-impedance condition has no logic significance and does not correspond with a logic state.

logic state One of the two possible states of a binary variable, these states usually being designated as the 1-state and the 0-state.

lone signal unit See *signal unit*.

long-distance back scatter See *indirect back scatter*.

long-line extension A PABX extension located so far from the PABX equipment that, owing to the length of the line, signalling and transmission limits for normal service are not met and some restrictions have to be imposed.

long-wire antenna A *travelling-wave antenna* consisting of one or more conductors long in comparison with the operating wavelength and fed at one end.

longitudinal circuit A *telephone circuit* consisting of one conductor (or two or more in parallel), with the return path provided by the earth.

longitudinal current A current flowing in the same direction in the two wires of a *pair*, and returning via the earth and/or some other conductors.

longitudinal gyro frequency See *gyro frequency*.

longitudinal interference *Interference* giving rise to *longitudinal currents* in the disturbed circuit.

longitudinal judder See *judder*.

loop antenna An antenna consisting of one or more turns of wire forming a closed circuit.

loop-disconnect signalling or **loop dialling** (US) A form of DC *signalling* in which currents corresponding with the looped and disconnected states of a line are used to represent signals.

loop extender See *range extender*.

loop network or **loop plant** See *local line network*.

loop switching system (US) Designation for a *pair gain system* that concentrates the traffic from a number of subscribers connected to a remote terminal, on to a smaller number of lines to a complementary terminal at the *local exchange*.

looped outlet In a cabled-distribution TV system, an outlet in a subscriber's premises through which a spur cable passes. The outlet box contains the required attenuation and usually safety isolation.

loss Between two points in a transmission system, the reduction in power between the two points, expressed as the ratio of the power at the first point to that at the second in *transmission units*—usually *decibels*.

loss system In automatic switching, a system in which a call attempt is lost if there is no free path for the required connection. Also known as *busy-signal system*.

lost call A call that is abandoned owing to congestion.

lost time In *facsimile*, that fraction of the *scanning line period* which cannot be used for the transmission of picture information, i.e. the *dead sector* scanning time.

lost traffic That portion of the traffic offered to a *loss system* which cannot be carried owing to congestion.

low-frequency wander In digital transmission, slow variations in the mean level of a pulse signal, owing to the use of AC coupling in the transmission path and/or the use of an unbalanced code. Wander reduces the useful open area of the *eye diagram* in direct proportion to the permitted imbalance of the signal as expressed by the *digital sum variation*. Its effects can be largely reduced by the use of *quantised feedback*.

low-level modulation *Modulation* of a signal at a point in a system or radio transmitter where the power level is low compared with the output power.

low noise-temperature antenna A highly directional antenna with very low-level *side lobes*, so that terrestrial noise sources do not degrade the *noise temperature* when the *main lobe* is directed above the horizon.

low-pass filter A frequency-selective network offering very little *attenuation* to waves with frequencies below a defined cut-off value, but attenuating all higher-frequency waves.

lowest useful high frequency The lowest frequency in the HF band (3–30 MHz) that can be used for a point-to-point service via the *ionosphere* at a particular time. It varies with factors such as *absorption* (1), antenna *gain*, type of service and *noise* conditions.

lumped loading See *loading*.

luneberg lens antenna An antenna in which the cross-section of the *lens* is circular, the *refractive index* varying in such a manner that a *feed* located at the edge of the lens produces a *major lobe* diametrically opposite the feed.

Luxembourg effect See *ionospheric crossmodulation*.

M

M-curve A characteristic showing the relationship between the amount by which the *modified refractive index* exceeds unity and the height above the earth's surface. In other words, a plot of the *refractive modulus* in M-units against height.

MF keypad A *keypad* producing multitone signals that can be used with suitable types of *exchange* both for call set-up purposes and subsequently to transmit slow-speed data. The signalling code standardised by the CCITT is a '2 out of 8' system as shown in *Figure M.1*.

M-reflection A propagation path in which the wave travels up to the *F layer*, down to a lower layer such as the *sporadic E layer* and back up to the F layer before returning to the ground.

MS43 A *line code* in which the incoming binary signal is divided into four-bit words, each of which is represented by a ternary

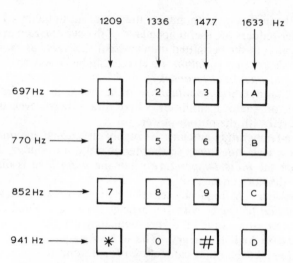

Figure M.1 Allocation of pairs of tones to a sixteen-button keypad

Table M.1

Binary words	Three-level signal alphabets* A			B			C		
0000	+	+	+	−	+	−	−	+	−
0001	+	+	0	0	0	−	0	0	−
0010	+	0	+	0	−	0	0	−	0
0011	0	−	+	0	−	+	0	−	+
0100	0	+	+	−	0	0	−	0	0
0101	−	0	+	−	0	+	−	0	+
0110	−	+	0	−	+	0	−	+	0
0111	−	+	+	−	+	+	−	−	+
1000	+	−	+	+	−	+	−	−	−
1001	0	0	+	0	0	+	−	−	0
1010	0	+	0	0	+	0	−	0	−
1011	0	+	−	0	+	−	0	+	−
1100	+	0	0	+	0	0	0	−	−
1101	+	0	−	+	0	−	+	0	−
1110	+	−	0	+	−	0	+	−	0
1111	+	+	−	+	−	−	+	−	−

*Alphabet A is used when the running digital sum is −1, alphabet B when it is 0 or 1, and alphabet C when it is 2.

word chosen from one of the three alphabets shown in the code conversion table (*Table M.1*). The choice of alphabet is

162

determined by the value of the running *digital sum* at the end of the preceding word in such a way that the digital-sum variation never exceeds five. MS43 coded signals have the desirable transmission properties listed under *four binary – three ternary code (4B3T)*, and a somewhat better spectral distribution with less energy at the higher and lower frequencies.

M-unit   The unit in terms of which values of *refractive modulus* are expressed.

M-wire   See *meter wire*.

machine-code programming   See *programming*.

machine ringing   Automatic ringing that continues until a call is either answered or abandoned.

machine word   See *computer word*.

magic T   See *hybrid T*.

magnetic-core antenna   See *ferrite-rod antenna*.

magnetic storm   An abnormal change in the earth's magnetic field, usually lasting for a day or so and characterised by large deviations from the usual value of at least one component of the field.

magneto bell   A polarised electric bell operated by low-frequency alternating current generated by a hand-operated generator called a magneto.

magneto-ionic double refraction   The combined effect of atmospheric ionisation and the earth's magnetic field whereby a linearly polarised wave entering the *ionosphere* is split into two components called the *ordinary wave* and the *extraordinary wave*. The component waves follow different paths, suffer different attenuations, have different phase velocities and in general are elliptically polarised in opposite senses. The ordinary wave is the component least affected by the earth's magnetic field. The *polarisation* (1) of each component depends on the direction of propagation relative to the earth's magnetic field. When the latter is normal to the direction of propagation the ordinary wave is linearly polarised, with its *electric field vector* in the direction of the earth's field. For the same conditions the electric field vector of the extraordinary wave is normal to the direction of the earth's field. In the more general case, the ordinary wave vector rotates counter-clockwise when the angle between the direction of propagation and the earth's field is acute, and clockwise when the angle is obtuse. The opposite relationships apply in the case of the extraordinary wave.

magneto system   In telephony, an early form of *local battery system* in which the current for *signalling* was obtained from a hand-operated generator.

main beam   The radiated energy or the space in the *main lobe* of a *directional antenna*.

main cable   In a *local line network*, designation given to a cable between an *exchange* and a *cross-connection point*. In the UK main cables are pressurised with dry air from the exchange end. They are sheathed with polyethylene bonded to an inner layer of aluminium foil, and cellular polyethylene is also used to insulate the wires. Conductor material is now aluminum, although a great deal of copper is still in use. Cable sizes range from 100 to 4800 *pairs*.

main distribution frame   A *distribution frame* providing for the termination of external cables on one side and internal wires from *exchange* equipment on the other.

main lobe   Of the *directivity pattern* of a directional antenna or array, the *lobe* defining the direction of maximum radiation or, in the case of a receiving antenna, the direction of maximum sensitivity. Also termed *major lobe*.

main switching centre   UK designation for any one of the fully interconnected switching centres in the *trunk transit network* (*Figure T.4*); see also *classification of exchanges*.

major lobe   See *main lobe*.

make-before-break contact unit   See *changeover contact unit*.

make contact unit   Of a *relay*: two contact members, normally separated, and arranged so that operation of the relay establishes a contact between them.

make pulse   In automatic switching, a pulse generated by closing and then opening a circuit.

man-made noise   *Interference* caused by electrical machines, car ignition systems, etc.

manual exchange or **manual central office** (US)   An exchange in which call connections are established and released by operators.

manual hold   In automatic telephony, a condition established when a call is made via an operator whereby the caller's line is held in the busy state until the operator releases it.

manual position   Part of a switchboard normally staffed by a single operator.

manual ringing   Ringing by means of a hand-operated generator.

manual switchboard   A telephone switchboard in which connections are established manually using *cord circuits* or *keys*.

manual switching system or **manual telephone system**   A system in which every call is established, supervised and released by an operator.

map-in-memory   See *network map*.

margin   In printing telegraphy, a measure of the ability of telegraph receiving apparatus to cope with timing errors in the received signal. Usually apparatus is more sensitive to errors occurring in a particular sense, i.e. to signal *transitions* that arrive earlier than they should rather than to those that are delayed, or vice versa. Margin is expressed as the smallest fraction of the *unit interval* by which a *significant instant* can depart from its theoretically correct time of occurrence without causing an error. The term is usually appropriately qualified. Thus *net margin* is the value obtained when the modulation rate at the input to the apparatus is standard. The *effective margin* is the value measured under actual operating conditions, and the *theoretical margin* refers to a value computed from constructional data assuming that the apparatus is operating under perfect conditions.

maritime satellite service (MARISAT) A service that enables calls to be made to ships in the Atlantic and Pacific oceans. The MARISAT system is operated by a consortium of four US companies, including Comsat and Western Union International. It has a *geostationary satellite* over each ocean, that over the Pacific being served by an *earth station* in California and that over the Atlantic by an earth station in Connecticut.

mark In a two-condition telegraph system, that significant condition which generally corresponds with the active condition of the receiving apparatus, i.e. the condition that causes a *Morse printer* to mark the paper.

marker Control apparatus that sequentially selects and sets up suitable paths through a *switching stage*.

marking In automatic switching, the assignment of a specified state to a device such as a switch.

marking interval In telegraphy, a period of time corresponding with the *mark* condition.

marking wave The wave emitted during a *marking interval*.

maser A stable, highly linear, low-noise amplifying device operating in the microwave region of the spectrum. Like the laser, the maser depends for its operation on the process *stimulated emission of radiation*. (Maser is an acronym for 'microwave amplification by stimulated emission of radiation'.) Masers are inherently very-low-noise devices, and versions employing ruby as the active material were used as input amplifiers for the reception of signals from the early communication satellites. These amplifiers had to be cooled to a temperature of around 2 K for satisfactory operation, however, and their relatively low bandwidth (≈ 30 MHz) made them unsuitable for use with later generations of satellites.

master clock See *clock*.

master system for the determination of reference equivalent See *SFERT*.

mastergroup An assembly of five *supergroups* separated by 8 kHz in a 1232 kHz band. The term also describes a *mastergroup link* with its associated terminal equipment. In North America the term describes an assembly of ten supergroups in a 2520 kHz band, the basic mastergroup extending from 564 to 3084 kHz.

mastergroup link, mastergroup section See *link*.

matched junction A *waveguide* component having four or more arms, and so arranged that if all ports except one are terminated in the correct impedance, there will be no reflection of energy from the junction when fed along the remaining arm, whichever this may be.

matched load or **matched termination** Of a *transmission line* or *waveguide*, a termination producing no reflected wave, so that the incident power is completely absorbed. The impedance of such a load must equal the *characteristic impedance* of the line in magnitude and angle.

matching loss (US) See *internal blocking*.

matching section A length of *transmission line* used for impedance transformation. In a *waveguide* the required change is usually obtained by progressively varying the cross-section of the guide or by the use of a *slug* (3).

material dispersion The variation with frequency in the value of the *refractive index* of a given material; also known as *optical dispersion*. Since the velocity of light in a medium depends on the refractive index, it follows that light of different wavelengths will travel at different velocities in the material. The significance of this effect in fibre optics is explained below.

material dispersion effect In an *optical fibre*, that component of *pulse dispersion* which is caused by the *material dispersion* of the fibre's core and cladding materials. Alternatively, the reduction in bandwidth resulting from the variation with wavelength of the propagation time along the fibre. This effect is of significance only if the *linewidth* of the light source is considerably greater than the modulation bandwidth due to the signal alone. At the present time this is unfortunately the case, the spectrum width for a typical *laser* being around 2 nm (720 GHz) and that of a *light-emitting diode* about 20 to 40 nm. It can be seen that the restriction in bandwidth caused by material dispersion is directly proportional to the length of the fibre and the linewidth of the light source. A bandwidth of 160 MHz has been quoted for a 1 km length of silica fibre fed by an LED.

matrix See *switching matrix*.

maximum justification rate or **maximum stuffing rate** (US) See *justification rate*.

maximum usable frequency In radio-wave propagation via the *ionosphere*, the highest frequency that can be used between two points at a particular time. This is normally the best frequency to use for long-distance transmission, but see *optimum working frequency*.

mean busy hour An uninterrupted period of sixty minutes, commencing at the same time on each of a number of weekdays, during which the highest average traffic is measured. Also known as *time-consistent busy hour*. The CCITT has recommended that the busy hour should be determined as a result of traffic observations taken over ten days, the traffic values observed for the same 15-minute period on each day being added together. The mean busy hour is then given by the four consecutive quarter-hour periods that together give the largest sum of observed traffic values.

mean interconnecting number The total number of outlets in a *grading* divided by the number of trunks serving it.

measured service (US) Telephone service in which charges are levied in accordance with the number of *message units* accrued during the charging period.

mechanical crosspoint A switching element consisting of a set of metallic contacts enabling *n* inlets to be connected to *n* outlets.

meet-me conference A PABX facility enabling a *conference call* to be established by each participating extension user dialling a designated conference code. Also termed *selector level conference*.

memory See *store*.

meridional ray In *optical-fibre* propagation, a ray that passes through the axis of the fibre in the course of internal reflection, and is confined to a single plane. See also *skew ray*.

mesochronous Qualifying term applied to digital signals whose *significant instants* occur at the same average rate. The phase relationship between corresponding transitions usually varies between specified limits. Compare with *plesiochronous*.

message (1) In general, an arbitrary amount of *information*. (2) In telegraphy or data transmission, an assembly of characters and sometimes digits used for control purposes, which is transferred as a whole from a transmitter to a receiver, the format being determined by the transmitter. (3) In call accounting in North America, a call that has matured.

message-alignment indicator In data transmission, that part of a *message* (2) which identifies the boundaries of the message during its transfer between the relevant *user part* and *message-transfer part* of the system.

message feedback In a data network, a method of operation in which received data is returned to the sending end and compared with a stored version of the original data in order to check for correct transmission.

message register (US) A cyclometer-type electromechanical meter used for *peg-count* measurements, e.g. as an overflow or subscriber's meter.

message relay A PABX facility whereby an extension user can record a message and arrange for it to be passed automatically to a nominated extension by a given time. If the system is unable to deliver the message by the specified time it is automatically relayed to the switchboard operator.

message switching A technique for reducing the idle time of traffic-carrying devices by the sequential switching of pre-stored messages. Also known as *store-and-forward switching*.

message-transfer part Of a particular *common-channel signalling* system, that part of the system which transfers *signal messages* for all users and provides facilities such as *error control* and *signalling security*.

message unit (US) In *automatic message accounting*, a unit of charge based on the destination and duration of a call.

messenger cable (US) A steel strand used to support an *aerial cable*.

metallic circuit A normal line circuit consisting of two conductors, as opposed to an *earth return circuit*.

meter pulse A pulse transmitted to a subscriber's meter in order to increase its total by one unit.

meter wire In automatic telephony, a wire used for the pulses operating a subscriber's meter. Also known as *M-wire*.

metre-amperes Of a linear vertical antenna less than a quarter-wavelength long, the product of the effective height and the RMS current at the base of the antenna. The concept is used in assessing the range of a ship's radio installation for regulatory purposes, the effective height being taken as the maximum height of the antenna above a specified datum level.

microphonics Electrical noise caused by mechanical vibration of one or more elements of a system.

microstrip See *strip line*.

microwaves Radio waves in the frequency range extending up from about 1 gigahertz to the lower end of the infra-red region of the spectrum, i.e. to about 3000 gigahertz. The corresponding wavelength range is from 30 cm to 0.1 mm.

minimum distance See *Hamming distance*.

minimum interval In telegraphy or data transmission, the smallest (ideal) interval of time between consecutive *transitions* in a signal formed according to a code in which the *significant* *interval* is not always an exact multiple of the *unit interval*.

mirror Of a *microwave* antenna, a reflecting surface such as a dish.

mismatch factor See *reflection factor*.

mixer (1) A circuit in which two input oscillations having different frequencies interact to produce an output oscillation having a frequency that is a linear combination of the input frequencies and is usually equal to their simple difference. (2) In audio and television broadcasting studios, equipment used to combine signals from two or more sources so that they do not interact with one another.

mobile earth terminal A radio station used for space communication and located on a vehicle, ship or aircraft.

mode (1) One of the states in which a vibrating system is resonant; for example, the flexural mode of a quartz crystal. (2) One of the field configurations that may be adopted by an electromagnetic wave propagating in a *waveguide*. The actual mode or modes adopted by a wave depend on the dimensions of the waveguide in terms of wavelength. For rectangular-section guides, modes are described by reference to the number of half-period field variations parallel to the transverse axis. See *TE mode* and *TM mode*.

mode dispersion In an optical fibre, that component of *pulse dispersion* occurring in a *multimode fibre* as a result of the different modes having different velocities of propagation and hence different arrival times. Sometimes called *multipath effect*, and explained in terms of the difference in the lengths of the paths travelled by rays making various angles with the axis of the fibre. Mode dispersion can be greatly reduced by the use of a fibre having a particular refractive-index profile; see *graded-index optical fibre*.

mode of ionospheric propagation A description of the path followed by a high-frequency wave, specifically mentioning any reflecting layers involved. For example, 1F + 1E indicates a two-hop path consisting of one hop with reflection from the *F layer* followed by one hop with reflection from the *E layer*.

mode purity In *waveguide* propagation, the ratio of the power present in a forward-travelling wave in a desired *mode* (2) to the total power present in all forward-travelling waves.

mode transducer or **mode transformer** A device for changing from one *mode* (2) of propagation to another in a *waveguide*.

modem An item of equipment that modulates the transmitted signal and demodulates the received signal at a *data station*. By extension the term is applied to equipment carrying out additional functions such as *multiplexing*.

modified AMI signal A signal coded in accordance with the general *alternate mark inversion* principle, but including violations as specified by a defined set of rules.

modified refractive index The sum of the *refractive index* of the air at a given height h above sea level and the fraction h/r, where r is the mean radius of the earth.

modulated continuous wave A *carrier* wave modulated by a steady audio-frequency tone. The term stems from the earlier days of radiocommunication, and was used even though such a carrier was often used for *on-off keying* telegraphy.

modulated wave A wave, one or more characteristics of which vary in accordance with a *modulating signal*.

modulating signal A signal that causes one or more characteristics of a *carrier* wave to be varied in a predetermined manner.

modulation The generic term for all those processes in which certain characteristics of a *carrier* wave or pulse train are varied in a desired manner. The term therefore covers processes in which some characteristic of a continuous wave, such as its frequency or amplitude, is varied in accordance with a *modulating signal* such as a speech, television or facsimile waveform. It also applies to processes used in alphabetic telegraphy and data transmission whereby coded signals are formed to represent the characters of a message.

modulation factor In *amplitude modulation*, the ratio of the peak variation of the envelope of the modulated wave from its unmodulated value to the unmodulated value, usually expressed as a percentage. For an asymmetric modulating signal, positive and negative modulation factors may be defined in terms of the positive or negative peak variation from the reference (unmodulated) value.

modulation index In *angle modulation* with a sinusoidal modulating wave, the frequency deviation of the modulated wave divided by the frequency of the modulating wave.

modulation rate In telegraphy, the number of *unit intervals* per second, i.e. the number of *bauds*; see also *symbol rate*.

modulation suppression In the reception of an amplitude-modulated signal, an apparent reduction in the depth of *modulation* of a wanted signal caused by the presence at the detector of a stronger unwanted signal.

mono callmaker UK designation for a device that enables a call to be made to a single preprogrammed number of up to 11 digits in length, merely by pushing a button on an associated telephone.

monomode optical fibre A *stepped-index fibre* in which the core diameter is so small that only a single wave *mode* (2) can propagate. For this condition to obtain, the radius must have a

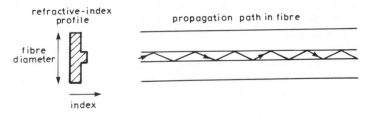

Figure M.2 Monomode optical fibre

value less than that of the expression $2.405\lambda/2\pi\sqrt{(n_1 - n_2)}$, where λ is the wavelength of light in free space and n_1 and n_2 are the refractive indices of the core and cladding respectively. Monomode fibres have the advantage that no **pulse dispersion** occurs as a result of multimode effects; so the effective bandwidth is larger than that of any other type of fibre. There are practical difficulties in coupling sufficient optical energy into such a small core, however, and a high-radiance light source such as a *laser* must be used with this type of guide. *Figure M.2* illustrates some of the properties of a monomode fibre.

monopole antenna See *unipole antenna*.

monostable element A *logic element* with one stable state, to which it returns a predetermined time after it has been triggered into its unstable state.

Morse code An early telegraph code in which the characters are formed from *signal elements* called dots and dashes. Thus the letter E is represented by a single dot, the letter T by a single dash, and the letter K by a dash-dot-dash combination. Ideally the dash has a duration of three dots, and the elements making up a character are separated by spaces with the duration of a single dot. The spacing between characters is equivalent to the length of a dash, that between words to the length of two dashes. The foregoing description applies to the *International Morse Code* (sometimes called the Continental Morse Code), which is still quite widely used for radio-telegraph services to ships at sea. An earlier version known as the American Morse Code differs in some characters and spacing arrangements. This code finds limited use only on some telegraph circuits in North America.

Morse key Essentially a contact unit that can be conveniently operated by hand to form signals according to the *Morse code*. See also *bug key*.

Morse printer Apparatus used to convert Morse signals recorded on a suitable medium, e.g. a punched tape, directly into printed characters.

mosaic telegraphy An early system of alphabetic telegraphy in which each printed character is formed of elementary parts, each of which is received as an individual *signal element*.

motor uniselector   A *uniselector* having a motor for driving the wipers.

motorised keyboard   A *keyboard* forming part of an instrument such as a *teleprinter* and utilising power from the instrument's motor to move the combination bars into the positions selected by the depression of a key.

mouth   The open end of a *microwave* antenna such as a *horn*.

mu-law encoding (also written *μ-law encoding*)   Encoding in accordance with CCITT Recommendation G711, which also specifies the A-law encoding characteristic. The mu-law is similar to the latter in that it too employs *non-uniform quantising* to achieve compression of the audio signal. However, the two characteristics differ in the size of the *quantising intervals* and in certain other respects. The mu-law is used with the standard 24-channel PCM systems employed in North America.

muldex or **muldem**   An item of equipment containing both a *digital multiplexer* and a *digital demultiplexer*.

multi-band antenna   An antenna capable of operating effectively without modification in any one of a number of predetermined radio-frequency bands.

multi-beam antenna   An antenna with several independent inputs, each of which corresponds to a distinct *directivity pattern*.

multidrop circuit   See *multipoint circuit*.

multiframe   In *pulse code modulation*, an assembly of a certain number of consecutive frames in which the position of each frame is defined by reference to a *frame alignment signal*. A four-frame multiframe is used in the standard 24-channel system, whereas the 30-channel version has a multiframe containing sixteen frames.

multi-frequency signalling   A form of *voice-frequency signalling* in which signalling information is represented by *compound signals*, each consisting of the simultaneous transmission of n voice-frequency currents selected from a set of m currents.

multimode antenna   A *microwave* antenna, generally of the horn or cone type, with a *directivity pattern* obtained by superimposing the radiation of several propagation *modes* (2) developed in various parts of the antenna.

multimode fibre   An *optical fibre* having a core large enough to permit optical energy to propagate in a number of different *modes* (2). Multimode fibres usually have core diameters in the range 25–75 nm and can support a great many modes (typically 500–1000).

multimode stepped-index optical fibre   An *optical fibre* having an

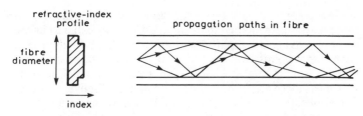

Figure M.3   Multimode stepped-index optical fibre

abrupt change of *refractive index* at the core/cladding interface and a core diameter of sufficient dimension to allow the propagation of optical energy in a large number of different *modes* (2). Owing to the size of its core this type of fibre can be used with an LED as a light source, although such a combination is severely limited in bandwidth by both multimode dispersion and *material dispersion*. *Figure M.3* illustrates some of the properties of a multimode stepped-index fibre.

multipath effect   In an optical fibre, see *mode dispersion*.

multiple   (1) To render a *circuit* accessible at a number of points, at any one of which a connection can be made. By extension, to connect in parallel; see also *multiple teeing*. (2) The permanent wiring provided to implement 1. (3) An aggregation of multipled points.

multiple access   See *satellite multiple access*.

multiple folded dipole   An antenna consisting of at least three parallel half-wave dipoles, one of which is centre-fed. The dipoles are spaced apart by a small fraction of the wavelength of operation and are connected together at their outer ends.

multiple image   See *ghost*.

multiple modulation   A succession of modulating processes so arranged that the modulated wave produced by one stage is used as the modulating wave of the next stage. In FDM carrier systems, only one *sideband* of the output wave is used as an input to the following stage.

multiple number   In automatic switching, a number designating an *inlet* or an *outlet* in a switching stage.

multiple switchboard   A manual telephone switchboard in which lines are connected to a *multiple* (2) so that a *jack* connected to any line is within easy reach of several operators.

multiple teeing   A method of improving the utilisation of a *local line network* by connecting some *pairs* in parallel at one or more *cross-connection points* so that they are accessible at several *distribution points*. The system is useful in areas where the growth rate is high, *party-line* working is used and material costs are low compared with those for labour. It avoids the need for cable rearrangements, enables standard sizes of cable to be used without leaving dead pairs, and ensures that individual cross-connection points are not exhausted before the main cables, thereby eliminating the need for piecemeal relief schemes. However, there are a number of concomitant disadvantages such as complicated records, difficult fault location and transmission degradation, particularly for data signals. The system is no longer used in the UK, and usage in the USA is declining.

multiple-twin quad cable   A cable made up of *quads* each of which consists of two twisted *pairs* twisted together.

multipled   See *multiple* (1).

multiplex system   A transmission system in which a common *channel* is divided into a number of separate channels of lower information-carrying capacity. See *frequency-division multiplex* and *time-division multiplex*.

multiplexing   The process of combining a number of signals so that they can share a common transmission facility.

multipoint circuit (US: *multidrop circuit*)   A *circuit* rented to a customer and providing for the transmission of data between a central site and a number of outstation terminals. Bothway transmission is possible between any terminal and the central site, but the terminals cannot communicate directly with one another.

multi-satellite link   A radio link between two *earth terminals* via two or more *communication satellites*. Such a link comprises one up-path, two or more satellite-to-satellite paths and one down-path.

multi-terminal circuit   Generic term covering both *omnibus circuit* and *multipoint circuit* arrangements.

multi-unit call (US)   A call for which more than one basic charge unit is levied for an initial minimum interval.

multi-unit message   In *common-channel signalling*, a signal message consisting of more than one *signal unit*, i.e. more than one block of digits.

multi-user PBX   An installation of PBX equipment on private premises, providing independent service to two or more subscribers.

multi-wire element   Of an *antenna*, an element consisting of a number of wires connected in parallel, the assembly behaving as the electrical equivalent of a single conductor of comparable cross-section.

musa array   A receiving array consisting of a line of identical *rhombic antennas*, the outputs of which are combined with adjustable *phase delay* so as to give steerable properties in the vertical plane containing the line of centres of the rhombics. (Musa is derived from 'multiple-unit steerable array'.)

muting (US: *squelch*) The process of inhibiting the output of a radio receiver by automatically reducing its **gain** (1) in the absence of an input signal meeting specified criteria. Usually the input signal must exceed a specified level before muting is removed. Alternatively a particular value of **signal-to-noise ratio** may be used as a criterion, or the muting circuit may respond to a signal having special modulation characteristics. In the latter case the process is called *selective muting* (*selective squelch*).

mutual interference chart A plot produced for a single transmitter/receiver combination showing the possibilities of interference with normal receiver operation as a result of spurious radiation from the transmitter and/or spurious receiver responses.

mutual isolation In a CATV-type system, the *attenuation* between two system outlets at any frequency within the system passband. A minimum figure is normally specified, to prevent spurious signals from a receiver connected to one outlet from interfering with a receiver connected to the other.

mutually synchronised network A *synchronised network* in which each clock exerts a degree of control over all the others. The network is said to be *democratic* if each clock exerts an equal degree of control over the others so that the operating rate of the network is the average of the natural rates of all the clocks. A *hierarchic network* is one in which some clocks exert more control than others so that the operating rate of the network is a weighted average of the rates of all the clocks.

N

NBMB balanced-disparity coding A method of coding in which each group of N binary digits in the input data is represented by a group of M binary digits having zero *disparity* or, where this is not possible, is represented alternately by one of two groups having equal and opposite disparity. The net disparity of the output signal is therefore zero.

NOSFER Designation for a high-quality, stable transmission system provided with means of calibrating its constituent parts in terms of absolute units and used in the CCITT laboratories for measurements based on comparisons of loudness. The acronym derives from the French phrase for 'new master telephone transmission reference system'.

n-ary digital signal A signal in which each element can assume

175

any one of n discrete states. The information content of such a signal will have its maximum value if each signal element represents an n-ary digit. If a signal having n discrete states is produced by line coding or AMI so that it is conveying digits of a lower radix than n, it is strictly no longer an n-ary signal; see *pseudo-n-ary signal*.

n-unit code   In telegraphy or data transmission, a code in which each character signal consists of n signal elements, each having the same duration.

n-unit code alphabet   An alphabet giving the correspondence between each member of a set of characters and the n signal elements forming the code combination that represents it.

NAND gate   A *logic element* having one output and two or more inputs, with the property that the output will stand at its defined logic 0-state if, and only if, all its inputs stand at their defined logic 1-states. The term derives from 'NOT AND', i.e. an *AND gate* with a negated output.

narrow-band interference   *Interference* having a spectral width narrow in comparison with the bandwidth of the receiver used to measure it.

national number   A combination of digits that, for the purpose of distance dialling, uniquely identifies a main station in an area of the world identified by a *country code*. A national number consists of a directory number preceded by the relevant *trunk code*—in the UK by the STD code. This definition is not satisfactory for international purposes because the STD code includes the trunk prefix 0. A similar situation exists in some other countries, and the CCITT has therefore defined a *national (significant) number* as the number to be dialled following the trunk prefix to obtain a subscriber in the same country but outside the local network or numbering area.

national numbering-plan area (US: *basic numbering-plan area*)   A geographical area where the national boundaries and the *country code* are uniquely related.

natural frequency   Of an antenna, the lowest frequency at which the antenna resonates without the addition of any inductance or capacitance.

natural noise   Interference such as *atmospherics*, as opposed to man-made disturbances.

nature-of-circuit indicator   Information sent forward during call set-up about the type of circuit or any preceding circuits already used in the connection. This information can be used, for example, to prevent the tandem connection of satellite links or to enable a circuit equipped with the correct *echo suppressor* to be selected.

near-end crosstalk *Crosstalk* in which the unwanted energy transferred into the disturbed circuit propagates in the opposite direction to that of the signal in the disturbing circuit. The terminal of the disturbed circuit at which the crosstalk is observed and measured normally coincides with the sending terminal of the disturbing circuit.

near-field region or **near zone** See *reactive near-field region* and *radiating near-field region*.

negative feedback The process in which a fraction of the output signal of a device or system is fed back to the input in such a sense that it reduces the *amplitude* of the input signal. This has the effect of reducing the *gain* of the device, but at the same time *distortion* produced by it is reduced and the linearity and stability are also improved.

negative-impedance repeater A device used in a *two-wire circuit* to provide bothway amplification of voice-frequency signals. Amplification is obtained by introducing into the line, impedances whose resistive components are negative over the required frequency band. In order to maintain line matching both shunt and series elements are needed, and they may

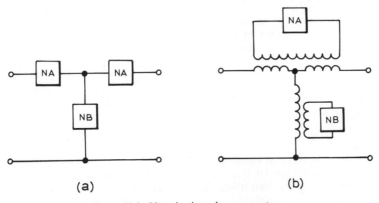

(a) (b)

Figure N.1   Negative-impedance repeater

conveniently be arranged in the form of a T network; see *Figure N.1*. Part (b) shows a generalised form of circuit for which only two sources of negative impedance suffice. Negative-impedance repeaters do not interfere with dial pulses and are thus suitable for use in the *local line network*.

negative justification See *justification*.

negative logic See *logic convention*.

negative modulation A form of *modulation* used in television transmission, in which an increase in brightness corresponds to a reduction in carrier power, i.e. the modulating video signal is inverted so that peak carrier power corresponds to the tips of the line-synchronising pulses.

negative wire   In an electromechanical exchange, that wire of a circuit within the exchange which, in the free condition, is connected to the negative pole of the exchange battery.

negator   A *logic element* with one input and one output, and with the property that its output always stands at the opposite logic state from that of its input, i.e. it performs the function of logic negation.

neper   The basic unit of a logarithmic scale used to express ratios of voltages, currents and analogous quantities. The neper is based on the use of natural logarithms and is named after their inventor, John Napier. Two voltages designated V_1 and V_2 are related by N nepers when $\log_e(V_1/V_2) = N$. The number of nepers in this case is thus simply the natural logarithm of the voltage ratio.

In conditions of equal impedance (the usual case for input and output quantities in telecommunications) a voltage of current ratio is equal to the square root of the corresponding power ratio. Hence:

$$\text{Number of nepers} = \log_e \left(\frac{P_1}{P_2} \right)^{\frac{1}{2}}$$

$$= \tfrac{1}{2}\log_e \frac{P_1}{P_2}$$

By extension this formula may be applied when the power ratio is not the square of the ratio of the corresponding voltages (or currents). It is then important to specify the convention adopted and to indicate the sphere of validity of the usage. The neper may be used to express levels of quantities such as voltages and currents in the same way as the *decibel*. See also *transmission units*.

net information content   A measure of the essential information in a message, expressed by the minimum number of *shannons* (or *hartleys*) required to transmit it with a specified degree of accuracy over a noise-free channel. See also *information content*.

net margin   See *margin*.

network map (US: *map-in-memory*)   A logic representation of the states of all the paths and *crosspoints* in a switching network, stored in the form of data in a common-control system.

network synchronisation   The synchronisation of the clocks and terminal equipment at the nodes in a digital network so that digital switching can take place without undue loss of information. See also *synchronised network* and *synchronisation network*.

network synchronisation plan The scheme defining the allocation of frequency tolerances, stability, etc. in a *synchronised network* so that the overall *slip* rate on a connection containing the maximum number of *switching nodes* allowed by the relevant *routing plan* is within the limits specified for the service in question.

neutral direct-current telegraph system (US) A simple system of *Morse code* telegraphy in which current is sent to line during marking intervals and no current is transmitted during spacing intervals.

new master telephone transmission reference system See *NOSFER*.

night alarm A device, such as a bell or buzzer, that can be used to attract attention when a switchboard is unattended.

night service connection A PBX facility whereby incoming calls can be switched to a designated extension whilst the switchboard is unattended.

node (1) A junction point in a network. (2) Of a *standing wave*: a point, line or surface in a transmission line or waveguide where the vectorial sum of a specified field quantity of the two waves is a minimum.

noise General term for any unwanted disturbances appearing in a *channel* or at the output of a receiver, and tending to obscure the information content of a wanted signal. The term is often used to describe *interference, crosstalk* and *intermodulation* products, particularly where they are not separately distinguishable.

noise factor or **noise figure** Of a linear receiver, amplifier or similar device, the ratio of the total output *noise* power when the input is terminated by an impedance at a specified temperature (usually 290 K) to the noise power that would be caused solely by this input termination. More precisely, noise factor may be defined for a given input frequency as the noise power per unit bandwidth available at the output terminals at the corresponding output frequency to that portion thereof caused solely by the input termination whose noise temperature is assumed to be standard. Numerically its value is given by $P_{\text{noise out}} / G \times P_{\text{noise in}}$, where the noise powers are those at a frequency f, and G is the gain of the device at that frequency.

noise level In a *channel*, the average *noise* power in the frequency range of interest, or in the case of some types of noise the reading of a specified test set.

noise limiter A device that prevents the amplitude of *impulsive noise* from exceeding the peak amplitude of the wanted signal. Also known as a *noise silencer* or a *noise suppressor*.

noise temperature Of a device such as an *antenna*, the temperature of a resistor that would generate as much *thermal noise* power per unit bandwidth at a specified frequency as the noise power available at the antenna output. The latter will include the thermal noise of the antenna itself plus any noise energy coupled into it. The *standard noise temperature* used for reference purposes is 290 K.

noise transmission impairment   A subjective measure of the effect of *noise* in a telephone circuit, determined by intelligibility or judgement tests and being equal to the amount of loss that has to be added to a substantially distortion-free circuit to give the same impairment as that caused by the noise.

noisy blacks   In *facsimile*, non-uniform reproduction of the darkest tones in a picture owing to level changes caused by *noise*.

nominal bandwidth   In sound-programme transmission, the bandwidth given by quoting the highest frequency in kilohertz at which the circuit gives effective transmission, e.g. a 10 kHz sound-programme circuit.

nominal justification rate   See *justification rate*.

nominal margin   The value specified for the effective *margin* of a receiver under standard conditions of operation and adjustment.

nominal stuffing rate   See *justification rate*.

nominal white [black]   Of a facsimile transmitter, the value of the chosen characteristic of the output signal, e.g. its frequency or amplitude, that corresponds to the brightest white [blackest black] that can be transmitted.

non-associated signalling   In *common-channel signalling*, a method of operation in which signals relating to the traffic carried by a group of circuits between two exchanges are carried by two or more *signalling links* connected in tandem at one or more *signal-transfer points*. This means that the signals will follow a different route from that of the traffic circuits to which they relate; see *fully dissociated signalling* and *quasi-associated signalling*.

non-deviative absorption   *Ionospheric absorption* occurring when a wave passes directly through an ionised layer with little or no bending. The absorption is highest in the *D region* and tends to be less the higher the frequency of the wave.

non-busy extension   A PBX extension that is used as an emergency telephone in a reporting centre and does not present the busy condition to further callers when in use.

non-dialled connection   A PBX facility enabling automatic calling to a specific service by removing the extension handset.

non-homing   In automatic switching, operation of a sequential selector (such as a *uniselector*) from its last position rather than the *home position*.

non-linearity distortion   Undesired changes to a signal waveform caused by a system or device having transmission properties that vary with the instantaneous magnitude of the input signal; see *amplitude/amplitude distortion, harmonic distortion* and *intermodulation*. The term non-linear is of course often used to describe a relationship between two quantities where ideally one would be directly proportional to the other. Thus non-linearity of the amplitude/frequency characteristic of an amplifier gives rise to *amplitude/frequency distortion*. Similarly non-linearity of the phase/frequency characteristic gives rise to *phase distortion*. Neither of these effects is classed as non-linearity distortion, however, and separately or together they give rise to *linear waveform distortion*.

non-resonant antenna   See *aperiodic antenna*.

non-return-to-zero signal   A digital signal using full-symbol-length pulses so that no change in signal level occurs when a symbol is repeated; see *Figure N.2*.

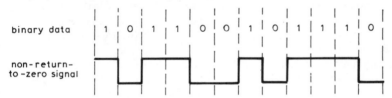

Figure N.2   Non-return-to-zero signal

non-synchronous network   A network in which the *clocks* are not necessarily synchronous or *mesochronous*.

non-synchronous transmission   See *anisochronous transmission*.

non-uniform encoding   In *pulse-code modulation*, the representation of non-uniformly quantised samples of an analogue signal according to a defined code.

non-uniform quantising   *Quantising* in which the quantising intervals vary in size with signal amplitude, usually in accordance with some specified law; see *A-law encoding*. This has the effect of reducing the *quantising distortion* caused at low signal levels.

non-urgent alarm   A visual indication in the apparatus room of fault conditions not requiring immediate attention. Also known as *deferred alarm*.

non-volatile store   A *store* that does not lose its contents when the power is removed; for example, a magnetic storage element such as a ferrite core.

NOR gate   A *logic element* having one output and two or more inputs, with the property that the output will stand at its defined logic 0-state if one or more of the inputs stand at their defined logic 1-states. The term derives from 'NOT OR', i.e. an *OR gate* with a negated output.

normal mode   In a *waveguide*, a *mode* (2) of propagation in which either the electric or magnetic field is mainly transverse with a negligible longitudinal component. See *TE mode* and *TM mode*.

notify call (US)   A call for which an indication of the end of the initial charge period is requested.

null-steerable antenna   An antenna with an omnidirectional *directivity pattern* in azimuth, except for one sharp null, the direction of which is electronically steerable.

null-zone detection   In digital transmission, a method of error detection in which marginal decisions are discarded by the receiver. In the reception of a two-condition signal, for example, where the nominal signal value at the sampling instant should be either $+1$ or -1, all values lying between chosen limits of $+E$ and $-E$ could be rejected as being in doubt. This method will not detect errors in which the wrong value is indicated decisively.

number-received signal   A *signal* (2) sent in the backward direction, to indicate that sufficient *address information* has been received to enable the next stage in the *forward set-up* of a call to proceed.

number repetition   A PABX facility available at selected extensions whereby the user, having called a number, can dial an *access code* causing that number to be stored so that a repeat call can be made by dialling a short code. Normally the storing code must be dialled after each call attempt to prevent erasure of the stored number. In some systems there is no need to dial a storing code, as the last dialled number is stored automatically until overwritten by a different one from the extension having this facility.

number-unobtainable tone (NU tone)   An audible signal sent back to a caller to indicate that the call cannot be completed because (a) the required line or equipment is out of service or faulty, (b) access to the number or service is barred, (c) an invalid number has been dialled, or (d) misoperation or equipment malfunction has occurred. The tone is also returned to callers who fail to send any effective calling signals within a specified time.

numbering plan   Any scheme for the allocation of *directory numbers, trunk codes* or *country codes*. A numbering plan may be drawn up for a single exchange, for a large conurbation such as London, for a group of countries such as those in North America, or it may be formulated on a world-wide basis; see *world numbering plan*. A comprehensive plan drawn up for a large area such as North America (including Canada, the US, Bermuda and the Caribbean Islands) is usually described as an *integrated numbering plan*.

numbering-plan area An area consisting of a subdivision of the territory covered by a national or integrated numbering plan and identified by a particular numbering-plan *trunk code*.

numbering zone One of the nine geographical areas into which the world is divided according to the *world numbering plan*.

numeric word See *word*.

numerical aperture A measure of the light-gathering ability of an *optical fibre*, expressed by the sine of the angle θ between its optical axis and the most divergent ray accepted by it. The value of the numerical aperture is given by the expression

$$NA = \sqrt{(n_{co}^2 - n_{cl}^2)}$$

where n_{co} and n_{cl} are the refractive indices of the core (the maximum value of a *graded-index optical fibre*) and the cladding respectively. For practical purposes operational values are usually derived from measurements of the acceptance or radiative patterns.

numerical selection In a *step-by-step automatic system*, the process in which the wipers of a selector are positioned by the pulses sent by a dial, relay, etc.

Nyquist bandwidth In digital transmision, the bandwidth corresponding to half the signalling rate. Thus if the latter is n bits/second the Nyquist bandwidth is $n/2$ Hz. See also *Nyquist interval* and *Nyquist rate*.

Nyquist interval (1) In digital transmission, a concept developed in connection with the transmission of digital signals over band-limited channels and usually defined as the reciprocal of the *Nyquist rate*, as discussed under that term. (2) In sampling, the maximum interval of time that can be allowed between regularly spaced instantaneous samples if the waveform of the sampled signal is to be completely determined. For a signal containing frequency components from zero to ω Hz it is equal to $1/2\omega$ seconds, in other words the sampling rate must be at least twice the highest angular frequency present in the wave.

Nyquist rate In digital transmission, a concept usually defined as the maximum rate at which independent signal values can be transmitted over a specified band-limited channel without exceeding a given amount of *intersymbol interference*. In many contexts, however, the term refers to the rate at which intersymbol interference vanishes.

The concept can be clarified by considering a hypothetical channel consisting of an ideal *low-pass filter* having unity transmission up to a cut-off frequency ω_c, zero transmission above this frequency and a linear phase/frequency characteristic;

183

see *Figure N.3*. The amplitude response of such a filter to a unit impulse can be calculated and has the form of a sin x/x function, where $x = \omega_c t$; see *Figure N.4*. Zero on the time axis corresponds to the instant at which the peak of the received pulse occurs, and it can be seen that the amplitude response is zero at all axis crossing points where $\omega_c t = \pm n\pi$, i.e. at instants separated from zero by an interval of time equal to half the reciprocal of the cut-off frequency ω_c of the filter, or by a whole multiple of this (Nyquist) interval. It follows that independent impulses separated by this time interval can be transmitted through the filter without interference between the peaks of the received pulses, provided that they are sampled instantaneously and accurately in time. Since the pulses occur at a rate of $\omega_c/\pi = 2f_1$ per second, the transmission rate is equal to twice the

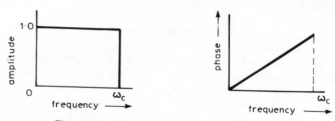

Figure N.3   Characteristics of ideal low-pass filter

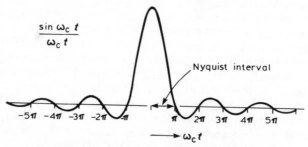

Figure N.4   Impulse response of ideal low-pass filter

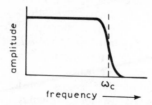

Figure N.5   Filter character-istic with symmetrical roll-off

184

cut-off frequency of the filter. Nyquist showed that in general this is the highest rate at which it is possible to recognise independent arbitrary values at the output of the filter, since any increase in the rate would result in the lowest frequency in the spectrum of the input signal being higher than the cut-off frequency f_1. For the ideal low-pass filter the Nyquist rate is therefore twice the cut-off frequency. In practice it is impossible to construct an ideal filter, and in any case the energy present in the tails of the response to each pulse would cause prohibitive intersymbol interference at any other rate than exactly $2f_1$. Nyquist also showed, however, that if the characteristic of the ideal filter is modified by adding transmission above the cut-off frequency and by making a corresponding symmetrical reduction below it (*Figure N.5*) the same axis crossings appear in the response and the energy in the pulse tails falls off much more rapidly; some deviation from the exact sampling instants is therefore possible, albeit at the expense of a certain amount of intersymbol interference. There are any number of symmetrical modifications that preserve the spacing of the nulls; one of great practical significance is the **full cosine roll-off**—see *Figure F.1(a)*. The total bandwidth in this case is double that of the ideal low-pass filter, but the response has a number of desirable properties as described under the definition. On the basis of freedom from intersymbol interference the Nyquist rate for a channel with a symmetrical roll-off about a frequency f_1 is therefore $2f_1$ and the *Nyquist bandwidth* corresponds to the 3 dB bandwidth of the channel.

It should be pointed out that Nyquist's results are based on a model in which the signal can assume only one of a permitted set of n levels at the transmitter during each signalling interval, and in which the received wave during each corresponding interval can assume only one of n levels in a one-to-one correspondence to those transmitted. This requirement effectively excludes systems—such as **duobinary coding**—that may appear to send at a rate in excess of twice the bandwidth, i.e. at a higher rate than the Nyquist rate. Such systems map the input signal values into a larger number of received values, and moreover decoding of the received signal may depend on the correct determination of a sequence of pulses, i.e. each value cannot be independently determined. Thus a system that transmits binary information by means of a three-level signal should properly be compared with a Nyquist system that sends and receives ternary data.

O

O-wave Ordinary wave; see *magneto-ionic double refraction*.

object code See *programming*.

oblique-angle beam array A directional array with at least one plane of symmetry and consisting of a number of radiating elements whose feed phases are such that the axis of the *main lobe* makes only a small angle (generally less than 30°) with this plane.

oblique-incidence ionospheric recorder See *ionospheric recorder*.

oblique-incidence ionospheric sounding Measurement of ionospheric properties using radio waves impinging obliquely on the ionised layers.

oblique-incidence transmission The transmission of a radio wave from a transmitter to a receiver via the *ionosphere* by reflection or refraction of waves impinging obliquely on one or more ionised layers.

occupation In traffic theory, each use of a device however caused. For traffic-engineering purposes each occupation of a circuit or device caused directly or indirectly by a subscriber is regarded as a call.

octave The interval between two frequencies having a ratio of two to one.

octet A group of eight *binary digits* treated as an entity, i.e. an eight-bit byte.

octonary signal A signal in which information is conveyed by means of eight discrete signal conditions; for example, an eight-phase PSK signal.

octuple phantom circuit A phantom circuit derived from two *quadruple phantom circuits* so that each leg consists of sixteen wires effectively in parallel.

odd parity See *parity*.

O'Dell grading A *progressive grading* formed by interconnecting only identically numbered outlets of adjacent grading groups.

off-hook signal A *signal* (2) indicating that a telephone instrument is being used for a call.

off-line A term applied to equipment or devices not under the direct control of a central processing unit.

offered load See *traffic offered*.

office class (US) A classification given to *exchanges* involved in the completion of *toll calls*.

office code (US) A combination of digits identifying a block of main-station numbers in a *numbering-plan area*.

oligarchic network A *synchronised network* in which a few selected clocks exert control over the remaining clocks in the network.

omnibus circuit A *circuit* rented by a customer and providing for the interconnection of a number of terminals so that any terminal can communicate individually with each of the other terminals or simultaneously with all of them.

omnidirectional antenna An antenna having a non-directional radiation pattern in azimuth; for example, a vertical *dipole antenna*.

on-hook calling A facility provided by some customers' installations (PABXs, *call connect systems*, etc.) whereby a user can make calls without removing the handset, by first pressing the appropriate button and then dialling or keying the wanted number. An integral loudspeaker in the telephone monitors the progress of the call.

on-hook signal A *signal* (2) indicating that a telephone instrument is in its quiescent or idle state.

on-line A term applied to equipment or devices under the direct control of a central processing unit.

on-off keying Simple binary *keying* in which the spacing condition corresponds with an absence of current or carrier wave.

one-unit message In *common-channel signalling*, a signal that is transmitted by means of a single *signal unit*, i.e. a single block of digits.

one-way A qualifying term applied to traffic to indicate that call set-ups take place in one direction only.

one-way trunk (US) A circuit used for calls originating at only one of the two *exchanges* it connects.

open-circuit working A form of direct-current telegraphy in which no current flows to line while the transmitting device is at rest.

open wire A conductor, usually bare, supported on insulators above the ground, e.g. on poles.

operating time In traffic engineering, the difference between the total *holding time* and the *conversation time* of a call.

operator-assured exchange-line access A PBX feature enabling all, or a group, of the outgoing exchange lines to be reserved for the exclusive use of the operator. Any calls in progress on the reserved lines when the relevant key is operated are not interrupted, switching being delayed until the lines are free.

operator call cancel A PABX feature enabling an operator to cancel any stored digits and release seized equipment at any stage in the setting-up of a call from the switchboard.

operator call-in signal A *signal* (2) sent from a PABX extension during the course of a direct incoming call, to attract the attention of the PBX operator.

operator call splitting A switchboard facility enabling an operator to speak separately on the calling and answering side of an operator-controlled or operator-held call.

187

operator code (US) A combination of digits dialled by an operator to gain access to another operator.

operator-controlled conference A PBX switchboard feature enabling an operator to arrange and control the connection together of a number of extensions and/or lines for the purpose of a *conference call*.

operator hold (1) A switchboard facility enabling an operator to hold an incoming or outgoing call without completing the connection and to leave the circuit in order to deal with another call; also known as *call in suspense*. (2) A PABX operator-controlled feature whereby an incoming call may be retained on the switchboard after the required extension has answered. (This feature applies to designs in which the call is normally released from the switchboard automatically when the extension answers.)

operator intrusion A PABX feature enabling an operator to gain access to an extension engaged on a call by keying the required number and operating an intrusion key. *Intrusion tone* is normally applied to advise the parties to the call that the operator is in circuit.

operator not working See *automatic switch to night service*.

operator number identification An arrangement used with *automatic message accounting* whereby the operator requests the identity of the calling station and feeds it into the system.

operator overlap A switchboard feature enabling an operator to ring on one circuit, call on another and speak on a third.

operator recall See *public-exchange operator recall*.

operator wait on busy A PABX switchboard facility enabling a call to be provisionally set up to an extension already engaged on a call, the required extension being rung automatically as soon as it becomes free. If the caller clears before the called party answers, the equipment is automatically released.

operator's console In an exchange with *stored program control*, a console providing the man/machine interface with the *central processor*.

optical axis The longitudinal axis of symmetry of an *optical fibre*.

optical conductors Materials, such as glass or plastic, that offer low *attenuation* to the transmission of light energy.

optical dispersion See *material dispersion*.

optical fibre A dielectric *waveguide* designed to operate at optical frequencies and consisting essentially of a fine cylindrical strand manufactured from highly transparent materials such as glass or plastic. Two basic forms of construction have been developed. In the first, a central region of the fibre, known as the core, is surrounded by and in intimate contact with a cylindrical cladding having a *refractive index* some one per cent lower than that of the core. In the second, the refractive index of the core material falls

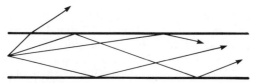

Figure O.1 Propagation of light in glass rod

in value with radial distance from the centre in an approximately parabolic fashion, and there is no direct core/cladding interface. Both forms of construction effectively prevent the loss of optical energy through the fibre wall, as explained below.

The propagation of light along the axial length of a dielectric rod takes place by internal reflection from the surface, as shown in *Figure O.1.* Provided the ratio of the refractive index of the surrounding medium to that of the rod's material exceeds the cosine of the angle at which the ray meets the boundary wall, total reflection will take place. Even under this condition, however, some of the optical field energy extends for about a wavelength outside the surface of the rod, and losses will occur if it encounters light-scattering or light-absorbing objects. These losses can be reduced to insignificant proportions if the rod is coated with a layer of low-loss optical material with a lower refractive index than that of the material from which the rod is made. Optical waveguides made in this way are termed stepped-index fibres, and may be designed to permit propagation in one or many modes; see *monomode optical fibre* and *multimode stepped-index optical fibre.* The other way of avoiding the surface losses is to confine most of the optical energy to the central part of the cross-sectional area of the fibre; see *graded-index optical fibre.*

optimum working frequency A frequency lower than the *maximum usable frequency* by an amount that allows for statistical or predicted variations in propagation conditions for the period considered.

OR gate A *logic element* having one output and two or more inputs, and having the property that the output will stand at its defined logic 1-state if one or more of the inputs stand at their defined logic 1-states.

Oracle Designation used by the IBA for its *teletext* service.

orbit The path followed by a planet, satellite or other body in space as it moves about the centre of another body under the influence of natural forces—mainly gravitational attraction. By extension, the term is applied to the course traced by a communication satellite that is subjected to small corrective forces exerted by its own propulsive unit in order to keep it in a desired path; see *station-keeping satellite*.

The path of a satellite moving around another body is described by making use of orbital elements that relate the shape, dimensions and position of the orbit to a specified frame of reference. For communication satellites a rectangular coordinate system with its origin at the centre of mass of the earth is employed. The basic reference plane containing the X and Y axes coincides with the earth's equatorial plane, and the Z axis has a south-to-north orientation. The position of a satellite in its orbit at a specified instant must be known in addition to the orbital elements if its position at any other time is to be determined.

orbital period   Of a *communication satellite*, the time between two successive passages through some specified point—usually the *periapsis*—in its orbit. Also known as *period of revolution*.

orbital plane   Of a *communication satellite*, the plane containing the centre of mass of the earth and the velocity vector of the satellite.

orbital test satellite (OTS II)   Designation given to the *geostationary satellite* launched on 11 May 1978 to serve as a test bed for equipment, techniques and systems to be used by the European Communication Satellite system of the 1980s. The satellite's position is 10° East longitude in the equatorial plane some 35 800 km above the Atlantic Ocean. It has three-axis stabilisation and six antennas giving coverage of the whole of Western Europe, the Middle East and the Atlantic Islands. The satellite contains two communication modules, each of which receives signals in the 14 GHz frequency band, frequency-changes and retransmits them to earth in the 11 GHz band. One module has two 40 MHz and two 120 MHz transponders contained within a total bandwidth of 210 MHz, each individual frequency band being used twice by means of orthogonal *linear polarisation*. The second module contains two 5 MHz transponders, frequency reuse in this case being by orthogonal *circular polarisation*. The satellite has a forecast operational life of five years. Many experiments on propagation, *depolarisation*, high-speed data transmission, *time-division multiple access* and other transmission techniques are planned to be held during this period. Although it is not intended that OTS II will be used operationally, the satellite has the capacity to carry 6000 phone calls and two television pictures simultaneously. (OTS I was lost owing to failure of the launch vehicle in September 1977.)

order wire   A circuit reserved for use in the alignment and maintenance of a transmission system.

ordinary wave   See *magneto-ionic double refraction*.

orientation   (1) A systematic difference between the *phase* of a receiver and transmitter in a synchronous telegraph system, introduced in order to compensate for the propagation time of the signals or delays in the response of the receiving apparatus. (2) Adjustment of the rest position of the camsleeve of a receiving instrument in order to improve its *margin*.

orifice   Of a waveguide or cavity resonator, an opening through which energy is transmitted.

originating   A qualifying term applied to *traffic* [*exchanges*] in a network to indicate that the sources of traffic are located in the network [are directly connected to the exchange].

orthogonal polarisation   *Polarisation* of a diametrically opposite sense to that of a given polarisation when both are represented on a *Poincaré sphere*. Hence two linearly polarised waves having their respective field vectors at right angles are said to be orthogonally polarised. Similarly, circularly polarised waves having opposite senses of rotation are orthogonally polarised. In the general case of elliptical polarisation, the condition is obtained if the ellipses traced by the respective field vectors are traced in opposite senses, have the same *axial ratio*, and have their major axes perpendicular to one another.

orthomode transducer   A device forming part of an antenna *feed* and serving to combine or separate orthogonally polarised signals.

oscillator   Generic term for a circuit generating an alternating current.

out-band signalling   The transmission of *signals* (2) over the channel or circuit used for a call, but in a different frequency band from that employed for the user's communication.

out-of-alignment time   In *pulse code modulation*, the interval of time during which *frame alignment* is lost. This includes the time taken to detect loss of alignment and the *frame-alignment recovery time*.

out-of-area line   A line provided in special circumstances to give service to a subscriber living outside the normal area of a *local exchange*.

out-slot signalling   Signalling in which the signals relating to the traffic carried by a *channel time slot* are transmitted in one or more other slots dedicated to signalling and time-shared by means of a *multiframe*.

outgoing   A qualifying term applied to circuits at some point in a network to indicate that the direction of call set-up is from that point to another.

outgoing traffic   *Traffic* passing through a given network to another network, regardless of its origin.

outgoing trunk   A *one-way trunk* carrying *traffic* or *signals* (2) from an exchange.

outlet   Of a switching stage, the terminals through which *outgoing traffic* leaves the stage.

output (1) The signal, current, voltage, data, etc. delivered by a device or circuit. (2) The terminals or port at which these quantities are available.

overflow route (US: *spillover route*) A route provided to carry traffic that cannot be carried on the primary route owing to congestion. Such traffic is known as *overflow traffic*.

overhead digit See *service digit*.

overlap In *facsimile*, a defect arising when the width of the scanning lines exceeds the *scanning pitch*.

overlap condition In a digital transmission system during a search for *frame alignment*, the condition in which some but not all the digits forming the *frame alignment signal* fall in the test interval.

overlap signalling A technique whereby the reception and onward transmission of *address signals* at a switching centre are overlapping processes.

overload point See *load capacity*.

overmoded waveguide A waveguide used for the propagation of a wave in a single *mode* (2), but capable of sustaining more than one mode at the frequency of operation.

overmodulation In *amplitude modulation*, modulation with an excessive level of the modulating wave so that the carrier wave is reduced to zero for some part of each cycle of the modulating wave.

overplugging The action of an operator in plugging into a *jack* of a switchboard *multiple* (2) in spite of a busy condition.

overshoot A form of waveform distortion in which a sudden change of level gives rise to a short-term exaggeration of the change.

P

PAL Designation for the 625-line colour television system used in the UK and much of Europe. The term derives from the words 'phase alternation line', which describe the technique of inverting the phase of one of the two chrominance signal components every alternate line. This makes the signal much less susceptible to *differential phase* distortion and eases the problems of transmission.

PBX final selector In a step-by-step public exchange, a *final selector* that, in addition to its normal operation, selects by a *hunting* action the first free line of any *PBX group* connected to its outlets.

PBX group A number of lines used to connect a *private branch exchange* to a public exchange.

PBX power [ringing] lead A *pair* from a public exchange to a *private branch exchange*, used only for supplying direct current [ringing current] to the PBX.

PCM multiplex equipment Designation given to equipment that converts a number of analogue signals into digital signals by the process of *pulse code modulation* and interleaves the resulting bit streams to produce a single digital signal at a defined rate at its output. The equipment also carries out the inverse function.

PCM multiplexing A combination of *pulse code modulation* with *time-division multiplex* to produce a single digital signal consisting of a given number of channels. The principal characteristics of two primary PCM multiplex structures have been standardised by the CCITT, and some of them are shown in *Table P.1*. The 1544 kbit/s system is widely used in North America under the designation T1. The 2048 kbit/s system, now coming into worldwide use, provides an improved signal-to-*quantising-distortion* ratio so that more links can be connected in tandem.

Table P.1

Parameter	1544 kbit/s primary multiplex	2048 kbit/s primary multiplex
Encoding law	μ-law of CCITT Recommendation G711	A-law of CCITT Recommendation G711
Sampling rate	8000 per second	8000 per second
Number of quantised values	225*	256
Number of 8-bit channel time slots	24	32
Number of bits per frame	193	256
Bit rate	$8000 \times 193 = 1544$ kbit/s	$8000 \times 256 = 2048$ kbit/s
Frame alignment signal	distributed in first bit position of every other frame	7 bit, bunched in time slot 0 of every other frame
Signalling	distributed in first bit position of every other frame*	bunched in time slot 16, 4 bit/channel every 16 frames

*Different arrangements have been agreed for some networks.

PCM word A group of signal elements representing the *quantised value* of a sample. Also known as a *character signal*.

p-i-n photodiode A *photodetector* consisting of a semiconductor junction diode in which the p-type and n-type regions are separated by a high-resistance layer of intrinsic material. This form of construction yields a better high-frequency *quantum efficiency* than a simple pn junction because, when the diode is reverse biased, the depletion region extends through the whole of the intrinsic layer. Moreover, the increased thickness of the field region results in the generation of fewer charge carriers in areas where diffusion processes degrade the speed of response. See also *photodiode*.

P-wire   See *private wire* (1).

packet   A block of digits with a defined format transferred as a composite whole over a *packet-switching* network. In general packets have a three-part format: a *header field* containing address and control data, an *information field* usually containing user's data, and an *error control field* containing bits used for error checking purposes. In a given system a maximum length of packet is normally specified, so a user's message may require the transmission of a number of packets.

packet assembly/disassembly facility   A facility provided in a *packet-switching* exchange to enable communication to take place between asynchronous character-mode terminals and synchronous packet-mode terminals. Two functions are basic to any PAD facility. First, it must be able to assemble data received from start-stop terminals into *packets* for onward transmission as *virtual calls* to packet-mode terminals. Second, it must be able to disassemble received packets and transmit the data at the correct asynchronous transmission rate to various start-stop character-mode terminals. PAD facilities presently form the subject of provisional CCITT Recommendation X3.

packet-mode terminal   A terminal connected to a *packet-switching* exchange by a private circuit, and having facilities for the assembly of data into packets and for their transmission, reception and disassembly into data in accordance with agreed

packet switching   A method of operating a data service whereby data is transferred in *packets* assembled in accordance with agreed *protocols* and normally containing address, routing and error-control information in addition to customers' data. This method of operation improves the utilisation of interexchange transmission links and enables customers with various types of terminal, operating at different rates, to communicate with one another. The technique is essentially an extension of the old store-and-forward telegraph system. A packet-switching exchange receives packets from its various terminals and transmits them sequentially over links to other exchanges in accordance with the address information provided. Although no direct connection is established between a calling and a called terminal, the speed of operation of the switching centres and interexchange links is sufficiently high to provide a conversational mode of communication between the terminals. Adequate buffer storage has to be provided at each switching centre, which must also be able to control the mean rate at which packets are received from any of its terminals. A packet-switching exchange has the ability to receive data at one rate from a given terminal and to transmit it at a different rate to another. Hence packets intended for a high-speed terminal and received from a number of lower-speed terminals can be interleaved and transmitted at the higher rate. As each packet is clearly identifiable, the receiving terminal can associate the packets from a given terminal to form a coherent message.

A *packet-switching network* consists of a number of packet-switching exchanges linked by high-speed data-transmission facilities. Each exchange is connected by a private or leased circuit to its packet-mode terminals. *Packet assembly/disassembly facilities* can be provided at the exchanges to enable users having asynchronous start-stop character terminals to use the network, access generally being via the PSTN.

Packet switching is a comparatively recent development, the first public network employing the technique in Europe being the Experimental Packet Switched Service (EPSS) set up in the UK in 1977. In the interests of international standardisation the CCITT has published a number of provisional Recommendations in the X series relating to the operation of packet-switched data transmission services. The International Packet Switched Service (IPSS) across the Atlantic uses the X25 protocols for the customer interface for synchronous packet-mode terminals operating at 2400, 4800 and 9600 bits per second. Character-mode terminals operating at certain lower rates are also able to gain access to the service via the PSTN and the PAD facilities at the packet-switching exchange.

pad A network of resistors used to introduce a fixed amount of *attenuation* or for impedance-matching purposes.

page printer An instrument, used for alphabetic telegraphy, that prints characters in page formation.

paged pick-up A PABX facility enabling a person who has been advised by a paging system that there is a call to his extension, to pick that call up at any extension by dialling his own number, followed by a special code.

pager See *radiopaging*.

paging service A facility available to the users of a PABX connected to a paging system whereby paging may be initiated by dialling a suitable code. The person being paged can respond by using the *paged pick-up* facility. These services are sometimes known as *staff location systems*.

pair Two similar conductors insulated from one another and generally associated to form a *circuit*.

pair gain system General term for a system that enables a given number of *pairs* in a *local line network* to provide service to more subscribers than there are pairs. See *line concentrator, line connector, loop switching system, subscriber loop multiplex* and *subscribers carrier system*. The term is not used to describe *party line* systems.

pair group (US) In a *local line network*, the unique bundle of *pairs* extending out from the *exchange* to feed a particular allocation area. The pairs are not necessarily all in the same cable sheath.

paired disparity codes A class of codes in which some or all of the input digits may be represented by one of two signal levels of opposite polarity, the signal levels being used in such a way that the overall imbalance or *disparity* of the signal is minimised; see *alternate mark inversion*.

paired selected ternary code A code in which the input signal is divided into pairs of binary digits, each pair being represented by a pair of ternary digits. Two of the four possible pairs of binary digits are represented by zero-disparity pairs of signal levels. The remaining two pairs of binary digits are represented alternately by pairs of signal levels chosen from two sets in such a way that the imbalance of the output signal is minimised.

panel system (US) An automatic switching system in which the *bank* contacts over which the wipers move are mounted vertically in flat rectangular panels, the wipers being positioned by a motor common to a number of the selecting mechanisms.

parabolic reflector Of an antenna, a circular reflector whose shape is a portion of a paraboloid of revolution or a part of a cylinder of parabolic shape.

parallel plate lens A microwave antenna *lens* made up from thin parallel conducting plates.

parallel resonance The condition that exists in a circuit consisting principally of inductance and capacitance connected in parallel, when the inductive reactance equals the capacitive reactance at the frequency of the applied voltage. Also known as *anti-resonance*.

parallel-to-serial converter A device for converting digits present simultaneously at its inputs into a corresponding sequence of digits at its output. Also known as a *dynamiciser*.

parametric amplifier (also known as a *reactance amplifier*) A *microwave* device in which signal amplification is obtained as a result of energy released by a reactive non-linear circuit element—usually a variable-capacitance diode—which is fed by a pumping oscillator running at a higher frequency than the signal. The correct phase relationship has to be maintained across the diode, so, except in the case of harmonically related frequencies, it is necessary for power to flow at another frequency equal to the difference between the pump and signal frequencies. This is known as the *idler frequency*. In essence, therefore, a parametric amplifier consists of a series of *tuned circuits* resonant at the pump, idler and signal frequencies. The non-linear reactance is common to all three circuits. In one-port versions incoming and outgoing circuits have to be separated by non-reciprocal circuit elements.

parasitic element   Of an antenna, an element that is not connected to a radio transmitter or receiver either directly or via a feeder, but is coupled to the *driven element* only by the fields. Also known as *passive element*.

paraxial rays   In an *optical fibre*, rays that are very nearly parallel with the optical axis; in calculations $\sin \theta$ can therefore be replaced by θ radians.

parent exchange   An *exchange* housing operators handling *assistance traffic* from one or more automatic exchanges. See also *satellite exchange*.

parity   Of a binary code, a characteristic of the code whereby the number of 0s (or 1s) in any permitted code word is always even (*even parity*) or always odd (*odd parity*).

parity bit   A bit appended to a string of bits forming a word or block in order to establish a desired *parity*.

parity check   A test carried out for error detection purposes on a received word, block, etc. to see whether the correct *parity* exists.

parked   See *parking*.

parking   A method of reducing the possibility of congestion in a PABX by preventing false *seizing* or holding of common equipment in the period immediately following a call. Thus if an extension is still off-hook after a connection has been released, it does not seize calling equipment and receive dial tone but is 'parked', *number-unobtainable tone* being transmitted to it for 30 seconds or until it hangs up, whichever is the shorter. Calls to a parked extension receive *busy tone*, but if the extension has not cleared at the end of the 30-second period number-unobtainable tone is returned.

part-time private wire or **part-time leased circuit**   A *circuit* available for the exclusive use of a customer for prearranged regular periods.

partial common trunk   A trunk accessible to some but not all the groups of a *grading*.

partial gain   Of an antenna for a given *polarisation* (2) and in a given direction: the ratio (usually expressed in *decibels*) of that part of the total *radiation intensity* attributable to the given polarisation to the radiation intensity that would be obtained if the power accepted by the antenna were radiated isotropically. The sum of the partial gains for any two *orthogonal polarisations* gives the *absolute gain* of the antenna. In the case of antennas designed for a particular polarisation, the partial gain for that polarisation may be used to indicate the total gain.

partial-response coding Generic term for methods of coding in which the binary signal is passed through a linear network having a rise time greater than one bit period, so that a multilevel signal is produced. Usually the technique includes precoding to modify the spectral distribution of the signal and to simplify reception.

partial secondary working In a *step-by-step automatic system*, a method of interconnecting two ranks of *selectors* so that early-*choice* outlets of the first rank are directly connected to the second rank, but late-choice outlets only have access via secondary selectors.

partial switching stage In a link switching system, a connecting stage that may be associated with one or more similar stages by a common control unit to switch a call from an inlet to a selected outlet.

partial tone reversal In *facsimile*, defective reproduction of tone changes so that a transition from white to black [black to white] on the original document is followed by a secondary change towards white [black] on the reproduced copy. This can be caused by the incorrect setting of black and white limits in the *frequency modulation* of a sub-carrier.

partially restricted extension A PABX extension that can only make *exchange line calls* via the PABX operator.

party line A line serving a number of subscriber stations, usually with *selective ringing* and a separate exchange number for each station.

passive A qualifying term applied to devices that do not require power (apart from that contained in a signal) for their operation; for example, a *filter* built of resistors, capacitors and inductors only.

passive element See *parasitic element*.

passive network An electrical network containing no source of energy.

passive reflector A reflector used to change the direction of propagation of a *microwave* beam; for example, a reflecting surface mounted on a hilltop and used to reflect signals to a convenient receiving site in a valley.

passive repeater A *passive reflector* or two antennas connected by a short length of transmission line, one serving to receive incident radiation and the other to transmit the signal in a new direction.

passive satellite See *communication satellite*.

passive transducer A *transducer* without an internal source of energy.

patch (1) A temporary connection between *jacks* using a short length of cable with plugs at both ends and called a *patchcord*. (2) In data processing, to carry out an improvised modification.

path allocation The function of testing and reserving a *path* for a call according to a set of rules.

path attenuation In radio communication, the ratio between the power received and the power radiated over a given radio path using an identical loss-free antenna at each end. The type of antenna, the frequency and the time of day must be specified. The *basic path attenuation* is that when *isotropic radiators* are specified.

path setting The activation of *crosspoints*, devices and transmission links selected to form a particular path.

Pawsey stub A device for connecting an unbalanced coaxial *feeder* (2) to a balanced antenna.

paytone A tone, heard by a customer making a call from a pay-on-answer coinbox, to indicate that the wanted party has answered and that money should therefore be inserted in the coinbox.

peak clipper or **peak limiter** See *limiter*.

peak limiting In PCM *quantising*, the effect occurring when the peak amplitudes of an input analogue signal exceed the virtual decision values of the quantiser.

peak program meter A measuring instrument used to check the level of a sound program in a channel in terms of the amplitude peaks averaged over a specified period.

peak-to-peak amplitude Of a periodic waveform, the value given by the difference between the highest maximum and the lowest minimum values in one period.

peaking The process in which the response of a device is increased over a desired frequency band.

peg count (US) A traffic measurement in terms of the number of calls offered to a group of circuits or handled by an operator during a specified period. The term is also applied to counts of busy or overflow conditions.

pencil-beam antenna An antenna producing a beam in the shape of a cone with a very small angle at the vertex.

penetration frequency See *critical frequency* (1).

percentage immediate appreciation In telephone transmission testing, the percentage of spoken sentences, each conveying a simple concept, that are immediately understood without any conscious deductive effort.

perforated-tape retransmitter Telegraph apparatus comprising a linked receiver and perforator feeding tape directly into an automatic transmitter.

perforator Apparatus that records telegraph signals on a paper tape by punching holes in accordance with a specified code. If the device includes a keyboard for controlling the perforation, it is termed a *keyboard perforator*. If it also prints the character or symbol corresponding with each punched code combination, it is called a *printing perforator*.

periapsis That point in the *orbit* of a *satellite* at which its distance from the centre of mass of the primary body has its minimum value.

perigee That point in the elliptical *orbit* of a *communication satellite* at which it is at its minimum distance from the centre of the earth. The altitude of the perigee is quoted with reference to a specified hypothetical surface serving to represent the surface of the earth.

period of revolution Of a satellite, see *orbital period*.

periodic metering A method of assessing the charge for a call by operating the *subscriber's meter* at intervals determined by the tariff rate in force at the time.

permanent store See *store*.

permanent virtual circuit A specially allocated data transmission path following a fixed route between two terminals in a *packet-switching* network. Such a circuit resembles a *private wire* (2), in that it can only be used for the transmission of packets between the two terminals. However, it is similar to a *virtual call* in that the network transmission facility is only allocated when packets are actually being transferred over the circuit.

permanently locked envelope In a data network, a mode of transmission in which *envelopes* are always separated by a number of bits corresponding to a whole number of envelopes.

permissible interference *Interference* that does not cause the performance of a communication system to fall below some specified criterion.

personal call or **person-to-person call** (US) A call made via an operator and intended for a particular person. Apart from the fee for the service, charging only begins when the wanted party, or an acceptable substitute, is available to take the call.

phantom circuit A circuit derived from two normal *pairs* known as *side circuits* in such a way that the wires of each pair are effectively in parallel; see *Figure P.1*. The principle can be extended so that a *double phantom circuit* can be formed from two phantom circuits, and so on.

phase Of a periodic quantity, that fractional part of a period (expressed in degrees or radians) through which the quantity has

200

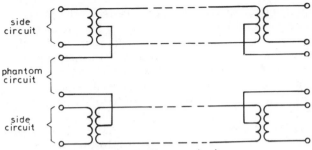

Figure P.1 Phantom circuit

advanced since some arbitrary time origin. Usually the origin is taken as the last previous passage of the quantity through zero value in the direction from negative to positive values.

phase/amplitude distortion In a non-linear system, *distortion* caused by lack of constancy in the *phase* shift between the input signal and the output signal as the former is varied in amplitude.

phase bandwidth Of a network or device, the width of the continuous frequency range over which the *phase/frequency characteristic* does not depart from linearity by more than a given amount, i.e. the range over which the *phase delay* is effectively constant.

phase centre Of an antenna, the location of a point that, when used as the origin for the *phase function*, yields a substantially constant value of phase for a given component of the radiation field. Usually it is sufficient to consider the phase over a limited sector of the *directivity pattern* of the antenna. For some types of antenna a unique phase centre may not exist.

phase-change coefficient or **phase constant** The imaginary part of the *propagation coefficient*, i.e. that part which expresses the rate of change of *phase* of the relevant quantity in the direction of propagation, in radians per unit length. Also known as the *wavelength constant*.

phase-continuous FSK See *frequency-shift keying*.

phase-corrected horn A *horn* antenna for which the emergent electromagnetic *wavefront* is substantially plane at the mouth.

phase delay For a single-frequency wave propagated between two points, the time obtained by dividing the *phase* shift in radians by the angular frequency in radians per second.

phase detector A device producing an output proportional to the deviation of the *phase* of an input signal from a reference phase.

phase deviation In *phase modulation*, the peak difference between the instantaneous phase angle of the modulated wave and the phase of the unmodulated sine-wave carrier.

phase diagram A graphical representation of the *phase function*

201

of an antenna. Also termed *phase pattern*. The phase function may be given for all directions in space, for directions lying in a plane containing the axis of the antenna, or for directions in a cone with its vertex lying on the axis of the antenna.

phase-discontinuous FSK   See *frequency-shift keying*.

phase-displacement antenna   A directional antenna consisting of a *driven element* and an assembly of *reflector elements* arranged so that the phase of the *secondary radiation* of each reflector element is such that the antenna has a desired *directivity pattern*.

phase distortion   General term for distortion caused by non-linearity of the *phase/frequency characteristic* of a system; see *delay distortion*.

phase/frequency characteristic   Of a system or device, a plot of the *phase* shift in radians introduced between the input and output as a function of the angular input frequency in radians per second. For distortionless transmission such a characteristic should be a straight line passing through the origin.

phase function   Of an *antenna*, a function giving (for each direction in space) the *phase* of a specified field component produced by the antenna with respect to a reference phase in a specified direction, these phases being evaluated on a sphere of fixed radius whose centre is defined with respect to the antenna. The phase function in the *far-field region* is most usually considered. See also *phase centre*.

phase inversion   Binary *phase-shift keying* in which the change of significant condition corresponds to a 180° change of phase of the carrier wave.

phase modulation   *Modulation* in which the *phase* of a sine-wave carrier is the characteristic that is varied in accordance with a modulating wave.

phase pattern   See *phase diagram*.

phase-shift keying (also known as *digital phase modulation*)   The process whereby the instantaneous *phase* of the modulated wave is shifted between a set of predetermined discrete values in accordance with the *significant conditions* of the modulating digital signal.

phase-shift signalling   *Signalling* in which the various signals are represented by specified changes in the *phase* of a constant-frequency carrier.

phased array   An array whose beam direction or *directivity pattern* is controlled mainly by adjusting the relative *phases* of the currents in the different radiating elements.

phased satellite   Deprecated term for *synchronised satellite*.

phasing   In *facsimile*, the process of adjusting the position of the midpoint of the *scanning field* at the receiver so that it coincides with that of the corresponding point at the transmitter, thereby ensuring that the picture is correctly located on the recording medium. If the phasing signal consists of nominal white interrupted by a short pulse of nominal black during the lost time, the process is called *phasing on white*. If black and white are interchanged, the last sentence defines *phasing on black*.

phonogram service   A service providing for the transmission of telegrams by telephone between telegraph offices and subscribers' stations.

photodetector   A device for converting electromagnetic radiation in the infra-red, visible and/or ultra-violet regions of the spectrum into an electric current.

photodiode   A type of *photodetector* consisting essentially of a pn (or p-i-n) semiconductor junction diode whose reverse current varies with the amount of light falling on the junction. The operation of a photodiode depends on the fact that certain semiconductor materials absorb light when the energy of the incident *photons* exceeds the band-gap energy of the material. Each photon absorbed gives rise to a pair of equal and opposite charge carriers, i.e. a negatively charged electron and a positively charged hole. In a pn junction photodiode the charge carriers coming under the influence of the electric field in the depletion region are separated, electrons and holes moving in opposite directions across the junction to form the photoelectric current of the device. Since this separation takes place in the depletion layer the conversion efficiency is critically dependent on the width of this layer, which is maximised in the case of a simple pn junction by using a fairly high value of reverse bias. *Figure P.2* shows a set of current/reverse-bias voltage characteristics to illustrate photodiode operation. Two other ways of maximising the depletion region are the use of a layer of intrinsic material

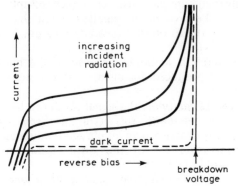

Figure P.2   Photodiode characteristics

203

sandwiched between the p and n regions (see *p-i-n photodiode*) and the adoption of a special structure (see *reach-through photodiode*). *Figure P.2* also shows how the use of high values of negative bias can increase the sensitivity of a device, as explained under *avalanche multiplication*.

Because the energy of a photon is a function of the frequency of the radiation, the *quantum efficiency* of devices manufactured from a particular semiconductor material is dependent on the wavelength. Silicon diodes yield efficiencies of the order of 90 per cent in the 0.85 μm spectral region and are still usable at wavelengths around 1.05 μm, albeit with a reduced efficiency of about 30 per cent. Devices fabricated from materials such as gallium arsenide, indium arsenide and gallium antimonide are under development for use with systems operating in the 1.25 μm region of the spectrum, where current silica *optical fibres* have relatively lower values of *attenuation*.

photon An elementary packet (*quantum*) of radiant electromagnetic energy (light) whose value is equal to the product of Planck's constant and the frequency of the radiation in hertz.

phototelegraphy See *facsimile*.

pick-up services Generic term for PABX facilities enabling calls to one extension to be answered at another; see *designated extension group pick-up, incoming call storage and retrieval* and *paged pick-up*.

pictogram A form of graphical symbol used to convey information independently of language, for example on how to operate a public telephone.

picture black In *facsimile*, that value of the chosen characteristic of the signal (e.g. its frequency or amplitude) which represents the darkest areas of the document being transmitted.

picture element In *facsimile*, the smallest area of the original document that can give rise to a recognisable signal when scanned, or the area of the smallest detail that can be satisfactorily reproduced on the recording medium. Also known as *scanned element*.

picture inversion In *facsimile*, reversal of the black and white areas in the reproduced document so that a negative picture is produced.

picture signal In *facsimile*, the signal produced by *scanning*.

picture tone In *facsimile*, this term has been defined as the frequency of the carrier in an amplitude-modulated system. This is an unfortunate use of the word 'tone'; *picture carrier frequency* would be better.

picture white In *facsimile*, that value of the chosen characteristic of the signal (e.g. its frequency or amplitude) which represents the brightest areas of the document being transmitted.

piezoelectric effect The production of voltages between the opposite faces of certain crystals when they are deformed as a result of mechanical stress; conversely the deformation that results when voltages are applied between the faces. This effect occurs in crystals of quartz, tourmaline and rochelle salt, and is exploited in *transducers* such as microphones and loudspeakers. A slice cut from a piezoelectric crystal can also be used as a frequency-control element since it will resonate with an applied EMF at a frequency determined by its dimensions. It behaves, in fact, as a *tuned circuit* with a very high *Q-factor* and stability.

pilot The generic term for a single-frequency wave transmitted for various purposes in a carrier transmission system; see *reference pilot, regulating pilot, switching pilot* and *synchronising pilot.*

pilot carrier In *single-sideband transmission* or *independent-sideband transmission,* a reduced-amplitude carrier transmitted so that it can be utilised for *local carrier reception* or for *reconditioned carrier reception.*

pilot signal or **pilot wave** See *pilot.*

pine-tree array An array consisting of a number of horizontal dipoles arranged in a vertical plane, separated by half a wavelength and so fed from a balanced transmission line that the currents in every element are always in the same direction.

piston In a *waveguide,* a longitudinally movable metallic plane surface that reflects substantially all the incident energy. Also termed *plunger.*

planar array An antenna array in which the centres of the *radiating elements* are in one plane.

plane of polarisation Of a wave having *linear polarisation,* the plane containing the direction of the electric field and the direction of propagation.

plane polarised wave In a homogeneous isotropic medium, a wave for which the direction of the electric field and the direction of propagation are permanently in one plane.

plane wave In radio propagation, a wave whose equiphase surfaces constitute a family of parallel planes.

plesiochronous Qualifying term applied to digital signals whose *significant instants* occur at nominally the same rate, any variation in rate being kept within specified limits. No such limits apply to the *phase* relationship between corresponding signal transitions. Compare with *mesochronous.*

plunger See *piston.*

Poincaré sphere An imaginary sphere, used to represent different *polarisation* (1) states of electromagnetic waves. Each point on the surface of the sphere represents a different polarisation. Using the terminology applied to the earth, the north and south poles correspond with left-hand and right-hand circularly polarised waves respectively. Points on the equator correspond with linear polarisation, zero longitude representing horizontally polarised waves and 180° longitude vertically polarised waves. It follows that a point on the equator at longitude 90° represents a linearly polarised wave with the electric vector at 45° to the horizontal. Points intermediate between the equator and the poles represent elliptically polarised waves, the ellipse becoming more circular as the distance from the equator increases. Thus the *axial ratio* of the ellipse at any intermediate point depends on its latitude, while the inclination of the major axis depends on its longitude.

point-to-point circuit   A radio link between two fixed stations.

polar orbit   The path traced by a *satellite* whose orbital plane includes the axis of the earth.

polar signal   A digital signal in which opposite directions or polarities of current are used, as distinct from an on/off signal; see *Figure P.3*. See also *return-to-zero signal*.

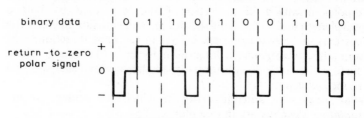

Figure P.3   Polar signal

polarential telegraph system (US)   A direct-current telegraph system employing *polar signals* in one direction and some form of *differential duplex transmission* in the other.

polarisation   (1) In radio-wave propagation, a fundamental property of a wave characterised by the direction of the electric field. The various types of polarisation are defined with reference to the path traced by the extremity of the *electric field vector* in a plane normal to the direction of propagation at some fixed location in space. See *elliptical polarisation, circular polarisation* and *linear polarisation*. (2) Of an antenna. In transmission, the polarisation of the radiated wave in the *far-field region* in a specified direction—usually the direction of maximum radiation. In reception, that polarisation of an incident plane wave from a given direction which yields maximum available power at the output port; if the direction is not specified, that corresponding with maximum received power is assumed.

polarisation conversion See *depolarisation*.

polarisation crosstalk In *dual-polarisation transmission*, the ratio of the power of the wanted signal at a specified output port to the power of the orthogonally polarised signal when the input ports of the remote transmitting antenna are excited by orthogonally polarised signal waves.

polarised relay A *relay* that will only operate for one direction of current through its coil.

polling A cyclic process in which sources of data are invited, one at a time, to transmit.

polybinary coding A method similar to *duobinary coding*, but producing a multilevel signal in which all even-numbered signal levels represent the *space* condition and all odd-numbered levels represent the *mark* condition.

polybipolar coding A method similar to *polybinary coding*, but producing a signal with an odd number of levels balanced about zero so that there is no DC component.

polyrod antenna See *dielectric antenna*.

port (1) An access point to a network, e.g. a pair of input terminals. (2) In *waveguide* transmission, an opening in a waveguide component through which energy may be supplied or withdrawn or where measurements may be made. A port may be specified by reference to a particular *mode* (2) of propagation and a given reference plane, a symbolic port being envisaged for each independent mode.

portable station In a mobile communication service, a station intended to be carried by or on a person.

position access control A PBX facility enabling the class of call to be handled at any switchboard position, to be selected by the operation of the appropriate key at the relevant position.

position meter A meter used to measure the number of calls handled at a switchboard position.

positive feedback The return of part of the output energy of a device or circuit to the input, in such a sense that the amplification or sensitivity is increased.

positive justification See *justification*.

positive logic See *logic convention*.

positive modulation (US: *upward modulation*) *Amplitude modulation* by a video signal so that an increase in brightness corresponds with an increase in carrier power. This method was used for the 405-line system in the UK.

positive-negative justification or **positive-negative pulse stuffir** (US) See *justification*.

207

positive pulse stuffing   See *justification*.

positive-zero-negative justification or **positive-zero-negative pulse stuffing** (US)   See *justification*.

post dialling delay or **post sending delay**   The interval of time between the completion of dialling and the return of a signal such as *ringing tone* or *busy tone*. With the extension of long-distance dialling and the introduction of automatic repeat attempt facilities, the delay before a subscriber receives any tone can be quite considerable. For this reason some system designs envisage the use of a recorded announcement, music or a comfort tone during this waiting period.

power-driven system   An *automatic switching system* in which the power required to move the *wipers* is obtained from a motor common to a number of selectors.

power flux density   See *field intensity*.

power level   See *level*.

power ringing   *Ringing* (1) in which current from a continuously running generator is connected via a *key* or *relay*.

pre-assignment   The semi-permanent allocation of circuits to a particular service or route in accordance with forecast traffic needs; for example, the allocation of blocks of satellite circuits for use between two *earth stations*.

precipitation static   *Interference* due to charges built up on structures as a result of rain, sleet or snow.

predistortion   A deliberate change in waveshape, introduced either to counteract the expected effect of a subsequent transmission path or to render the signal less susceptible to *noise*; see *pre-emphasis* and *companding*.

pre-emphasis   A process that increases the amplitude of some frequency components of a complex wave with respect to the amplitude of others.

preference facility   A PABX facility whereby the users of certain extensions can enter any PABX conversation in progress.

prefix   (1) Of a multi-component signal, the initial part of the signal; the prefix serves to prepare the receiving circuit for the reception of the remainder of the signal. (2) One or more digits that have to be dialled before a national or international number to indicate that the call is to be routed to some point outside the local area. This is known as a *prefix code* in the US.

pre-selector   A *selector* associated with a *subscriber's line* and used to connect it to a free outlet.

pressurisation of cables   See *cable pressurisation*.

Prestel   The *viewdata* service available in the UK.

primary block   In *pulse code modulation*, a basic group of channels assembled by *time division multiplexing*. In the US a primary block is known as a *digroup* and usually contains 24 channels. Some 24-channel systems are in use in the UK, but all new systems comply with the CCITT Recommendation for a primary block of 32 channels, two of which are reserved for signalling, timing and other purposes.

primary centre A CCITT term for a *switching centre* to which *local exchanges* are connected and through which trunk traffic is passed. In the UK such an exchange is called a *group switching centre*. In North America a primary centre is defined as a class 3 central office used for toll switching. It is thus one level higher than the *toll centre*, or class 4 office, which corresponds to the international definition in functional terms. See *classification of exchanges*.

primary radiator See *driven element*.

primary route The route that is selected as the first choice between specified points.

principal mode See *dominant mode*.

printer See *teleprinter*.

printergram A service in which a *teleprinter* is used to transmit telegrams in either direction between a subscriber and the local telegraph office.

printing perforator See *perforator*.

printing reperforator See *reperforator*.

printing telegraphy Telegraphy in which the received signals are automatically translated and printed as characters.

private automatic branch exchange (PABX) See *private branch exchange*.

private automatic exchange See *private exchange*.

private branch exchange (PBX) An *exchange* normally located in a subscriber's premises and having at least one line connecting it with the public network. The term is usually qualified to indicate whether the exchange is manual or automatic.

private branch exchange hunting A facility provided at a public exchange for automatically searching for a free line among a group of lines serving a *private branch exchange*.

private branch exchange trunk (US) A *subscriber's line* serving a PBX.

private exchange An exchange having no connection with the public network. The term is usually qualified to indicate whether the exchange is manual or automatic.

private manual branch exchange See *private branch exchange*.

private manual exchange See *private exchange*.

private wire (1) In automatic switching, the wire over which the functions of guarding, holding and releasing are controlled and via which metering may be effected in some systems; also known as *P-wire*. (2) A *circuit* placed at the exclusive permanent use of a customer.

problem-oriented language   See *programming*.

proceed-to-send signal (US: *start-dialling signal*)   A *signal* (2) sent back after a *seizing* signal has been received and the necessary conditions have been established for the receipt of further signals, usually those conveying *address information*.

processor   General term for equipment capable of performing operations on data. In the context of exchange equipment the term is used to describe functional units that operate in real time to control switching systems or parts thereof.

program   A schedule of actions expressed in a form suitable for execution by a functional unit such as a central processor or a computer. The term is also used as a verb to describe the act of *programming*.

programmable logic array   A logic element that can replace a conventional *read-only memory*, provided that only some of the possible words in the storage matrix and address decoder are required. Both the address decoder and the storage matrix are programmed to obtain the maximum reduction in chip size. Devices in which the programming can be carried out by the user are termed *field-programmable logic arrays*.

programmable read-only memory or **programmable read-only store**   A *read-only memory* that can be programmed initially by the customer but cannot subsequently be changed.

programming   The act of drawing up an ordered list of the steps to be taken by a computer or processor so that it can solve a particular problem or accomplish a given task. The original method of programming made use of instructions that could be directly acted upon by the computer concerned. This procedure, known as *machine-code programming*, has the disadvantage that it requires an expert programmer familiar with the details of the relevant computer. Nowadays programming is carried out by making use of one or more of the many programming languages that have been developed. A 'language' in this sense comprises the symbols, words, statements and syntax used to construct a program. *High-level languages* are those permitting instructions to be written in relatively fewer statements, couched in generally understood terms. Programs of this type are translated into a form suitable for direct control of a given computer by a process called *compilation*: each statement in the high-level language is expanded and converted into a set of machine instructions—the *object code*—by the use of a program called a *language compiler*.

Languages designed for specific purposes are termed *problem-oriented high-level languages*, and a number of them have been developed for use with exchanges having *stored-program control*. These languages have to take account of a number of conflicting factors such as ease of programming and program modification, efficient use of computer resources, and the desirability of international compatibility.

progressive grading A form of *grading* in which the number of grading groups connected to each outgoing trunk is larger for later-choice outlets.

progressive wave A wave propagating freely in a medium.

progressive-wave antenna See *travelling-wave antenna*.

prolate filter A type of *low-pass filter* named for the complex mathematical function on which its design is based and having the property of an optimum step response.

prompt alarm See *urgent fault alarm*.

propagation coefficient or **propagation constant** A measure of the reduction in amplitude and retardation experienced by a wave of a given frequency in travelling unit distance in the direction of propagation. It is expressed as the natural logarithm of the vector ratio of the steady-state values of the wave at two points separated by unit length, the transmission line being of infinite length or terminated in its characteristic impedance. In the case of a waveguide the value for a given *mode* (2) of propagation is given by the natural logarithm of the ratio of two values of a specified field vector component.

protection ratio In the planning of radio services, the minimum ratio deemed necessary between the power of a wanted signal and that of an unwanted signal under specified conditions of reception, if a specific standard of performance is to be achieved.

protective anode See *reactive anode*.

protectors General term for devices used to prevent excessive voltages and/or currents on a line from damaging exchange equipment or subscribers' apparatus. Protectors are usually fitted at the ends of overhead routes and in other circumstances of higher-than-average risk. Spaced carbon electrodes, gas discharge tubes, varistors and zener diodes are used to provide protection from voltage spikes such as those caused by lightning. Thermally operated devices such as heat coils and fuses may be used to give protection from excessive currents of longer duration.

protocols In data transmission, sets of rules specifying interface conditions, operating methods and procedures, data formats, etc. Protocols relating to the interface between *data terminal equipment* and *data-circuit terminating equipment* for terminals operating in the *packet-switching* mode are at present specified in CCITT Provisional Recommendation X25. For this application three levels of protocol are defined. Level 1 deals with the DTE/DCE interface characteristics, level 2 with link access procedure for data interchange across this interface, and level 3 with packet format and control procedures for *virtual call* and *permanent virtual circuit* facilities.

proving In *common-channel signalling*, the process of testing a signalling link that has previously failed, in order to ensure that it is again serviceable. Proving is usually carried out by checking that the *error rate* is below a predetermined value during a specified interval known as the *proving period*.

pseudo-Brewster angle See *Brewster angle*.

pseudo-*n*-ary signal A signal derived from an *n*-ary signal without change of symbol rate and with *n* having the value $2m - 1$. An example would be a pseudo-ternary signal derived from a binary signal in accordance with a *line code*.

pseudo-ternary codes A general class of codes used in digital transmission in which a three-level signal is used to represent binary information; see for example *alternate mark inversion* and *compatible high-density bipolar code*. A signal coded in this way occupies the same bandwidth and transfers information at the same rate as the binary input signal it represents. By contrast, each digit of a true ternary-coded signal conveys $\log_2 3$ *shannons* of information.

psophometer An instrument for measuring the disturbing effect of *noise* voltages present in a telephone circuit. In order to equate the disturbing effect of noise voltages of different frequencies, the instrument incorporates a frequency-selective weighting network whose parameters can be changed to suit different types of circuit.

psophometric EMF An EMF equal to twice the *psophometric voltage* that would be measured across a 600 ohm non-inductive resistor bridging the circuit at the point of measurement, the sending end being closed by its image impedance. The resistor can be connected to the circuit via an ideal transformer adapting the image impedance to 600 ohms.

psophometric power The power absorbed by a 600 ohm non-inductive resistor from a source of *psophometric EMF*. In the usual case square-law addition (power addition) of noise is assumed, and it is convenient to define psophometric power as follows:

$$\text{Psophometric power} = \frac{(\text{psophometric voltage})^2}{600}$$

$$= \frac{(\text{psophometric EMF})^2}{4 \times 600}$$

$$= \frac{(\text{psophometric EMF in mV})^2}{0.0024} \text{ picowatts}$$

psophometric voltage A measure of the interference caused to a telephone conversation by circuit *noise*, expressed as the value of an 800 Hz tone that would have an equally disturbing effect.

public call office or **public telephone station** (US) A telephone station available for use by members of the public.

public-exchange operator recall A PBX switchboard facility enabling the operator to recall the public-exchange operator on outgoing calls connected via, and held at, the public-exchange manual board.

pulse Of a quantity such as voltage or current, a short and sharp excursion from the steady value. Also called an *impulse*.

pulse amplitude The magnitude of a *pulse*, usually expressed as the peak, average, effective, instantaneous or other value with respect to the normal steady value of the quantity.

pulse amplitude modulation Modulation in which the amplitude of the pulses in a *pulse carrier* is varied in accordance with the instantaneous values of a modulating signal.

pulse-and-bar signal A *video-frequency* signal used to test television equipment and transmission links, and consisting of either a T-pulse or a 2T-pulse associated with a smoothed bar and a line synchronising pulse; see *Figure K.1* under *K-rating system*. The signal is normally repeated at the line frequency of the relevant TV system, and the parameters of the bar and short-duration pulses are related to those of the TV system in the manner described under *waveform testing*. Pulse-and-bar signals are used to test for short-time and line-time linear waveform distortions in luminance channels, and may be used to modulate a *sub-carrier* for chrominance channel tests.

pulse carrier A regular sequence of identical *pulses* intended for modulation.

pulse code In *pulse code modulation*, a set of rules defining the equivalence between each *quantised value* of a sample and the corresponding character signal.

pulse code modulation A process in which an analogue signal is sampled, the samples are quantised and converted by coding to a digital signal. The process can be used for the transmission of all kinds of analogue signals including television, facsimile and wideband signals produced by FDM. Its major application, however, is in the provision of voice channels for telephony, and the following brief and much simplified explanation is based on this usage. The audio signal to be encoded is sampled 8000 times per second to produce a stream of pulses each having an amplitude corresponding to the instantaneous amplitude of the signal at the sampling instant. The amplitude of each pulse is compared with a fixed scale of magnitudes in order to decide in which interval it lies. Each interval or quantising step is represented by a particular binary number, which is transmitted to line every time a sample falling within the relevant interval appears. At the receiving end of the link the binary numbers give rise to the generation of pulses having amplitudes corresponding to those of the original samples. These pulses are passed through a *low-pass filter* to produce a replica of the original audio signal.

In practical PCM systems, advantage is taken of the digital nature of the process to interleave pulses from a number of channels to form a composite signal. This *PCM multiplexing* is usually done by sampling each channel in turn. If the sampling rate is 8000 Hz there will be 125 μs between the sampling instants, and this can be divided up between the channels being multiplexed. In the case of the widely used 24-channel system a time slot of 5.2 μs will therefore be available for each channel sample. In a real system additional coding is normally used; see *line code*.

pulse correction In automatic telephony, the process in which an incoming pulse train (usually from a dial) is corrected insofar as the break-to-make ratio is concerned, the repetition rate remaining unaltered.

pulse dispersion In an *optical fibre*, the spreading in time of the energy in a short pulse of light transmitted along the fibre. Neglecting the losses caused by absorption and scattering, the energy in the received pulse will equal that in the transmitted pulse but will be dispersed in time, i.e. the pulse will be broader and its peak amplitude will be lower (*Figure P.4*). It can be seen that the effect is analogous to that caused by a transmission facility having inadequate bandwidth, so the amount of pulse dispersion caused by a fibre gives an indication of its bandwidth limitation. Pulse dispersion is stated in units of time and distance (usually ns/km), the figure quoted being the width at the $1/\epsilon$ point of the gaussian-shaped output pulse that would result if an ideal impulse (delta function) were to be launched into the fibre. Since an ideal impulse cannot be generated, practical measurements are made with a very short pulse, due allowance for its actual shape being made in the computation of the result. For mechanisms producing pulse dispersion, see *mode*

214

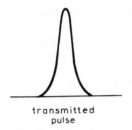 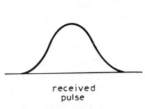

transmitted   received
pulse   pulse

Figure P.4 Pulse dispersion (arbitrary amplitude units; not to scale)

dispersion, material dispersion and *waveguide dispersion*.

pulse duration The interval of time during which the instantaneous amplitude of a *pulse* exceeds a specified fraction of its peak amplitude. Also sometimes known as *pulse length* or *pulse width*.

pulse duration modulation *Modulation* in which the duration of each pulse in a pulse train is varied in accordance with the instantaneous value of the modulating wave. Sometimes called *pulse length modulation* or *pulse width modulation*. The modulating signal may vary the time of occurrence of the leading edge, the trailing edge, or both edges of each pulse.

pulse frequency modulation *Modulation* in which the repetition rate of the pulses in a *pulse carrier* is varied in accordance with the instantaneous value of a modulating signal.

pulse interlacing or **pulse interleaving** (US) The process used in *time-division multiplexing* whereby pulses from a number of sources are interlaced in time to form a single digital signal.

pulse interval modulation *Modulation* in which the interval between corresponding features of the pulses in a *pulse carrier* is varied in accordance with the instantaneous amplitude of a modulating signal.

pulse jitter In digital transmission, small unwanted departures from the ideal times of occurrence of *pulses* in a digital signal. See also *jitter*.

pulse length See *pulse duration*.

pulse length modulation See *pulse duration modulation*.

pulse modulation A term used to describe both the *modulation* of a continuous carrier wave by *pulses* and the variation of some characteristic of a *pulse carrier* by a modulating signal.

pulse position modulation *Modulation* in which the times of occurrence of the pulses in a *pulse carrier* are displaced from their unmodulated values in accordance with the instantaneous amplitudes of a modulating signal.

pulse ratio In automatic telephony, the duration of a *make pulse* divided by the duration of the associated *break pulse*.

pulse regeneration   See *regeneration*.

pulse repetition   In automatic telephony, the process in which an incoming pulse train (usually from a dial) is repeated without change of speed or break-to-make ratio.

pulse repetition frequency or **pulse repetition rate**   The number of *pulses* per unit time. Strictly the first term should only be applied when the frequency is independent of the time interval over which it is measured, whereas the second can apply to the average number of pulses in unit time.

pulse response   The response to a *unit impulse*.

pulse rise time   The time taken for the instantaneous amplitude of a pulse to rise from a lower to an upper specified value—usually from 10 per cent to 90 per cent of its peak amplitude.

pulse signal   In analogue signalling, a signal of fixed duration usually representing a single function.

pulse spectrum   The distribution as a function of frequency of the relative amplitudes of the sinusoidal components of a pulse.

pulse stuffing   See *justification*.

pulse time modulation   General term for methods of *modulation* in which a time-related characteristic of a *pulse carrier* is varied in accordance with the instantaneous value of a modulating signal. See *pulse frequency modulation, pulse duration modulation, pulse interval modulation* and *pulse position modulation*.

pulse width   See *pulse duration*.

pulse width modulation   See *pulse duration modulation*.

pulsing (US)   The transmission of *address information* and other signals over a *circuit*.

pump frequency   The frequency of the alternating current supplied to a *maser* or a *parametric amplifier* to provide the stored energy released in response to an input signal.

pumping   (1) In a *maser* or *laser*, the process of supplying energy at a suitable frequency to lift electrons from lower to higher energy levels. (2) In a *parametric amplifier*, the process of supplying energy at the *pump frequency* to the variable reactance.

pure chance traffic   Traffic in which calls arrive individually and collectively at random, the rate of arrival being independent of the number of calls already in progress. Also known as *random traffic*.

push-to-talk circuit (US)   A circuit that can be used for speech transmission in only one direction at a time.

push-to-type circuit (US)   A telegraph circuit that can be used in only one direction at a time, e.g. because the same radio frequency is used for both directions of transmission.

pushbutton dial (US) A calling device that generates the *signals* (2) required to establish a wanted connection when the appropriate buttons are depressed.

pushbutton switching (US) Designation for the process in a *reperforator switching centre* where an operator selects the outgoing channel.

pyramidal horn A *horn* antenna with a rectangular or square cross-section so that it resembles a pyramid.

Q

Q-factor A figure of merit describing the performance of energy-storing devices such as capacitors and inductors, or of *tuned circuits* or other resonant systems.

quad An assembly of four insulated wires used as a unit in the construction of a cable. See also *star-quad cable* and *multiple-twin quad cable*.

quad-pair cable A cable made up of a number of units each comprising four twisted *pairs* twisted about a common axis.

quadrant antenna A symmetrical antenna having a substantially omnidirectional *directivity pattern* and consisting of two equal-length horizontal conductors forming a right-angled V, which is fed at its apex.

quadrature Qualifying term usually indicating a *phase* difference of 90° between two waves.

quadrature amplitude modulation In digital transmission, a process in which two sinusoidal carriers in phase *quadrature* are amplitude modulated by independent digital signals, the resulting quadrature components being summed to produce the output signal. With this process the number of possible states (*significant conditions*) of the output signal is equal to the product of the number of permissible levels of the input modulating signals. Four-level coding is often used in data transmission, each level of either modulating signal representing a pair of binary digits, i.e. 00, 01, 10 or 11. In this case, therefore, each of the sixteen significant conditions of the output signal conveys four bits of information.

quadruple phantom circuit A phantom circuit derived from two *double phantom circuits* so that each leg consists of eight wires effectively in parallel.

quadruplex system A system of telegraphy permitting the simultaneous independent transmission of two messages in each direction over a single *circuit*.

quantised feedback A technique used in data transmission to correct for *low-frequency wander*. This form of distortion is caused by a signal with a large *digital sum variation* and/or by the loss of DC and LF components of a signal as a result of AC couplings in a transmission path. It manifests itself as an irregular wander in the mean level of the signal. The technique for correction is to pass the received and regenerated pulses through a frequency-selective network complementary to that of the transmission path, and then to use the resultant signal to cancel the wander in the received signal; see *Figure Q.1*. Because

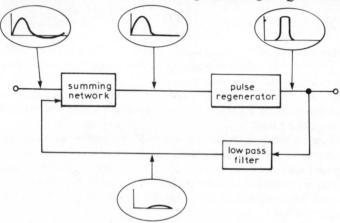

Figure Q.1   Quantised feedback

the amount of low-frequency *attenuation* varies from section to section of a line, the characteristic of the feedback network should ideally be adjusted in each case. In practice it is possible to introduce into the transmission path a dominant network having an LF cut-off frequency higher than that of any line section, so that the latter's effects are swamped. The feedback network can then be made complementary to this dominant network. Quantised feedback enables the use of codes with a relatively large digital sum variation. It also permits the use of higher LF cut-off frequencies, thereby improving the protection from lightning surges and other forms of low-frequency interference.

quantised value or **quantised level** In *pulse code modulation*, an amplitude value used to represent all samples falling within a given *quantising interval*.

quantising In *pulse code modulation*, a process in which samples are graded into a number of adjacent non-overlapping amplitude ranges (*quantising intervals*), any sample falling within a given interval being represented by a single value (the *quantised value*) selected from within the range.

quantising distortion (also termed *quantising noise)* In *pulse code modulation*, inherent distortion arising from the process of *quantising*. Quantising distortion is present only during the presence of a signal, and may be reduced by increasing the number of *quantising intervals* into which the input amplitude range is divided.

quantising interval In *pulse modulation*, a range of instantaneous signal amplitudes lying between two defined reference values known as *decision values*.

quantising noise See *quantising distortion*.

quantum General term for the smallest indivisible quantity of energy associated with any phenomenon. In the case of electromagnetic radiation the quantum corresponds with a *photon*, the value of which varies with frequency.

quantum efficiency Of a photodiode, a measure of the effectiveness with which the device converts incident radiation into output current, usually expressed as the percentage of incident *photons* that produce electron – hole pairs contributing to the output current. The term *DC quantum efficiency* is sometimes used to describe the responsivity (or sensitivity) of a photodiode in terms of amps of output current produced per watt of incident light. This overall figure includes the effect of electron – hole pairs that are generated outside the depletion layer but subsequently drift into an area where they come under the influence of the electric field. These charge carriers make a delayed contribution to the output current and hence degrade the response speed of the device, an effect that is equivalent to a bandwidth restriction when the device is used as a detector of modulated signals. For this reason the performance of photodiodes is often quoted in terms of the *high-frequency quantum efficiency*, which may be defined as the percentage of incident photons giving rise to the production of electron – hole pairs in the depletion region. The high-frequency quantum efficiency of devices can be improved by maximising the width of the depletion layer (see *p-i-n photodiode* and *reach-through photodiode*) and by treating the surface of the diode to minimise reflection losses.

quantum noise Of a *photodiode, noise* produced as the result of the random nature of the arrival of optical energy in the form of discrete quanta, i.e. *photons*. Its mean square value is $2qI_pB$, where q is the electron charge, I_p the photocurrent and B the bandwidth.

quarter-wave (circular) polariser A device for changing the *polarisation* (1) of a wave by applying, in a given plane, a phase delay of 90° relative to the orthogonal plane so that it can be used for conversion between linearly and circularly polarised waves.

quarter-wave skirt dipole   See *coaxial antenna*.

quarter-wave sleeve   An *antenna* element usually about a quarter of a wavelength long and consisting of a tubular conductive sleeve surrounding a conductive supporting cylinder and connected to it at one end. Such an element can be used to match a coaxial *feeder* (2) to a balanced antenna. Quarter-wave sleeves are often called *chokes* in the US.

quarter-wave transformer   A transmission line one quarter of a wavelength long and used for impedance-matching purposes.

quarter-wavelength line   A section of a transmission line having an *electrical length* that is one quarter of a wavelength at the *fundamental frequency* of operation.

quasi-associated signalling   In *common-channel signalling*, a variant of *non-associated signalling* in which signals are restricted to one specified route through the signalling network.

quasi-impulsive noise   *Noise* that is partly continuous and partly impulsive in character.

quasi-peak detector   In radio, an instrument used for the measurement of *impulsive interference*. It consists of a detector circuit whose output operates a meter, the electrical and mechanical time constants being chosen so that the indication is a fraction of the peak of the input signal, the reading increasing with *pulse repetition rate*.

quaternary centre   See *classification of exchanges*.

quaternary signal   A digital signal having four *significant conditions*. See also *n-ary digital signal*.

queuing delay   In *common-channel signalling*, the delay experienced by a signal message whilst it has to wait for previously submitted messages to be sent by the transmitting terminal of the *signalling link*. Queuing delays occur when signal messages are applied to a terminal more quickly than it can send them, and they are a consequence of the fact that many traffic channels and other users share the signalling facilities.

quiescent carrier modulation   *Modulation* in which the carrier is radiated only when a modulating signal is present and modulation can occur.

quiescent terminal   A telephone terminal, such as an extension, that is neither *parked* nor *busy*.

quiet automatic gain control   A combination of *muting* and *delayed automatic gain control* so that the receiver gives no output until an input signal exceeds the gain-control threshold.

220

R

RQ system See *continuous RQ, idle RQ, van Duuren ARQ system*.

R-wire See *ring wire*.

raceway (US) General term for conduit, underfloor troughing and similar structures used to support and/or enclose internal wires, busbars and cables.

rack A vertical metal structure on which apparatus may be mounted.

radiated interference Radio *interference* in the form of unwanted signals or *radiated noise*.

radiated noise Noise energy in the form of an electromagnetic wave.

radiating doublet See *doublet (electrical) radiator*.

radiating element Of an *antenna*, any basic unit intended to produce *radiation*.

radiating near-field region A region of space between the *reactive near-field region* and the *far-field region* of a transmitting antenna, in which the predominant components of the field produced by the antenna are those that represent an outward propagation of energy, the angular field distribution being dependent on the distance from the antenna. This region may not exist if the antenna has a maximum dimension that is not large compared with the wavelength.

radiating surface Of an *antenna*, a conductive assembly having dimensions that are large compared to the wavelength for which the antenna was designed, and effectively forming a continuous surface that functions as a *reflector*.

radiation (1) General term for the emission of energy from a source in the form of particles or waves. (2) In radio, either the outward flow of radio-frequency energy from a source such as an antenna or energy flowing in a medium in the form of radio waves.

radiation diagram See *radiation pattern*.

radiation efficiency Of an *antenna*, the ratio of the radiated power to the total power supplied to the antenna at a given frequency.

radiation function Of an *antenna*, a mathematical expression equal or proportional to a quantity characterising the radiation from an antenna in terms of spatial coordinates. Usually the radiation function for the *far-field region* is considered for a quantity such as the *directivity, radiation intensity, absolute gain* or *cymomotive force*. In the US the term *radiation pattern* covers this concept.

radiation intensity For a given direction in the *far-field region* of an antenna, the power radiated per unit solid angle, usually expressed in watts per steradian. The average radiation intensity is equal to the total power radiated by the antenna divided by 4π steradians. For polarised waves the radiation intensity can be regarded as the sum of the radiation intensities of two orthogonally polarised components.

radiation lobe See *lobe*.

radiation pattern (also termed *radiation diagram*) A graphical representation, using an appropriate coordinate system, of a quantity characterising the radiation from an antenna. Usually the radiation pattern in the *far-field region* is given in terms of angular coordinates for quantities such as the *cymomotive force, radiation intensity, absolute gain, relative gain* and *directivity*. In the latter case the terms *directivity pattern* or *directivity diagram* are often used. In the US the term directivity pattern is also widely used for the concepts *radiation function* and *radiation surface*.

radiation resistance Of an *antenna*, the total radiated power divided by the square of the effective (RMS) antenna current measured at the input.

radiation surface Of an *antenna*, the surface described by the end of a radius vector whose magnitude is proportional to a quantity characterising the radiation properties of the antenna in the direction of the vector. Usually the radiation surface in the *far-field region* is considered for a quantity such as the *radiation intensity, directivity, absolute gain* or *cymomotive force*.

radiation zone See *far-field region*.

radiative loss Of an *optical fibre*, loss of optical power owing to the escape of optical energy from the fibre. Radiative loss thus includes energy radiated out of the fibre as a result of *Rayleigh scattering* and irregularities in the core/cladding interface, as well as that lost by direct tunnelling through the cladding layer. The latter effect can be aggravated by mode mixing caused by excessive bends or imperfections in the fibre.

radio channel A *band* of frequencies allocated for use by a particular service or transmitter.

radio circuit A *circuit* provided by means of two unidirectional *radio links* together with the lines joining them to *terminal exchanges*.

radio communication Telecommunication using *radio waves*.

radio fade-out See *Dellinger fade-out*.

radio frequency A frequency that can be used for *radio communication*, loosely taken as any frequency between about 15 kHz and 3000 GHz.

radio horizon   The locus of points on the surface of the earth at which direct rays from a *microwave* transmitter become tangential to the surface. Under normal conditions of propagation the *refractive index* of the atmosphere falls gradually with height, and this causes the waves to follow a path

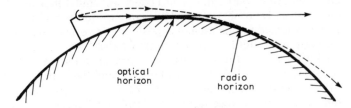

Figure R.1   Radio horizon

that is slightly curved in the same sense as the surface of the earth. For these conditions, therefore, the radio horizon extends beyond the true horizon, as shown in *Figure R.1*. See also *effective radius of the earth* and *line-of-sight radio link*.

radio interference   Interference with the reception of a wanted radio signal by another signal or by a radio-frequency disturbance in the form of *noise* or *atmospherics*. See also *harmful interference, permissible interference* and *acceptable interference*.

radio link   A *radio communication* system of specified characteristics between two points.

radio relay system   A *radio communication* system in which signals are received and retransmitted by one or more intermediate stations.

radio-wave propagation   The transfer of energy through space by means of *radio waves*.

radio waves   *Electromagnetic waves* in that part of the spectrum extending up from high audio frequencies to just below the infrared region, and not guided by wires, *waveguides* or other means.

radiopaging (US: *bellboy*)   A service enabling customers equipped with pocket-sized receivers to be given an audible indication that they are required to take some prearranged action, usually that of calling a particular phone number.

   Radiopaging receivers are often called *pagers* or *bleepers*, the latter term deriving from the characteristic sound of the alert signal they emit. The following description of the operation of a radiopaging system is based on the service presently offered in the London area, but is fairly typical of these systems. Each pager is allocated a unique ten-digit telephone number, which can be dialled from any telephone in the UK. A caller dialling a valid number is connected to the paging control equipment, which translates the number into the unique code number of the relevant pager and arranges for this code to be radiated by transmitters covering the service area. The caller is given a recorded announcement that his instructions have been accepted. On receipt of its particular code a pager will emit a short series of pulses of 2 kHz tone, provided it is switched to the 'on' position. If it is switched to the 'memory' position, however, it will store a received alert until switched back to the 'on' position; this facility is useful for meetings and similar situations. Battery economy is provided by cyclically switching the battery on and off for periods of about a quarter of a second and one and a quarter seconds, respectively. As a result a calling signal must be radiated for a longer period than the duration of the 'off' cycle.

A standard radiopaging code suitable for a large-capacity, wide-area service has recently been developed in Europe. This code provides for a number of options and may well form the basis for international standardisation. It has a capacity for over two million users, each of whom could receive four types of alerting signal plus a simple message such as the caller's telephone number. The code includes error detecting and correcting capability, and is inherently suitable for battery economy measures in a pager.

raised cosine pulse   See *sine-squared pulse*.

random-access memory or **random-access store**   A storage element into which data can be placed and from which it can be retrieved in any desired order. Such an element usually consists of a matrix store and an address decoder that enables a particular word in the store to be accessed by applying a coded input to the address leads.

random hunting   See *hunting*.

random noise   *Noise* caused by a large number of superimposed elementary disturbances and characterised by random occurrences in time and/or amplitude.

random traffic   See *pure chance traffic*.

range extender (US: *loop extender*)   Generic term for any device used to enable satisfactory **signalling, supervision** and/or *transmission* to be obtained on a *subscriber's line* having a higher loop resistance than that normally allowed for in the *exchange* equipment design. The functions that may be adversely affected by a high loop resistance are call detection, dialling, ring trip, provision of feed current to the telephone, speech transmission and ringing.

The simplest form of range extender to gain wide acceptance deals with the signalling and supervision problem in electromechanical exchanges, where non-operation of the line relays is usually the limiting factor. The solution is a solid-state circuit that detects the presence of loop current when the telephone goes off-hook, and then places a temporary shunt across the line to operate the relay. The latter is held in the operated state by the normal loop current, because the hold current of a relay is substantially less than its operate current. Another way of securing the same result, and at the same time eliminating other deficiencies, is to increase the voltage applied to the line. More sophisticated devices also detect and repeat dial pulses, detect and amplify ringing currents, detect and repeat ringing trip signals, and amplify speech currents in both directions.

raster An ordered arrangement of *scanning lines*.

rat race (US) See *hybrid ring*.

ray A path followed by electromagnetic radiation, its direction being normal to the wavefront.

Rayleigh region See *reactive near-field region*.

Rayleigh scattering In *optical fibres*, irregular dispersal of light owing to inhomogeneities of smaller dimension than the wavelength of the light.

reach-through photodiode An *avalanche photodiode* with an improved high-frequency *quantum efficiency* owing to the use of a structure that combines a thin high-field region, in which avalanche action occurs, with a thick high-resistance depletion region in which charge carriers are generated.

reactance The imaginary part of impedance which is not due to resistance. Reactance may be capacitive or inductive, and is a measure of the opposition to alternating current flow offered by a circuit or circuit element. *Reactive* circuit elements store and transfer electromagnetic energy, as opposed to *resistive* elements, which dissipate it.

reactance amplifier See *parametric amplifier*.

reactance modulation The process in which the *reactance* of a circuit element is varied in accordance with a modulating wave in order to phase-modulate or frequency-modulate a *carrier* (1).

reactive anode A substantial billet of metal buried in the ground and connected to a metallic structure such as a cable sheath to provide *cathodic protection*. The anode must be more electronegative than the metal to be protected, and usually consists of magnesium or zinc alloyed with small proportions of other metals. Also known as a *protective anode* or *sacrificial anode*.

reactive attenuator An attenuator that does not absorb energy.

reactive near-field region A region immediately surrounding a transmitting *antenna* where the predominant components of the field produced by the antenna are those that represent an exchange of reactive energy between the antenna and the medium. Also known as *inductive field region* or *Rayleigh region*.

reactive reflector antenna See *reflective array antenna*.

read In data processing, to acquire data from some form of storage device.

read-only memory or **read-only store** A storage element, the data content of which is either fixed during manufacture or can only be altered under certain special conditions. The data may be read repeatedly by applying suitable words to the address inputs of the device.

ready-access terminal (US) See *distribution point*.

real-time operation Term used rather loosely to describe the mode of operation of a computer in which the latter's functions are carried out on demand as and when required by a user. The user may be a process or system interacting with the computer, so the time allowable for a real-time operation depends on the speed of the related process.

rear feed Of a *microwave* antenna, a feed that passes through the *reflecting surface*.

reasonableness check In *common-channel signalling*, a procedure applied to a received signal message to confirm that its *information content* is reasonable in relation to the sequence of previously received messages for that circuit.

recall signal A *signal* (2) sent by an operator to recall another operator or by a subscriber to recall the operator at a manual exchange. The term is sometimes applied to a signal sent from a PABX extension during the course of a direct incoming call, to attract the attention of the PBX operator. Such a signal is more correctly described as an *operator call-in signal*.

receive loss Of an *echo suppressor*, the specified loss in *decibels* introduced into the circuit under break-in conditions to reduce the effect of echo during double-talking.

receiver noise *Noise* generated solely by a receiver.

receiver radiation Unwanted electromagnetic radiation from a receiver, usually that caused by the *local oscillator*.

receiving-end crossfire See *crossfire*.

receiving-loop loss (US) That part of the *repetition equivalent* allocated to the subscriber's apparatus, line and battery-feeding apparatus at the receiving end of the circuit.

receiving perforator See *reperforator*.

reconditioned-carrier reception A technique used mainly for the reception of single-sideband *reduced-carrier transmissions*, whereby the received *carrier* is separated from the *sideband(s)* and is filtered, amplified and limited to remove unwanted modulation and noise before it is used in the demodulation process. See also *local carrier reception*.

reconstructed sample In *pulse code modulation*, a signal amplitude appearing at the output of a decoder when a specified character signal is applied to its input. The reconstructed sample is thus proportional to the *quantised value* of the corresponding encoded sample.

recorded spot See *scanning spot* (2).

recorder warning tone A periodic tone applied to a connection to indicate to the parties using it that their conversation is being recorded. In the US the tone consists of a half-second burst of 1400 Hz tone repeated at 15-second intervals. Also known as *recording tone*.

recording-completing trunk (US) A low-loss circuit between a public *exchange* or PBX and a *toll centre* that can be used to pass the details of a wanted call to an operator and subsequently to complete the toll connection.

recording tone See *recorder warning tone*.

recording trunk (US) A circuit between a public *exchange* or PBX and a *toll centre* that is used only for passing details of wanted calls to an operator, usually when *delay working* is in force. The losses in a recording trunk may prevent it from forming part of a toll circuit.

rectangular wave A periodic wave that alternately assumes one of two fixed values, the transition time between these values being negligible in comparison with the duration of either fixed value. A *square wave* is the special case in which the duration of each fixed value is the same.

recurrent code See *convolutional code*.

reduced-carrier transmission A method of transmitting an amplitude-modulated signal in which the amplitude of the *carrier* is reduced relative to the *sidebands* to enable more of the transmitter's output power to be used for the information-bearing sidebands. See also *pilot carrier*.

redundancy (1) In the transmission of information, the fraction of the *gross information content* of a message that can be disregarded without the loss of essential information. Numerically this is equal to unity minus the ratio of the *net information content* to the gross information content, but it is usually expressed as a percentage. (2) In a communication system, surplus capability usually provided to improve the reliability and quality of service. The term also covers the duplication or partial duplication of key units such as *processors* in switching equipment.

redundant code A code using more *signal elements* than strictly necessary to represent the required message information.

redundant digit A digit that is not required for the transmission of message information, but is used for some other purpose such as a *parity check*.

redundant *n*-ary signal A digital signal in which each *signal element* can take up one of *n* discrete states and where the average *equivalent binary content* per signal element is less than the theoretical maximum of $\log_2 n$. The percentage *redundancy* (1) of such a signal is given by the expression:

$$1 - \frac{r_e}{r_d \log_2 n} \times 100$$

where r_d is the *symbol rate* of the *n*-ary signal and r_e is the *equivalent bit rate*. Redundant *n*-ary signals are produced by line codes such as *alternate mark inversion, four binary – three ternary* and *MS43*.

reed contact unit Two overlapping reeds of magnetic material separated by a small gap and sealed in a glass tube containing an inert gas such as nitrogen. The reeds are made of a material such as a nickel – iron alloy, which has high permeability, low remanence and the required mechanical properties. The overlapping tips are plated with a material such as gold or rhodium, depending on the switching application. A reed contact unit operates when the reeds are magnetised by a sufficiently strong field produced by a coil, or in certain cases by a permanent magnet.

The unit described above is the simple make-contact unit, which is used in vast quantities in *reed relays* and switch matrices. Other varieties providing changeover action also exist.

reed electronic exchange An *exchange* using electronic techniques to control a switching network consisting essentially of *crosspoints* comprised of *reed contact units*.

reed relay One or more *reed contact units* enclosed in an operating coil. The advantages of reed relays include low cost, high speed of operation and release, low power requirements, and freedom from the need for adjustment or cleaning.

re-entrant trunking See *entraide*.

refer back A PABX facility associated with *hold for enquiry* whereby the extension user making the enquiry call is able to return to the original call while holding the third party for further reference or transfer. The user is thus able to alternate between the enquiry call and the original call, so the service is sometimes known as *shuttle* or *broker's call*.

reference burst In a *time-division multiple access* system, a discrete group of digits transmitted by a nominated earth station and serving to define the start of a *frame* (2). The reference burst is used by the other earth stations to control the times at which their own *standard bursts* are transmitted.

reference clock See *clock*.

reference equivalent Of a complete telephone connection, a figure in *decibels* giving the result of a comparison of the system's transmission performance with that of the CCITT's master system known as *NOSFER*. The measurement is based on a comparison of the loudness of received speech.

reference pilot Of a *carrier transmission* system, a single-frequency wave transmitted to facilitate maintenance and adjustment. Thus the levels of reference pilots can be readily checked, and they can be used for alarm purposes. A *group* [*supergroup*] reference pilot is applied where the group [supergroup] is assembled and accompanies it through the system up to the point where the group [supergroup] is broken down into its constituent *channels* [groups].

reference system for the determination of articulation reference equivalents See *SRAEN*.

reference telephonic power The volume that corresponds to the zero graduation of the speech-level meter forming part of the CCITT's master system for determining reference equivalents. A zero reading on this meter is obtained when a sinusoidal voltage of 800 to 1000 Hz at a level corresponding to 6 mW in 600 ohms is applied.

reflected binary code See *Gray code*.

reflecting surface Of an antenna, a conductive assembly having dimensions that are large compared with the wavelength for which the antenna was designed, and effectively forming a continuous surface that functions as a passive *reflector*.

reflection coefficient At a given point in a transmission line or medium, the ratio of the value of some quantity associated with a reflected wave to the value of that same quantity in the incident wave under specified conditions. In a transmission line the voltage reflection coefficient is often used, and is given by the complex ratio of the reflected voltage to the incident voltage. If the characteristic impedance of the line is Z_c and the terminal impedance is Z_t:

$$\text{Reflection coefficient} = \frac{Z_t - Z_c}{Z_t + Z_c}$$

reflection factor The ratio of the current delivered by a source to an unmatched load to the current that would be delivered to a load of matched impedance. Also known as *mismatch factor*.

reflection loss The ratio in *decibels* of the power delivered by a source to an unmatched load to the power that would be delivered under matched conditions. If the impedances of source and load have opposite phases and appropriate magnitudes, a reflection gain may be obtained.

reflective array antenna An *antenna* consisting of a feed and an assembly of reflecting elements arranged on a surface and adjusted so that the *phase* of the reflected wave from each channel is such that the array has a desired *directivity pattern*. Also known as a *reactive reflector antenna*. The reflecting elements are usually lengths of *waveguide* containing electrical phase shifters and terminated in short circuits.

reflector Of an *antenna*, one or more conductors or conducting surfaces positioned with respect to the *driven element(s)* so that radiation is increased in the desired direction and reduced in other directions.

reflector element Of an *antenna*, a parasitic element located behind the *driven element* with respect to the forward direction of radiation.

refracted wave That portion of a wave incident on a transition between two media that passes on into the second medium. Also called the *transmitted wave*.

refraction The phenomenon whereby the path of an electromagnetic wave is bent as it passes obliquely from one medium into another in which its velocity of propagation is different.

refractive index The ratio of the *phase* velocity of an electromagnetic wave in free space to that in the given medium.

refractive-index profile Of an *optical fibre*, a plot showing the value of the *refractive index* across a diameter of the fibre.

refractive modulus The difference between the *modified refractive index* and unity, expressed in millionths. It is represented by the symbol M, so the unit used to express its value is known as an *M-unit*.

refund key (US) The switchboard key used by an operator to return the money deposited in a prepay coin telephone.

regeneration In digital transmission, a process in which a digital signal that has suffered *attenuation* and *distortion* is used to control the generation of a new signal having the waveform and other specified characteristics of the original signal prior to its attenuation and distortion.

regenerative repeater A device for signal *regeneration* and other

230

ancillary functions.

regenerator A device performing signal *regeneration*.

regenerator section A *regenerator* together with the transmission path from the preceding regenerator or sending equipment. This term is now deprecated in CCITT contexts, being covered by (digital) *elementary cable section*.

regional centre (US) A class 1 office to which a number of sectional centres are connected; see *classification of exchanges*.

register (1) Generic term for a device that stores information in data-processing equipment and computers. (2) In automatic switching, apparatus that receives and stores dialled information that is then used to control the establishment of part or all of a wanted connection. In modern systems the register function often includes *translation* and the transmission of *signalling information*.

register recall signal A *signal* (2) sent by either the caller or the called party after a connection has been established, to indicate to the *local exchange* that the call should be held pending the receipt of further digits from the subscriber.

register signalling A method of signalling in which *signals* (2) are passed between *registers* (2) associated with a circuit during the call set-up phase.

register – translator In automatic switching, older designation for apparatus combining the functions of a *register* (2) and a *translator*.

regularity return loss See *structural return loss*.

regulating pilot A *pilot* used to control the *gain* of a transmission system. Pilots located at different frequencies may be used to control the attenuation/frequency characteristic—sometimes called the *slope*—of the system.

rejection filter See *band rejection filter*.

rejector circuit A parallel *tuned circuit* that offers a high impedance to currents of the frequency to which it is tuned, and a comparatively lower impedance to currents of other frequencies.

relative gain Of an *antenna*, for a given direction, with respect to a specified reference antenna: the ratio (usually expressed in *decibels*) of the power accepted by the reference antenna and the given antenna so that each antenna produces in the *far-field region*, at the same distance and in the same direction, a field component of the same *polarisation* (1) and magnitude. The reference antenna is assumed to be oriented so that its maximum *directivity* is in the given direction, the latter corresponding with the direction of maximum *radiation intensity* from the given antenna unless otherwise stated. Typical reference antennas are *half-wave dipoles, elementary electric dipoles, horns* and short *vertical monopoles.*

relative level (also known as *transmission level*) Of a signal, an expression in *decibels* of the difference between the power of the signal at a certain point in a transmission channel and the power of the signal at a specified reference point, usually the starting point of the circuit. It is thus a statement of the gain or loss between the two points. If an amplifier has a gain of 20 dB, the relative level of a signal at its output terminals will be + 20 dBr relative to its value at the input terminals. See also *signal level*.

relay Generic term for an electrically operated switch. The most basic form of electromechanical relay consists of one or more sets of contacts (make, break, changeover) that may be operated by passing a current through a coil. Such relays form an essential part of most switching systems, and versions that are (comparatively) slow to operate or release are produced by modifying the magnetic circuit. See also *reed relay*.

relay set In automatic switching, an item of equipment consisting mainly of *relays* which is usually allocated to a path to carry out certain functions such as *signalling*.

relay slug A conducting cylinder placed around part of the core of a *relay* to modify the establishment or decay of flux in the magnetic circuit.

relay switch A rectangular array of *crosspoints* in which the means of operation is individual to each crosspoint. Such a switch can be assembled from *relays*, as the name implies.

release The act of returning a *selector*, line, etc. from the busy state to the free state or, in the case of a *relay*, to the unoperated state.

release guard The protection of equipment from seizure or attempted use during the period that it is releasing.

release guard signal A *signal* (2) serving to protect a circuit or channel from seizure at its outgoing end while equipment at its incoming end is releasing, following the receipt of a *clear-forward signal*.

release wire In some automatic switching systems, a wire provided solely to control the *release* of *selectors*.

remanent relay A *relay* that is held in the operated state by magnetic remanence after the operating current is switched off, and that has to be released by the application of a reverse current.

remote concentrator A *line concentrator* (1) located at a point in the network some distance from the *exchange*.

remote manual board A manual board serving an automatic *exchange* located in another building.

reorder tone (US)   An audible signal used to advise a toll operator to make another attempt to complete a call, the previous attempt having failed owing to the unavailability of a free circuit, use of an incorrect code, etc.

repeat last number   A *callmaker* facility whereby the last number dialled may be repeated by pressing a button.

repeated call   A call that fails to find a free trunk owing to congestion, and is offered again after an interval of time.

repeated signal   In *analogue signalling*, a signal that is repeatedly transmitted as long as the condition it represents persists. If intervals are included to permit the reception of an acknowledgement signal, it is known as a *repeated-until-acknowledged signal*.

repeater   Generic term for apparatus inserted in a *line circuit* to amplify the signals therein. The term was first used in connection with telegraph apparatus consisting essentially of a *relay*, but is now widely used to describe amplifying equipment in audio and carrier circuits. See also *two-wire repeater, four-wire repeater, regenerative repeater, negative-impedance repeater* and *telegraph repeater*.

repeater distribution frame   A frame in a *repeater station* providing for the interconnection of amplifiers, transformers and signalling units.

repeater station   A building or a part of a building housing *repeaters* and associated equipment.

repeating coil   Old term for a *transformer*.

reperforator (also termed *receiving perforator*)   Telegraph apparatus consisting essentially of a linked receiver and *perforator* so that received signals cause the tape to be punched in accordance with the received characters. If the characters and symbols are also automatically printed the apparatus is termed a *printing reperforator*.

reperforator switching centre   A telegraph message-relaying centre equipped with *reperforators* feeding directly into transmitters, the outputs of which can be switched to various outgoing channels. If switching is done under control of coded routing details on the tape, the process is called automatic reperforator switching, as opposed to semi-automatic switching in which the outgoing channel is selected by an operator.

repertory callmaker or **repertory dialler** (US)   See *callmaker*.

repetition equivalent (US)   A measure of the transmission performance of a complete telephone connection, determined as a result of *articulation* tests and expressed as the loss of a reference system adjusted to give the same *repetition rate*.

repetition rate (US)   In telephony, a measure of the effectiveness of transmission over a *circuit*, given by the number of repetitions necessary per 100 seconds of conversation time.

reproduction ratio In *facsimile*, the ratio between the size of the recorded copy and the original document.

reproduction speed Of a *facsimile* receiver, the area of recording medium acted upon in unit time.

request repeat system In data transmission, a method of operation in which the detection of an error in a received message automatically initiates a request for retransmission of the erroneous signal.

re-radiation See *secondary radiation*.

rerouting Recommencement of *route selection* from the first point of routing control, when congestion is encountered at some intermediate switching point in the connection it is desired to establish. See also *alternative routing*.

residual error rate In data transmission, the ratio of bits, characters or blocks that are incorrectly received but are neither detected nor corrected by the *error control* system, to the total number of bits, characters or blocks transmitted. Also called *undetected error rate*.

resistance noise See *thermal noise*.

resistive attenuator See *absorptive attenuator*.

resolution In *facsimile*, a measure of the ability of a system to reproduce fine detail. Resolution in the direction of the *scanning lines*—longitudinal resolution—may differ from that perpendicular to the scanning lines, known as transverse resolution.

resonance In a *resonant circuit*, the condition in which the capacitive *reactance* balances out the inductive reactance. Since these are frequency-dependent quantities, resonance can only occur at a single frequency in a simple circuit consisting of an ideal inductor and capacitor.

resonant cavity In *microwave* technology, a space enclosed by conducting walls and so dimensioned that standing electromagnetic waves can be excited. A resonant cavity is effectively a *tuned circuit* operating at microwave frequencies.

resonant circuit A circuit consisting of an inductor and a capacitor connected in series or in parallel. At resonance the impedance of the series circuit falls to a low value while that of the parallel circuit rises to a high value.

resonant frequency The frequency at which the inductive reactance and capacitive reactance of a resonant circuit balance out. It is given by $f = 1/2\pi\sqrt{(LC)}$, where L and C are in henries and farads respectively.

resonant line An *open wire* or *coaxial line* that is an odd number of quarter-wavelengths long and is either short-circuited or open circuit at one end.

responsivity Of a *photodiode*, the current generated per unit of incident optical power of a specified wavelength, usually expressed in amps per watt.

restitution In telegraphy, the conditions assumed by the appropriate part of a receiving apparatus as a result of the receipt of the *signal elements* constituting a telegraph signal.

retiming In digital transmission, adjustment of the intervals between corresponding *transitions* of a digital signal by reference to a timing signal.

retrieval In *common-channel signalling*, the procedure for guarding against the loss of *signalling information* when a *signalling link* fails and changeover is initiated. Retrieval involves the retransmission of lost or mutilated messages.

retrograde orbit Of a *satellite*, an *orbit* such that the projection of the satellite on a plane through the equator rotates in the opposite direction to the earth.

return-current coefficient The *reflection coefficient* when the quantity concerned is current.

return loss At a discontinuity in a transmission system, the difference between the incident and reflected powers, or the ratio in *decibels* of these two quantities. This ratio is equal to the reciprocal of the magnitude of the *reflection coefficient*.

return-to-zero signal A digital signal in which the pulse length is shorter than the spacing between the symbols, so that intervals occur between successive symbols; see *Figures R.2* and *P.3* (*polar signal*).

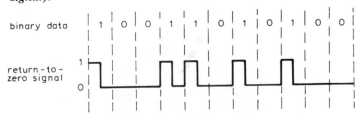

Figure R.2   Return-to-zero signal

reverse-charge call (US: *collect call*)   A call for which the called subscriber agrees to accept the charges.

reversed-frequency operation   A method of operating a point-to-point *radio relay system* whereby the frequencies used for transmission and reception by a station A are transposed by the relay station R so that the subsequent station B operates on the same frequency as A.

235

reversible antenna, reversible array   A *directional antenna* (array) with the property that the direction of the *main lobe* can be reversed by simply changing the feeding arrangements.

reverting call   A dialled call from one subscriber to another served by the same telephone line.

revertive control system   In automatic switching, a system in which the controlled devices feed back information to the controlling units to enable the latter to achieve their control functions. An example of such a system is one in which *registers* (2) control *selectors* by reference to position signals sent back by the selectors.

rhombic antenna   A *directional antenna* consisting of wire elements several quarter-wavelengths long arranged in the form of a horizontal diamond, which is connected to a feeder at one end and is terminated in its characteristic impedance at the other. See *Figure R.3*. Rhombic antennas have a number of desirable properties and are widely used in the HF band. The *directivity pattern* is a result of the combined radiation of the four sides

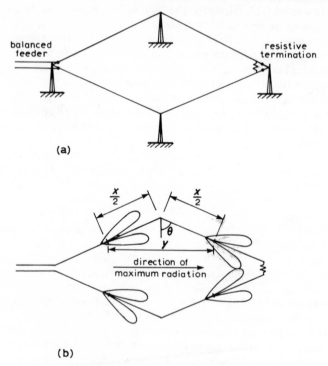

(a)

(b)

Figure R.3   Rhombic antenna: (a) general view, (b) plan showing major lobes of individual sides

considered individually as long-wire radiators—*Figure R.3(b)*. The *tilt* angle is selected in conjunction with the length of the legs, in wavelengths, to obtain a desired directivity pattern. Ideally one of the two **main lobes** of each wire's pattern should be in the direction of the rhombic's axis, and at the same time the radiation from the four lobes in this direction should add in phase. This latter requirement is met if the distance x along the wire between the midpoints of adjacent legs is half a wavelength greater than the direct distance y. In practice rhombics operate successfully over a frequency range of more than two to one without too large a change of directivity.

ridge waveguide A circular or rectangular *waveguide* with one or two longitudinal interior projections in contact with the wall, usually for the purpose of lowering the *critical frequency* (2).

right-hand polarised wave See *clockwise polarised wave*.

ring Of a telephone plug, the ring-shaped contacting part located immediately behind the *tip* but insulated therefrom.

ring-back signal A signal sent back to recall a subscriber whose line is held by an operator under a *manual hold* facility.

ring-back tone (US) See *ringing tone*.

ring down (US) The process in which ringing current is applied to a line to operate a device producing a steady signal (usually visual) to gain the attention of an operator.

ring-forward signal (US) See *forward-transfer signal*.

ring when free See *camp on*.

ring wire That wire of an *exchange* circuit which is connected to the *ring* of a plug or with the corresponding contact of a switchboard jack. Also termed *R-wire*.

ringer isolator (US) A device fitted at a *party line* subscriber's premises to isolate the ringer from the line at times when ringing currents are not present. This preserves line balance and prevents false ringer operation by induced longitudinal power-frequency currents. By extension, the term is applied to devices used at the station ends of high-resistance loops to provide both isolation and improved ringing capabilities.

ringing (1) In telephony, the process whereby an alternating or pulsating current is applied to a line to actuate a calling device such as a bell or lamp. (2) In video transmission, a damped oscillatory response following any sharp transition in the input waveform.

ringing tone (US: *ring-back tone*) An audible tone connected to a calling subscriber's line to indicate that the required service or subscriber's line is being rung.

ripple An alternating component of a direct current, usually having its origin in sources within the power-supply equipment.

Ripple may be caused, for example, by inadequate smoothing in rectifier equipment or may arise from the commutator action of a DC generator.

rise time Of a pulse, the interval of time between the instants at which the instantaneous amplitude passes through specified upper and lower limits, usually 10 per cent and 90 per cent of the peak amplitude. In the case of a pulse of radio-frequency energy, or of a carrier modulated by a pulse, it is the instantaneous amplitude of the envelope of the signal that is considered. The term is also used to describe the response of a receiver, amplifier, etc. to an input *step function*. The *equivalent rise time* is then the time that would be taken to attain the steady-state magnitude if the rate of increase were constant at the value corresponding to half the steady-state response. Also known as *build-up time*.

riser cable Vertical sections in the internal wiring of a building.

rotary attenuator A variable attenuator in a circular *waveguide* in which absorbing vanes are fixed in one section, which may be rotated about the common axis.

rotary joint A coupling device between two *waveguides* or transmission lines providing for the propagation of electromagnetic energy while one of the structures is rotated.

rotary selector See *uniselector*.

rotating-field antenna An omnidirectional antenna whose *phase function* for any direction in the horizontal plane is sensibly equal to the angle describing this direction. Such an antenna can be formed of two identical radiating elements oriented at right angles about a common axis of symmetry and fed in phase *quadrature*.

round-the-world echo Term applied to a radio signal that propagates around the world and reaches the receiving point after the direct signal. The signal is regarded as a *forward* echo if it propagates in the same direction as the direct signal and a *backward* echo if it propagates in the reverse direction. See also *echo*.

route (1) A group of *circuits* having the same terminating points. (2) A transmission path utilised for a call in a communication network.

route optimisation A PABX feature whereby the maximum use is made of any private network to which the subscriber has access. The equipment automatically routes calls over the private network whenever possible, regardless of the route selected by the extension user.

route restriction A PABX facility for checking the dialled digits from an extension against the *class of service* allocated to it, in order to prevent unauthorised calls from being made.

238

route selection The process of choosing one of several possible groups of paths suitable for a particular connection.

routiner Equipment that tests circuits and equipment automatically.

routing The selection, according to a *routing plan*, of paths through a network for calls or specific types of traffic.

routing code One or more digits used to direct a call towards its destination. The term is often applied to the digits produced by a *translator* in an exchange.

routing information Information required for *routing*, for example that part of a signalling message which defines the wanted earth station in a *satellite multiple access* system.

routing pattern (US) The *routing plan* applying to a particular automatic exchange.

routing plan An overall scheme for directing traffic through a network, taking account of any constraints imposed by transmission parameters.

S

SCARAB An unmanned submersible craft developed by an international consortium to assist in the recovery, repair and replacement of damaged submarine cables buried in the seabed. The term is an acronym for 'submersible craft assisting recovery and burial'.

SFERT Designation given to the CCITT's earlier European master system for the determination of reference equivalents, now superseded by the new system known as *NOSFER*. Values determined in accordance with SFERT are still valid, however.

SPADE Acronym for 'single-channel-per-carrier, pulse-code-modulation, multiple-access demand-assignment equipment'. The SPADE system was developed to make more efficient use of the transmission capacity of the Intelsat IV satellites, particularly in the provision of lightly loaded routes. Its essential feature is the creation of a pool of satellite circuits, each of which may be allocated for use between participating *earth stations* on a demand-assignment basis, i.e. only when actually required for traffic. Further economy in satellite capacity is achieved by making use of the fact that on average each (unidirectional) channel of a circuit used for speech is idle for over 50 per cent of the time. In the SPADE system each carrier is transmitted only when actually required for speech, so that the transponder in the satellite is able to handle a much larger number of circuits before overload restrictions apply. An outline description of the system is as follows.

The 45 MHz bandwidth of a single Intelsat IV transponder is used to derive eight hundred 45 kHz frequency bands, each of which can be occupied by a single carrier to form a unidirectional channel. Channels are associated in pairs to form slightly less than 400 circuits, because a small fraction of the bandwidth is reserved for control and signalling purposes. Participating earth stations are each equipped with a demand-assignment signalling and switching unit (DASS) and these units collectively control the operation of the system. They are linked by a common signalling channel (CSC), which is shared on a time-division basis. In this way information regarding the setting-up and clearing of calls can be exchanged and the DASS at each earth station is able to maintain a record of the circuits allocated for traffic at any given time. When a request for a circuit is received by a DASS unit it selects a pair of free channel frequencies and advises the distant station via the CSC of its choice. The DASS units at the other stations use this information to update their channel-utilisation records so that the selected frequencies are no longer available for new calls. The frequency selected by the DASS unit at the outgoing end is generated in a channel unit and used both as the outgoing carrier and as the local oscillator for the received signal (the channel pairings having been selected to make this possible).

Speech incoming from the terrestrial network is sampled 8000 times per second and the samples are encoded in accordance with CCITT Recommendation G711. Each sample is represented by a seven-bit word, so the bit rate is 56 kbit/s at the output of the PCM *codec*. Because the carrier is transmitted only when speech is present, each speech burst has to include additional bits to enable the distant receiver to acquire and hold word synchronisation. Timing, buffering and framing functions are performed by a synchronisation unit that has an output of 64 kbit/s. This bit stream is applied to a four-phase PSK *modem* to produce the modulated carrier. Both incoming and outgoing carriers pass through an IF sub-system, which interfaces with the earth station up and down converters. At the end of a call the controlling DASS unit releases the circuit and advises all the other units of the re-availability of the circuit.

SRAEN Designation for a high-quality, stable transmission system provided with means of calibrating its constituent parts in terms of absolute units, and used in the CCITT laboratories for measurements based on comparisons of *articulation*. The acronym derives from the French phrase for 'reference system for the determination of articulation reference equivalents'.

ST signal   See *end-of-pulsing signal*.

S-wire   See *sleeve wire*.

sacrificial anode   See *reactive anode*.

sample   The instantaneous value of a wave determined as a result of *sampling*.

sampling   A process in which a wave is examined, usually at regular intervals, in order to determine its value at each sampling instant. If sampling is carried out at a sufficiently high rate, the original wave can be completely reconstructed from the samples. Nyquist showed that the minimum sampling rate for satisfactory determination of a wave should be at least twice the highest frequency present in the wave. In PCM systems used for telephony, samples are usually taken at a rate of about 8000 per second since this corresponds with twice the highest speech frequency to be transmitted.

satellite   A body following a path about the centre of another body of preponderant mass, the motion of the satellite being determined primarily by the gravitational force exerted by the larger body. See also *communication satellite*.

satellite exchange   An *exchange* having trunk or junction circuits to only one other exchange, known as its *parent*. A satellite PABX usually has no operator's switchboard but may be provided with one or more outgoing-only exchange lines.

satellite link   A radio link between a transmitting *earth station* and a receiving earth station via a single *communication satellite*. Such a link is unidirectional and consists of one up-path and one down-path connected in tandem.

satellite multiple access   Any technique whereby a number of *earth stations* are able to share the transmission capacity of a *communication satellite*. See *frequency-division multiple access, time-division multiple access* and *SPADE*.

satellite network   One *communication satellite* and its cooperating *earth stations*.

saw-tooth keyboard   Of a telegraph instrument, a keyboard in which each key, on depression, engages with the sloping faces of teeth on the combination bars, thereby moving each of them directly into the desired position.

saw-tooth wave   A periodic wave whose instantaneous amplitude in each period increases or decreases in a linear manner with time and then returns quickly to its initial value. Such a wave is used for *scanning* and as part of a signal for measuring differential gain.

scanned element   See *picture element*.

scanning   (1) In automatic switching, the sequential periodic examination of the state of circuits and devices carried out by a common control system. (2) In *facsimile* transmission, the process in which the surface of a document is systematically examined by a reading head, which produces an electrical signal corresponding with the luminance of successive elements of the document. (3) In facsimile reception, the process in which a recording medium is acted upon element by element in accordance with the received signal, to synthesise a copy of the original document.

scanning density In *facsimile*, the number of *scanning pitches* per unit length.

scanning field In *facsimile*, the total area scanned by a reading or recording head in connection with the transmission of a document.

scanning line In *facsimile*, the area covered by the *scanning spot* in travelling from one side of the *scanning field* to the other.

scanning-line frequency In *facsimile*, the number of lines scanned in unit time. In the case of equipment using a drum this is equal to the number of drum revolutions in unit time.

scanning-line period The reciprocal of the *scanning-line frequency*.

scanning pitch The distance between the centres of consecutive *scanning lines*.

scanning speed The linear rate at which the *scanning spot* travels over a scanned document or recording medium.

scanning spot (1) In *facsimile* transmission, the elemental area of the original document examined at a given instant by the reading head. (2) In facsimile reception, the elemental area of the recording medium acted upon at a given instant by the recording head. Sometimes called *recorded spot*. (*Note* Generally the scanning spot is circular in shape. If it is not, the effective dimension in the direction of scanning is called the X dimension and that at right angles to the direction of scanning is called the Y dimension.)

scatter loss In an *optical fibre*, loss of optical power owing to the scattering of light by unwanted particles, bubbles or other inhomogeneities such as irregularities in the density and composition of the core and cladding materials. Most of the losses are caused by *Rayleigh scattering*, which is inversely proportional to the fourth power of the wavelength. Hence scatter loss is less important at wavelengths in the infra-red region of the spectrum, but it effectively prevents the operation of systems towards the blue end of the visible spectrum.

scattering In radio-wave propagation, dispersal of some fraction of the energy of radio waves propagating in a medium, owing to their encountering discontinuities or irregularities having dimensions of the order of a wavelength. Usually the scattered waves of interest are either those propagated in the same general direction as the incident radiation (called *forward scatter*) or those travelling in the opposite direction (called *back scatter*). See also *ionospheric scatter* and *tropospheric scatter link*.

scattering area or **scattering cross-section** Of an antenna excited by an incident plane wave with a specified *polarisation* and direction of propagation: the ratio of the total power that an *isotropic radiator* would have to radiate to produce a *radiation intensity* equal to that caused by re-radiation from the given antenna in a specified direction, to the power flux density of the incident wave.

scintillation (1) In radio-wave propagation, small random fluctuations of the instantaneous amplitude of a received signal about its average value. The effect is not really understood, but may be due to a mechanism similar to that causing the twinkling of stars, from which phenomenon the name derives. (2) Undesired rapid fluctuations in the frequency of a *carrier* wave.

scrambler (1) In telephony, equipment fitted in a subscriber's premises to modify the speech signals transmitted to line so that they are unintelligible until passed through a corresponding device at the distant subscriber's end. (2) In digital transmission, see *data scrambler*.

screening (US: *shielding*) The use of a barrier, usually composed of conductive material, to prevent electric, magnetic or electromagnetic fields from penetrating the screened area or to prevent such fields from escaping from that area.

screening (US) The process whereby calls can be accepted or rejected according to the line class or similar information.

scroll See *helix*.

second-channel response See *image frequency*.

second detector (1) In *superheterodyne reception*, the circuit that demodulates the intermediate-frequency signal. (2) In a double superheterodyne receiver, the frequency-changing stage between the first and second intermediate-frequency amplifiers.

secondary centre See *classification of exchanges*.

secondary radiation Radiation produced by a conductive or dielectric body subject to incident radio radiation. Such re-radiation is usually intended to augment that of a primary radiator (*driven element*) in a given direction or directions.

sectional centre (US) A class 2 office acting as a toll switching centre and usually connected to a number of primary centres, toll centres or toll points. See also *classification of exchanges*.

sectoral horn A *horn* of rectangular cross-section in which one of the transverse dimensions increases progressively towards the open end, so that two opposite sides are parallel and the other two diverge.

segmented encoding law In *pulse code modulation*, an *encoding law* providing an approximation to a smooth law by means of a number of linear segments.

seizing An action in which available equipment (e.g. a *switching stage* or a *circuit*) is engaged and taken into use, usually for the purpose of establishing a call.

seizing signal (US: *connect signal*) A *signal* (2) sent at the start of a call, primarily to prepare the incoming end of the circuit for the reception of subsequent signals. It may also have subsidiary functions, such as switching or the busying of the far end of a bothway circuit.

selecting In automatic switching, the process of choosing a particular path or device, usually in the course of setting up a call.

selection In telegraphy, part of the process of *translation* consisting of choosing the character to be printed or transcribed in accordance with the received signal.

selection signals In a data network, a sequence of characters providing all the information needed to establish a call, including any facility requests and/or the address (or addresses).

selective answering A switchboard feature such that a separate *call indicator* is provided for each group of circuits, e.g. extensions, exchange lines or inter-PBX lines. The calling indicators are *multipled* to each position so that an operator can select from which group of circuits calls will be answered. See also *common answering* and *individual answering*.

selective calling See *selective ringing*.

selective fading Fading which varies with frequency so that the components of a modulated wave are unequally affected and the received signal is distorted.

selective ringing A method of ringing used on *party lines* whereby only the bell of the required party is rung. Also known as *selective calling*.

selective squelch See *muting*.

selectivity A measure of the ability of a receiver to discriminate between a wanted signal on one frequency and unwanted signals on other frequencies.

selector (US: *bank and wiper switch*) The generic term for a switching device having either one inlet and many outlets or one outlet and many inlets. External or internal control elements may be operated to connect one inlet to one outlet.

selector level conference See *meet-me conference*.

244

self information   See *information content*.

self-supporting cable   An *aerial cable* incorporating a steel supporting wire in the sheath.

semi-automatic reperforator switching   See *reperforator switching centre*.

semi-automatic switching system or **semi-automatic telephone system**   A system in which the information needed to establish a connection is passed orally to an operator, who completes the call automatically.

sender   Apparatus that generates and transmits signals in response to information received from other equipment.

sending-end crossfire   See *crossfire*.

sensitivity   Of a receiver, a measure of the ability of the receiver to respond to weak signals, usually expressed as the minimum input signal level that will yield a specified *signal-to-noise ratio* at the output.

separator   In a CATV-type system, a frequency-dependent device such that signals occupying a band of frequencies at its input are divided between two or more outputs, each of which passes only those signals in a given part of the input frequency band. Some types of separator can be used in the reverse sense for combining signals.

septate waveguide   A *waveguide* consisting of two coaxial cylinders joined along their length by a metal plate.

sequential hunting   See *hunting*.

serial-to-parallel converter (US: *deserialiser* or *staticiser*)   A device that converts a sequence of digits presented to its input into a group of corresponding digits, each of which is presented simultaneously at one of its outputs.

serial transmission   A method of transmitting data in which the bits, bytes, characters or words comprising a signal are transmitted successively, usually over a single channel. It is possible, however, to transmit the words or bytes serially but the bits of which they are composed in parallel.

series call   A PABX facility whereby an operator can cause an incoming *exchange* line to be presented to the same position after each extension clears. In this way an incoming caller can speak successively to a number of extensions without making a further call. The service is also available to an extension user wishing to make a number of exchange-line calls in succession via the operator. Also known as *call chaining*.

series-loaded antenna   An antenna having one or more *reactances* in series with its radiating element(s) to modify the current distribution therein.

series resonance   Resonance in a circuit consisting of a coil and capacitor connected in series so that the inductive and capacitive *reactances* cancel out at the frequency of the applied voltage. In this condition the impedance of the circuit is purely resistive and the current through the circuit is in phase with the applied voltage.

series T (also known as *E-plane T junction*) A waveguide *T-junction* in which the *electric field vectors* of the *dominant mode* are everywhere parallel to the plane containing the longitudinal axes of the waveguides. In this case the impedances of the two side arms of the main guide are substantially additive when viewed from the leg of the T. A series T constructed from rectangular waveguide of the same dimensions has the leg projecting from one broad face of the main guide, the narrow faces of the main guide and the leg being in two common planes. See also *shunt T*.

server (US) In the teletraffic context, an item of equipment or a transmission path that responds to call attempts.

service (US) A measure of the overall performance of a telephone system in terms of *blocking* or *congestion*.

service area The area within which a radio transmitter provides a specified quality of service.

service bit See *service digit*.

service code One or more digits dialled by customers to obtain access to a service such as directory enquiries, *test desk* or long-distance operator.

service digit (1) See *service code*. (2) In digital transmission, one of the digits added to a digital signal (usually at regular intervals) to enable equipment to function properly, and sometimes to provide extra facilities; also known as an *overhead digit*.

service indicator In some types of common-channel signalling system, that part of a *signal unit* which identifies the user to which a *signal message* belongs, thus enabling it to be transferred to the correct *user part* at a signalling terminal.

service interception The diversion of a subscriber's incoming telephone calls to a monitoring or enquiry position in an exchange.

service observations Monitoring of calls to obtain information on the quality of service provided under normal traffic conditions, i.e. without using test calls.

service-oriented part See *user part*.

service signal In telegraphy or data transmission, a signal sent automatically to a calling terminal by the network to indicate why a call has not been connected.

serving area (US) In a *local line network*, a geographical area provided with telephone service via a particular flexibility point

246

known as a *serving-area interface*.

serving-area concept (US)   A plan for the provision of service in a *local exchange* area whereby the distribution network for each *serving area* is fully provided initially, ideally at least two *pairs* being available from each potential residence to the serving-area interface. This is a *cross-connection point* where the distribution pairs can be connected to pairs in the feeder cables to the exchange, as required. The scheme minimises expensive rearrangements of the buried distribution network, and is broadly similar to UK practice.

servophone   A specially developed loudspeaking telephone provided for customers whose mobility is severely restricted. It enables them to make and receive calls using only suck/blow techniques or light pressure on a switch to control the apparatus.

set   (1) To place a storage element, e.g. a bistable, into a specified state. (2) In path selection, to activate selected *cross-points*.

set-top converter   In a CATV-type system, a device that changes the frequencies used for the distribution of signals over the network to those for which the receiver was designed.

setting-up time   The interval of time between the initiation of a call and the instant when the called party answers.

shadow factor   (1) A measure of the reduction in field strength of a ground wave owing to the curvature of the earth, expressed as the ratio of the field strength that would result from propagation over a sphere to the strength that would result from propagation over a plane with the same electrical properties. (2) In a *reflector* antenna, see *shadow loss* (2).

shadow loss   (1) The attenuation caused to a radio signal by obstructions in the propagation path. (2) In a *reflector* antenna, the relative reduction in the effective aperture of the antenna owing to the masking effect of antenna parts, such as the feed obstructing the radiation from the reflector.

shannon   The unit of information in a binary scale, i.e. the amount of *information* that can be derived from knowledge of the occurrence of one of two equiprobable, exclusive and exhaustive events. In earlier years the term *bit* was used for this concept, since under the right conditions one shannon of information can be conveyed by a single binary digit. If there is any redundancy in a signal, however, the information rate and the bit rate are not the same. See also *information content*.

shaped-beam antenna   General term for a type of antenna designed to produce a beam having a well specified spatial distribution of *radiation intensity*; see for example *contoured-beam antenna*.

shaping network   An electrical network designed to process an input signal in such a way that the output waveform has a desired shape.

shared-service line Designation used in the UK for a local line providing service to two subscriber stations, each of which has its own meter and number. In North American terms this is equivalent to a *party line* with selective ringing capable of serving only two subscriber's stations.

shielded-loop antenna An *antenna* consisting of one or more turns of wire enclosed in a tubular cross-section screen in the form of a loop with a small gap in it.

shielding (US) See *screening*.

shift-lock keyboard A keyboard constructed so that a key cannot be depressed unless the appropriate shift key has been depressed.

shift pulse A pulse used to control the movement of data in a *shift register*.

shift register A binary logic element consisting of a number of storage cells so arranged that the state of each cell can be transferred to an adjacent cell in a preselected manner by the application of a *shift pulse* to the appropriate input.

short-code calling or **short-code dialling** See *abbreviated dialling*.

short-distance back scatter See *direct back scatter*.

shot noise *Noise* due to small random fluctuations in the value of a current.

shunt T (also known as *H-plane T junction*) A waveguide *T junction* in which the *electric field vectors* of the *dominant mode* are everywhere perpendicular to the plane containing the longitudinal axes of the waveguides. In this case the admittances of the two side arms of the main guide are substantially additive when viewed from the leg of the T. A shunt T constructed from rectangular waveguide of the same dimensions has the leg projecting from one narrow face of the main guide, the broad faces of the main guide and the leg being in two common planes. See also *series T*.

shuttle See *refer back*.

side circuit A circuit forming part of a *phantom circuit*.

side frequency The frequency of a wave component in a *sideband*.

side lobe Of an antenna, a radiation lobe other than the *main lobe* or the *backward lobe*.

side-stable relay A *polarised relay* with two stable states.

sideband interference or **sideband splash** (US) *Interference* from an adjacent channel in radio reception, or interference due to an imperfectly suppressed sideband in a line carrier system.

sidebands (1) The frequency bands above and below the *carrier* containing the wave components produced in the process of modulation. (2) The wave components in those bands.

In the case of amplitude modulation the upper sideband contains components with frequencies equal to the sum of the carrier and the modulating frequencies, the lower sideband containing the difference frequencies. Each sideband contains all the information in the modulating signal, leading to the concept of *single-sideband transmission*. With phase or frequency modulation, multiple pairs of sidebands are produced. In the case of modulation by a single-frequency tone, side frequencies spaced from the carrier by integral multiples of the tone frequency appear above and below the carrier. For low values of *modulation index*, where the frequency deviation is less than half the modulating frequency, the second- and higher-order side frequencies are comparatively small and the frequency band required for the signal is similar to that needed with amplitude modulation. For higher values of modulation index, such as those used for VHF broadcasting, the frequency interval in which the sidebands of importance are contained is approximately equal to the sum of the frequency deviation and the modulating frequency.

sidereal period of revolution   Of a *communication satellite*, the interval of time between two successive intersections of a line in a plane by the projection of a satellite on to this plane. The line in the plane extends from the centre of the earth to infinity. Both the line and the normal to the plane are fixed in relation to the stars.

sidereal period of rotation   Of the earth or other body in space, the period of rotation about its own axis in a frame of reference fixed in relation to the stars.

sidetone   The reproduction by a telephone receiver of speech and noise picked up by the associated microphone. Sidetone is normally suppressed to an optimum level by the use of a balancing circuit including an *induction coil*.

signal   (1) A phenomenon usually varying with time and conveying information (*Note*   An unvarying phenomenon such as a direct current can convey information by its very presence and hence may be classed as a signal.) (2) In the specific context of *signalling*, a signal conveys information relating to the establishment, control, supervision and release of a call. Inter-equipment signals are sometimes called *electrical signals* to distinguish them from the *tone signals* heard by subscribers.

signal adaptor   In a cabled television distribution system employing a non-standard method of transmission, a device for converting the signals into a form suitable for reception by a normal broadcast receiver.

249

signal component In AC *signalling*, any part of a signal that remains uniform in character throughout its duration. Spaces between pulses of current in a multi-component signal are therefore classed as signal components.

signal element Of a digital signal, a single part of the signal that can be distinguished from the other parts in a distinctive manner, for example by its nature, magnitude, duration, position in time, or a combination of some of these features. In the US the term is used to describe the part of the signal occupying the shortest interval in the *signalling code*; it is assigned unit duration and hence corresponds with the *unit interval*.

signal imitation In *voice-frequency signalling*, an effect caused by speech or other currents that are not genuine signals but have frequencies in the signalling band.

signal interval (US) See *unit interval*.

signal level The magnitude of a signal at a point in a telecommunication circuit. This can be expressed as an absolute power level in *decibels* relative to one milliwatt (dBm). It is also convenient, however, to express the value that the signal would have had if it had been measured at the starting point of the circuit or any other point of zero *relative level*. (By convention the reference power at the starting point is 1 milliwatt, so this is a 0 dBr point.) Signal levels expressed in this way are called 'absolute power levels referred to relative zero', the abbreviation used being dBm0. An absolute value in dBm is readily converted into dBm0 if the relative level of the measuring point is known.

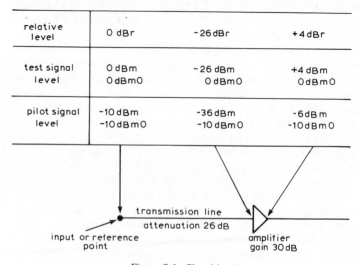

relative level	0 dBr	-26 dBr	+4 dBr
test signal level	0 dBm 0 dBm0	-26 dBm 0 dBm0	+4 dBm 0 dBm0
pilot signal level	-10 dBm -10 dBm0	-36 dBm -10 dBm0	-6 dBm -10 dBm0

transmission line
attenuation 26 dB

input or reference point

amplifier gain 30 dB

Figure S.1 Signal levels

250

Thus a signal of +30 dBm at a point of relative level of 20 dBr will have a value of +10 dBm0. *Figure S.1* should clarify the concept. See also *through level, relative level* and *terminated level*.

signal message In *common-channel signalling*, a message comprising *signalling information* together with associated *message-alignment indicators* and *service indicators*, where provided. A signal message is transmitted over a *signalling link* in the form of one or more *signal units*.

signal recording telegraphy Telegraphy in which the received signal elements are automatically recorded (for example on a paper tape) for subsequent interpretation by an operator.

signal spillover See *spillover*.

signal tilt In a CATV-type system, the difference in level between signals, deliberately established at some point in the system in order to counteract the slope of the following transmission line.

signal-to-crosstalk ratio At a specified point in a circuit, the ratio in *decibels* of the power of the wanted signal to the power of the unwanted signal, the signals being adjusted so that they are of equal *amplitude* at the points of zero *relative level* in their respective channels.

signal-to-noise ratio The ratio of the magnitude of a signal to that of the *noise* at some point in a circuit, usually expressed in *decibels*. This ratio is one of the most important parameters of any transmission system, and it is measured and expressed in different ways depending on the type of signal and noise concerned. With impulsive noise a peak-to-peak signal to peak-to-peak noise ratio is often used. In the case of random noise RMS values are generally used, but if the noise is in an audio channel weighted *psophometric power* may be the quantity measured. In the special case of a video television signal it is convenient to use the ratio of peak-to-peak signal (including synchronising pulses) to weighted RMS noise.

signal transfer point In a *common-channel signalling* network, a centre providing for the transfer of signals from one *signalling link* to another. The transfer process usually involves some change to the *routing information* in the signal but does not affect the signalling information itself.

signal unit In *common-channel signalling*, a group of information and check bits normally subject to a single error-detecting process. In the CCITT System No. 6 a signal unit consists of 28 bits, the last eight being used for error-detecting purposes. Signal units are termed *initial, subsequent* and *final* in the case of multi-unit signal messages, or *lone* in the case of a single-unit message.

251

signal-unit indicator Information in a *signal unit* that identifies its type.

signalling The transfer of information relating to the establishment, control and release of connections and sometimes of information concerning network management.

signalling channel In *common-channel signalling,* a *data channel* together with terminal equipment at its end. See also *signalling link*.

signalling code A set of rules defining the correspondence between *signalling* functions and the properties of the signals used to represent them.

signalling 500/20 A *signalling* system employing AC at a frequency of 500 Hz interrupted at a frequency of 20 Hz.

signalling information In *common-channel signalling*, that part of a *signal message* which contains information relating to a call, management action, etc.

signalling link In *common-channel signalling*, an assembly of two *data channels* operating together but in opposite directions to provide a bidirectional transmission facility for signalling data. A signalling link therefore consists of a *data link* together with terminal equipment.

signalling module An assembly of *signalling links* that act together to provide signalling facilities, including security, for a group of user circuits.

signalling path That part of a circuit which is used for *signalling* rather than speech.

signalling security In *common-channel signalling*, the ability to maintain a signalling capability in spite of equipment failure. Security arrangements generally take the form of the provision of one or more reserve *signalling links*, with automatic means of transferring signalling traffic to the standby link(s) without loss of information.

signalling system A specification defining the exact form of the *signals* (2) to be used for signalling, together with rules for their interpretation and use.

signalling time slot In *pulse code modulation*, a time slot occupying a defined position in a frame and used specifically for *signalling*. The slot may not be used in every frame. In the standard 24-hour channel system the first *digit time slot* of each *channel time slot* is available for signalling in every other frame. In the 30-channel system, however, channel time slot 16 is available for signalling information in 15 out of every 16 frames. (It is used for multiframe alignment purposes in the first frame of each *multiframe*.)

significant condition Of a digital signal, a condition of a *signal*

element the meaning of which is defined by an appropriate code. Telegraph codes are traditionally described by the number of distinct significant conditions used. Thus the *Morse code* is a two-condition code, the conditions being termed *mark* and *space* respectively.

significant instant Of a digital signal, each of the successive instants at which some defined feature of the signal occurs, for example the instants at which each *significant condition* is deemed to begin.

significant interval Of a digital signal, the ideal time interval between two consecutive *significant instants*.

silent listening Monitoring by an operator or supervisor with the microphone switched out of circuit.

silent period In AC *signalling*, the specified period during which no transmission of AC takes place immediately before or after the sending of a signal.

silent zone That portion of the *skip area* surrounding a transmitter that is not reached by the ground wave, so that the only signal available will be that due to *scattering* or anomalous propagation. Also called *skip zone*.

simple computation service A feature of some *stored-program control* PABXs whereby an extension user can carry out simple arithmetical calculations using the extension telephone keypad.

simple-ratio channels In *time-division multiplex* systems, channels that are connected to the common transmission path for periods of time bearing a simple ratio to one another.

simple signal In AC *signalling*, a signal consisting of the transmission of a single frequency only.

simplex A qualifying term denoting a capability for transmission in either direction over a *link* or *circuit*, but not simultaneously.

simplex circuit (1) A circuit operating in the *simplex* mode. (2) In America, a DC telegraph circuit obtained by using the two conductors of a *speech circuit* in parallel for one leg and earth return for the other.

sinad ratio (US) The ratio, expressed in *decibels*, of the signal plus *noise* plus *distortion* to the noise plus distortion at the output of a mobile radio receiver as a result of the reception of a modulated *carrier*.

sine-squared pulse A pulse having a shape equal to the square of one half-cycle of a sine wave. Mathematically the pulse is defined by $y = K \sin^2(t/2T)$ for values of t lying between 0 and $2T$, K being the amplitude and $2T$ the duration of the pulse. The half-amplitude duration of the pulse is then T. A sine-squared pulse is equivalent to one whole cycle of a cosine wave, starting and finishing at its negative peaks and lifted so that the peaks coincide with the zero line. The frequency of the cosine wave will be twice that of the sine wave, and the relationship is described by the trigonometrical identity $\sin^2 A = \frac{1}{2}(1 - \cos 2A)$; hence the alternative term *raised cosine pulse*. See also T-pulse and 2T-pulse under *waveform testing*.

singing Unwanted self-oscillation in a transmission system or *transducer* caused by *positive feedback*. In transmission systems singing is usually caused by poor balance at two-wire to four-wire connections. In amplifiers low-frequency singing is often called *motor-boating* and higher-frequency singing is termed *howling*.

singing margin Of a possible *singing* path, the excess of loss over operating gain at any frequency, usually expressed in *decibels*.

singing point The smallest value of gain that is just sufficient to make a circuit break into oscillation.

singing suppressor A speech-controlled device inserted in a *four-wire circuit* to provide sufficient loss in the forward and return channels to prevent the occurrence of *singing*. The occurrence of speech in one channel causes the removal of the loss in that channel but maintains the loss in the return channel.

single-ended synchronisation At a specified *synchronisation node* in a digital network, a method of synchronisation in which *synchronisation information* at the specified node is derived from the phase difference between the local clock and the digital signal incoming from the other node. Compare with *double-ended synchronisation*.

single-frequency operation (US: *single-frequency simplex*) A radio system in which the same frequency is used in both directions of transmission, so that only one station can transmit at a time.

single-frequency signalling A method of AC *signalling* in which the various *signal components* all have the same frequency within the telephone frequency range.

single-frequency simplex See *single-frequency operation*.

single-mode optical fibre See *monomode optical fibre*.

single-polarised antenna An antenna having a single port for connection to the feed line and intended to radiate or receive radio waves with only one *polarisation* (1). Usually the desired sense of polarisation is maintained only for certain directions or within the major portion of the antenna's beam.

single-sideband transmission A method of operation in which either the upper or lower *sideband* of an amplitude-modulated wave is transmitted, the unwanted sideband being filtered out. The *carrier* may be partially or wholly suppressed. Since one sideband contains all the information, this method of transmission reduces the **bandwidth** (2) required for transmission and makes more effective use of the available frequency band.

single-tone keying   A method of **keying** in which one **significant condition** corresponds with an unmodulated carrier and the other corresponds with modulation by a single-frequency tone.

single-unit message   A **signal message** transmitted within one **signal unit**.

single-wire transmission line   A form of **waveguide** consisting of a circular-section metallic conductor treated with a coating of a material, such as a dielectric, that has different electrical properties from those of the conductor. Also known as a **guide wire** or **goubau line**.

siphon recorder   A form of **undulator** using a fine siphon to feed the ink to the stylus.

skew   In **facsimile**, defective reproduction caused by a difference between the **scanning speeds** at the transmitter and receiver, so that lines that should be at right angles to the direction of scanning are inclined to it. It is expressed numerically as the tangent of the angle between the correct and reproduced directions of a line.

skew ray   In **optical-fibre** propagation, a ray that never intersects the axis of the fibre in the course of internal reflection. See also **meridional ray**.

skinner   The length of insulated wire between a connection to apparatus, e.g. a **jack**, and the laced cable form.

skip area   The area surrounding a transmitting **antenna**, determined by plotting the **skip distance** in every direction.

skip distance   For a transmission on a given frequency at a specified time, the smallest distance in a given direction from the transmitter at which reception by ionospheric reflection is possible. This normally excludes any reflection caused by **sporadic ionisation** of the **E layer**.

skip zone   See **silent zone**.

skipping   In the formation of a **grading**, a method of interconnection in which identically numbered choices of non-adjacent grading groups are joined together.

sleeve   Of a telephone plug, the cylindrical contacting part located immediately behind the **ring** (or the **tip** in the case of a two-pole plug) but insulated therefrom.

sleeve-control cord circuit   A **cord circuit** using the **sleeve wire** to control terminal apparatus associated with the line.

sleeve-control switchboard   A switchboard equipped with **sleeve-control cord circuits** having no transmission bridges.

sleeve dipole   A **dipole antenna** the central portion of which is enclosed in a coaxial conductive sleeve.

sleeve monopole or **sleeve stub antenna** An antenna formed of half a *sleeve dipole* projecting from a plane conductive surface.

sleeve wire That wire of an exchange circuit which is connected to the *sleeve* of a plug or to the corresponding contact of a switchboard *jack*. Also termed *S-wire*.

slicer A device or circuit arranged so that only the portions of an input waveform lying between two predetermined boundaries are passed on.

slip In digital transmission, an unwanted and uncontrolled loss or gain of a set of consecutive digit positions, owing, for example, to a momentary loss of *synchronism* (2). Formerly this term was also applied to a controlled loss or gain of digits in a digital network, for example the deliberate deletion of a complete frame when a buffer store is nearly full. The word *jump* is now applied to the latter process, however.

slipped banks *Banks* forming a *multiple* (2) and connected so that contact n of the first bank is joined to contact $n + 1$ of the second bank, contact $n + 2$ of the third bank, and so on.

slipping In the formation of a *grading*, a method of interconnection in which differently numbered choices of grading groups are joined together.

slope In the context of broadband transmission systems, a term deriving from an *amplitude/frequency characteristic* and used, for example, to express the difference in *decibels* between the values of *gain* of an amplifier at two specified frequencies. Similarly the term describes the difference in decibels in the *attenuation* between designated points in the network at two frequencies, usually those corresponding to the upper and lower limits of the band transmitted by the system.

slope overload distortion See *delta modulation*.

slot antenna General term for an antenna formed by cutting one or more correctly dimensioned slots out of a metal conducting surface. A slot one-twentieth of a wavelength wide by half a wavelength long in a large surface behaves like a *half-wave dipole* with the electric and magnetic fields interchanged.

slot radiator A slot cut in a conductive sheet, e.g. the wall of a *waveguide*.

slotted-cylinder antenna An antenna consisting of one or more slots in a cylindrical metal surface.

slotted-guide antenna An antenna formed from a length of waveguide containing one or more *slot radiators*.

slotted line or **slotted section** A length of *coaxial line* or a section of *waveguide* containing a longitudinal non-radiating slot through which a measuring probe can be inserted.

slow-scan TV transmission A technique whereby individual frames of a television signal may be transmitted in digital form over a standard data circuit, for example via the PSTN. The rate at which pictures can be displayed at the receiving end depends on the definition required and the data rate of the circuit, and hence may range from one picture every few seconds to one every few minutes. Such a rate is suitable for applications where real-time presentation is not essential, for example for security or traffic-surveillance purposes.

slug (1) Of a *relay*, a heavy sleeve of copper occupying part of the winding space and serving to lengthen the operate and release times by virtue of the eddy currents induced in it. (2) A movable metal core of a coil. (3) A piece of metal that can be adjusted longitudinally in a *waveguide* for impedance matching purposes.

smart multiplexer (US) In data transmission, a general term for *time-division multiplex* equipment incorporating intelligence in the form of a microprocessor, *stores*, etc., so that it can provide enhanced user facilities and/or make more efficient use of a common transmission path. See *adaptive multiplexer, statistical multiplexer* and *data compression*.

smooth traffic Traffic with a variance-to-mean ratio of less than one, so that the probability of a call arriving decreases with the number of calls in progress.

smoothing The process of reducing the amplitude of the *ripple* in a direct current.

software All the information in the form of *programs*, procedures and related data needed by a computer or processing system to carry out one or more specified tasks.

software multiplexing A technique whereby a computer can separate out time-division multiplexed data from a number of terminals by recognising the format used by each terminal. This avoids the need for a hardware demultiplexer, but *programming*, storage and machine-time costs are incurred.

solar array A group of interconnected *solar cells* arranged in a form convenient for exposure to radiation from the sun.

solar cell A photovoltaic cell that converts incident radiation from the sun directly into electrical energy.

solar flare A violent eruption on the surface of the sun, associated with sun spots and giving rise to intense radiation.

sound (1) Periodic vibrations, at a frequency in the audio range, propagating in a suitable elastic medium such as air, water or a metal. (2) The sensation produced in the brain when waves in the frequency range from about 20 Hz to 20 kHz impinge on the eardrum.

sound articulation See *articulation*.

sound-in-sync A method of transmitting the sound signal of a television program in the video signal in the form of *pulse code modulation* during the synchronising pulse intervals.

sound level The intensity of a sound at a given frequency, expressed as a weighted *sound pressure level* in *decibels* with respect to a reference pressure of 2×10^{-5} newtons per square metre. The weighting curve used in the measurement must be specified.

sound-level meter A microphone, amplifier, indicating-meter combination equipped with frequency-weighting networks and used for the measurement of *sound levels* in a specified manner.

sound-powered telephone A telephone using a moving-coil, permanent-magnet microphone to generate the audio-frequency speech currents.

sound pressure level The sound pressure in *decibels* relative to a reference pressure, which must be stated. As pressure is a field quantity, the sound pressure level is usually taken as 20 times the logarithm to the base 10 of the ratio of the pressure of the sound to the reference pressure. It should be noted, however, that this practice is not always strictly correct, since the sound pressure ratios are not always proportional to the square root of the corresponding power ratios.

sounder See *telegraph sounder*.

space One of the conditions in a two-condition telegraph code, the other being *mark*. In printing telegraphy the spacing condition corresponds to a passive operation of the receiving device.

space diversity The use of a number of physically separate paths for transmission of the same signal.

space-diversity reception The technique whereby a radio signal is received at two or more locations separated by a few wavelengths, the received signals being combined, selected, or both, in order to minimise the effects of *fading*, rain *attenuation*, etc.

space-division switching Switching in which connections between inlets and outlets of one or more *switching stages* are provided by a plurality of separate metallic paths.

space signal In alphabetic telegraphy, a signal consisting of a code combination that has the effect of advancing the printing position by one character without printing.

space wave A radio wave that travels between a transmitting antenna and a receiving antenna situated above the earth. It includes the direct wave and the ground-reflected wave.

spacing wave (US: *back wave*) In radio telegraphy, the radio wave transmitted during the spacing intervals of a telegraph code.

span That part of an overhead conductor or cable between two consecutive supports, usually poles.

spark killer (US) or **spark quench**   A circuit or device for reducing sparking at contacts operating in an inductive circuit.

speakerset   Apparatus associated with a customer's telephone to amplify incoming speech so that it can be heard by a group of people, or to permit the use of both hands by the user while the other party is speaking. Outgoing speech is transmitted via the handset in the normal way.

special assistance code   A code, other than the normal *access code*, giving the user of a selected extension the ability to call the switchboard.

special coinbox discriminating tone   A tone sent to an operator to indicate that a call is from a customer's coinbox.

special communication group   A selected group of PABX extensions enjoying special facilities such as *abbreviated dialling* between extensions in the group.

special dial tone   A different form of *dial tone* used to advise a customer that his line is unable to receive incoming calls owing to the operation of a supplementary service such as call transfer.

specific cymomotive force   The *cymomotive force* in the given direction when the power supplied to the antenna is one kilowatt.

spectral   A qualifying term relating to wavelength or frequency. Hence the spectral power density of a wave is the power density per unit of bandwidth.

spectral bandwidth   Of a *light-emitting diode, laser* or other light source: the difference between the wavelengths at which the spectral radiance is some stated fraction (usually 50 per cent) of its value at the peak wavelength.

spectrum   (1) A continuous band of frequencies within which waves have some common characteristics, for example the radio-frequency spectrum. (2) The distribution of the amplitude of the components of a complex wave as a function of frequency.

speech chopping (US)   See *speech clipping*.

speech circuit   A *circuit* suitable for the transmission of speech in analogue or encoded form. In practice such a circuit may be used for another service such as data transmission or voice-frequency telegraphy.

speech clipping (US: *speech chopping*)   The loss of the initial portion of a word or syllable owing to the action of a *singing suppressor, echo suppressor* or other speech-operated device.

speech digit signalling (US: *bit stealing*)   In digital transmission, *signalling* in which time slots used mainly for the transmission of encoded speech are used on a periodic basis for *signalling information*. In a typical system the eighth bit in each *channel time slot* is used for the signalling relating to that channel in every sixth frame.

speech frequency See *voice frequency*.

speech interpolation See *time-assignment speech interpolation*.

speed calling See *abbreviated dialling*.

spike A short-duration *transient* during which the instantaneous amplitude of a waveform considerably exceeds its average amplitude.

spillover In *voice-frequency signalling*, that part of a signal which passes through a switching centre before *splitting* takes place.

spillover factor Of a reflector antenna, the ratio of the power intercepted by the *reflector* to the power radiated by the associated feed.

spillover route See *overflow route*.

spiral four See *star-quad cable*.

splice (US) To join two or more cables together so that all the individual *pairs* are connected through and the jointing point is suitably protected.

splicing chamber (US) See *cable chamber*.

split An unwanted spacing condition of short duration occurring in the printing of a dot or dash in the reception of a Morse code signal.

split-type echo suppressor See *half echo suppressor*.

splitter In a cabled television distribution system, a device having one inlet and two or more outlets such that signal energy applied to the input is divided between the outlets in a desired manner.

splitting In *voice-frequency signalling*, short-term disconnection of the through-transmission path at a switching centre during the process of signalling. Splitting is used at the outgoing end of a link to prevent possible interference from previous links or equipment from affecting a transmitted signal. It is applied at the incoming end of a link as soon as the signal receiver recognises the beginning of an incoming signal, thereby protecting equipment in subsequent links from false operation by the signal. The period between the start of a signal and actual disconnection is termed the *splitting time*.

sporadic E layer An area in the E region of the *ionosphere* in which *sporadic ionisation* is of sufficient extent and continuity to form a temporary layer.

sporadic ionisation Abnormally intense ionisation of the atmosphere occurring in an erratic manner and caused by particulate radiation from the sun.

spur feeder See *feeder* (1).

spurious emission Any unwanted radio-frequency energy emitted by a transmitter.

spurious response In a receiver, any output due to signals having frequencies differing significantly from that of the signal to which the receiver is tuned.

square-law detection   The process in which the output voltage is substantially proportional to the square of the voltage of the input signal.

square wave   See *rectangular wave*.

squelch   See *muting*.

squint angle   The angle between the true direction of maximum radiation of an antenna and the direction that would be expected from theoretical consideration of the geometry of the antenna.

stabilisation   General term for a process whereby one or more parameters of a system are constrained to have stable values. Thus the gain of an amplifier can be stabilised by the use of a large amount of *negative feedback*.

stability   Of a *circuit*, the maximum amount by which the gain can be increased beyond the working value equally and simultaneously in both directions of transmission without causing *singing* or, in the case of a circuit fitted with a *singing suppressor*, without causing perceptible speech mutilation.

staff location system   See *paging service*.

stagger (US)   In *facsimile*, an effect caused by a periodic error in the position of the recorded spot along a *scanning line*.

staggering (US)   Adjustment of the frequencies of two *carrier* systems following the same route, so that the *sidebands* do not exactly coincide and the possibilities of mutual interference are reduced.

standard burst   In a *time-division multiple access* system, a discrete group of digits transmitted by a particular earth station and occupying a unique *time slot* in the *frame* (2). A standard burst begins with a preamble containing a timing pattern, station identification, signalling digits, etc. The remainder of the burst consists of digits representing encoded information, and it may be used for the transmission of speech, data, facsimile etc.

standard cable   A hypothetical cable with arbitrarily assigned parameters used in early telephone practice for specifying transmission losses.

standard frequency signal   A signal whose frequency has a specified relationship with a *frequency standard*.

standard M-gradient   The uniform increase in the value of the *refractive modulus* with height above the earth's surface that is taken as a standard for comparison and normally has a value of 0.12 M-units per metre.

standard noise temperature   See *noise temperature*.

standard propagation   The propagation of radio waves over a smooth spherical earth with uniform electrical properties under conditions of standard *refraction* in the atmosphere.

standard radio atmosphere An atmosphere with the *standard M-gradient*.

standard radio horizon The *radio horizon* that would obtain with propagation through the *standard radio atmosphere*.

standard refraction The *refraction* that would arise in a *standard radio atmosphere*. Higher and lower values are known as *super-refraction* and *sub-refraction* respectively.

standard refractive-modulus gradient See *standard M-gradient*.

standing wave In a transmission line, a stationary field pattern created by the interference between two waves of the same frequency propagating in opposite directions but in the same *mode* (2) along a uniform line or *waveguide*. Standing waves are produced when a wave is reflected from a discontinuity or mismatch. If the two waves are of equal amplitude the stationary pattern will have zero value at points called *nodes* and maximum values at points called *anti-nodes*.

standing-wave antenna An *antenna* for which the fields and currents giving rise to the *directivity pattern* can be regarded as the result of two or more waves travelling along the antenna in both directions.

standing-wave meter An instrument incorporating some form of detector for locating the position of *nodes* and *anti-nodes* and measuring the value of a field quantity at these points. The detecting device may be a crystal diode, thermocouple or *bolometer*, and may be capacitively coupled if the line is operating at a high power level.

standing-wave ratio In a transmission line, the ratio of the magnitude of a specified field component of a *standing wave* at an *anti-node* to its magnitude at an adjacent *node*, or the reciprocal of this ratio. Its value is given by $(1 + r)/(1 - r)$ (where r is the *reflection coefficient* at the discontinuity causing the standing wave) or by the reciprocal of this ratio, depending on usage. In general the definition yielding values greater than unity is used in the US, while the reciprocal is used in the UK. Use of the term *voltage standing-wave ratio* for this concept is now deprecated.

star-quad cable A cable containing *quads* each of which consists of four insulated conductors twisted about a common axis. The non-adjacent wires of a quad are used to form a *pair*. Also called *spiral four*.

start-dialling signal (US) See *proceed-to-send signal*.

start element A *start signal* consisting of a single element, usually having the duration of a *unit interval*.

start-of-pulsing signal (US: *KP signal*) A *line signal* sent forward

262

to indicate that *address signals* are about to be transmitted.

start signal In a *start-stop system*, a signal that precedes a character signal or block, and prepares the receiving equipment for the reception and registration of code elements.

start-stop distortion In a *start-stop system*, departure from the ideal timing of the *significant instants* in telegraph *modulation* or *restitution*, with reference to the significant instant of the *start element* immediately preceding them. The degree of distortion is usually expressed as a percentage given by $(A/B) \times 100$, where A is the maximum difference between the real and theoretical time intervals separating any significant instant from that of the start element preceding it and B is the *unit interval*.

start-stop margin The maximum degree of *start-stop distortion* permitting the correct translation of all character signals appearing singly or consecutively at the highest speed consistent with the standard modulation rate. If the latter is adjusted to the most favourable value with respect to the timebase characteristic of the machine under test, the figure obtained is called the *synchronous margin*.

start-stop modulation [restitution] Telegraph *modulation [restitution]* that is isochronous for each character or block but has an undefined interval between consecutive blocks or characters.

start-stop system A telegraph or data transmission system in which each equal-length group of code elements forming a *character signal* (1) or *block signal* is preceded by a *start signal* and followed by a *stop signal*.

static (US) See *atmospherics*.

staticiser (US) See *serial-to-parallel converter*.

station identification A facility for determining which of the subscribers served by a *party line* is making a call.

station-keeping satellite A *communication satellite* that is controlled in such a manner that its position relative to a fixed point on the earth or to other satellites in the same system remains substantially unchanged. Geostationary satellites have to be provided with station-keeping facilities because they may be attracted eastward or westward by non-uniformity in the earth's gravitational field. Also the combined effect of the gravitational pull of the sun and moon tends to move the orbital plane away from the earth's equatorial plane. Small thrusters are normally fired at intervals of about two months to correct the position of a satellite.

statistical multiplexer (US) In data transmission, *time-division multiplex* equipment that makes efficient use of the transmission capability of the common channel by allocating time slots only to active terminals, and by buffering and storing data at times when the total transmission capability is in use. Simpler fixed multiplexers allocate dedicated time slots to each terminal on a permanent basis, and since a terminal may be active for only a small percentage of the time the transmission capacity of the common channel is considerably under-utilised. Individual designs of statistical multiplexers differ, but they usually include facilities for *error control, data compression* and alternative modes of operation.

steady state   The condition existing in a circuit either when the magnitude of currents and voltages are constant or, if they are periodic, when they have a constant frequency and constant peak values.

steerable-beam antenna   An *antenna* in which the direction of the *main lobe* can be changed either by mechanical means or by varying the excitation of its various elements. See also *musa array*.

step-by-step automatic system   A switching system in which the *selectors* are operated in succession in response to trains of pulses.

step-by-step selector   A *selector* having electromagnetic ratchet mechanisms for moving the *wipers* into engagement with the *bank*. The wipers may move in one or in two senses.

step function   A signal having zero value for all time up to a certain instant, and a constant finite value immediately after that instant. Such a signal is useful for testing the *transient response* of amplifiers and similar apparatus.

stepped-index fibre   An *optical fibre* in which there is an abrupt change of *refractive index* at the core/cladding interface; see *monomode optical fibre* and. *multimode stepped-index optical fibre*.

stepped stop-start system   A *start-stop system* in which the start signals are constrained to occur at regular intervals.

stepper (US)   An *exchange* using *step-by-step selectors*.

stimulated emission of radiation   A phenomenon occurring in the atoms of certain paramagnetic materials, whereby electrons that have been raised to an unstable high-energy state revert to their equilibrium state under the stimulus of an applied electro-magnetic field, radiating energy as they do so. The process may be explained with reference to the laws of quantum physics that define the interaction between electromagnetic radiation and the electrons inside individual atoms. According to these laws electrons can exist inside an atom only at certain discrete energy levels, the values of which are characteristic of the element concerned. An electron can move from one energy level to

264

another only if a *quantum* of energy is emitted or absorbed by the atom. In the case of electromagnetic radiation the quantum corresponds to a *photon*, the value of which is a function of frequency. It follows that for each pair of energy levels there is an appropriate resonant frequency at which an applied field will lift electrons from the lower to the higher level. Conversely, if the applied field is removed the electrons will fall back to the lower level, emitting energy at the resonant frequency in the process. The way in which this phenomenon is used to provide amplification in a ruby *maser* is explained below.

In a solid-state ruby maser the active atoms are triply-ionised atoms of chromium dispersed in a crystal of aluminium oxide. There are four energy levels in the ionised atoms, and hence six resonant frequencies corresponding to the transitions between the various levels. Under equilibrium conditions the electron population in the crystal at each energy level will be greatest at the lowest level (L1), and will be successively smaller at each higher level. If a microwave field at the resonant frequency corresponding to an L1/L3 transition is applied to the crystal, electrons will be lifted up to saturate level 3 and the population at level 1 will fall to a value smaller than that at level 2, i.e. there will be a temporary population inversion. If the crystal is now subjected to an electromagnetic field at the frequency corresponding to an L2/L1 transition the excess electrons will be stimulated to revert to level 1, giving up energy to reinforce that of the signal. In practice, microwave power at a frequency of about 30 GHz is supplied by an oscillator to pump the electrons to the higher level, the signal frequency corresponding to the L2/L1 transition being about 4 GHz. The values of the energy levels in the atom, and hence the frequencies of operation, can be adjusted by varying the strength of a permanent magnetic field in which the crystal lies.

stop element   A *stop signal* consisting of a single element having a duration equal to or greater than a specified minimum value.

stop signal   In a *start-stop system*, a signal that follows a character signal or block, and prepares the receiving equipment for the reception of a subsequent character signal or block.

storage keyboard   A telegraph *keyboard* in which the combination selected by depression of a key is stored for subsequent control of a transmitter.

store   The generic term for equipment in which data can be placed and retained, and from which it can be retrieved. Although store is the internationally approved term for this concept, the term *memory* is also widely used, and because it forms part of abbreviations such as RAM, PROM, etc. such usage is likely to continue. A store whose content can be changed is known as an *erasable store*, in contrast with a *permanent store*.

store-and-forward switching   See *message switching*.

stored-program control   A method of control realised by storing the appropriate instructions in the form of a *program* held in an electrically alterable *store*. The term is in general use to describe modern processor-controlled switching systems, which may differ widely in architecture and size but which all enjoy a number of advantages resulting from this method of control. The principal advantage is the ease with which new subscriber facilities can be introduced and exchange functions can be amended, such changes only requiring new programs to be written into the appropriate program stores.

straight banks   *Banks* forming a *multiple* (2) in which any given contact of one bank is connected to the identical contact on all the other banks.

straight receiver   A simple receiver in which signals are amplified at the received frequency and then undergo detection. Sometimes known as a *tuned radio frequency* (t.r.f.) receiver.

string   In data processing, generic term for a series of entities such as characters, symbols or binary digits.

strip line   A *transmission line* for use at UHF and microwave frequencies, and consisting of a conducting strip above a parallel conducting surface or between extended parallel conducting surfaces. The conducting strip is normally separated from the ground plane (or planes) by dielectric material, the strip line being formed by the techniques used to manufacture printed wiring boards. Also known in the US as *microstrip* and *strip-type transmission line*.

strobe   The action of selecting a desired epoch in a recurrent phenomenon, e.g. some part of a periodic signal.

Strowger selector   An electromechanical, two-motion *step-by-step selector* in which the wipers first move vertically so that each is opposite a given arc of bank contacts and then rotate to engage with these contacts.

structural return loss   A measure of the loss caused by lack of uniformity in the characteristics of a *coaxial cable* as a result of irregularities in its structural geometry. The irregularities give rise to the generation of forward and backward *echoes*, which represent a loss of signal energy. Because this loss is analogous to that caused by a mismatch between a source and a load, the result is described in terms of a *return loss*. The irregularities present along a length of cable can be separated into minor variations distributed in a random manner and larger changes occurring periodically as a result of the repetitive nature of the manufacturing process. Some cables also exhibit non-uniform characteristics as a result of their design, for example variations caused by the spacers present in a semi-airspaced cable.

In general echoes caused by small random irregularities have an insignificant effect on signals transmitted over cables. Periodically distributed variations in structure, on the other hand, can cause significant transmission impairments because their effects are additive at certain frequencies. A plot of the return loss of a cable as a function of frequency is often called a *regularity return loss* characteristic, and such a plot is a useful indication of a cable's performance. Regularity return loss can be measured using a swept-frequency sine-wave oscillator as a test signal source, the cable impedance being referred to a reference standard by a hybrid bridge technique. This method is useful for tests on low- and medium-quality cables but suffers from limitations due to errors produced by test leads, connectors, etc., and from the masking effects of any large impedance changes at joints, etc. A more sensitive method suitable for testing high-quality cables is known as the CW burst technique because the test signal is generated in bursts under the control of a pulse generator. By adjusting the burst length and using a sampling technique to detect the returned signal, spurious results due to the test equipment can be eliminated. Moreover, any particular portion of the cable can be tested so that the masking effect of joints etc. can be avoided. Even this method gives only near-end information, however, and the results cannot be used to predict the values of forward echoes with any real degree of accuracy. Since knowledge of this parameter is important in the context of digital transmission, other methods of measuring it have been developed; see *excess-attenuation testing* and *through-pulse-echo testing*. See also *forward echo*.

stub or **stub tuner**   A short adjustable length of transmission line open- or short-circuited at one end and connected in series or parallel with the main transmission line at the other end.

stuffable digit time slot   See *justifiable digit time slot*.

stuffing digit   See *justifying digit*.

stuffing rate   See *justification rate*.

stuffing ratio   See *justification ratio*.

stuffing service digit   See *justification service digit*.

sub-audio frequency   See *infrasonic frequency*.

sub-carrier   A *carrier* modulated in an intermediate process and then applied as part of the modulating signal used to modulate another carrier.

sub-frame   In *pulse code modulation*, sets of digit time slots distributed in a *frame* (1), each set being repeated at a whole

267

multiple of the frame repetition rate.

sub-group In carrier telephony, an assembly of *n* channels by *frequency-division multiplex*, where *n* is a sub-multiple of twelve.

sub-harmonic frequency A frequency that is some integral fraction of the frequency of a reference wave, which must be non-sinusoidal in character. Sub-harmonic components are produced in some forms of *non-linearity distortion*.

sub-refraction See *standard refraction*.

subscriber-busy signal A *signal* (2) sent back from the *exchange* nearest to the called party to indicate that the subscriber's line(s) is (are) busy. This causes the exchange nearest to the calling party to connect *busy tone* to this line. Some systems do not employ this signal but return busy tone to the caller directly from the exchange nearest to the called party.

subscriber loop (US) See *subscriber's line*.

subscriber loop carrier (US) See *subscribers carrier system*.

subscriber loop multiplex (US) Designation for a *pair gain system* that combines the technique of *concentration* by switching with *time-division multiplex* transmission to enable 80 subscribers to be given service over four pairs of wires.

subscriber trunk dialling The term used to describe the direct dialling of trunk calls in the UK.

subscribers carrier system (US: *subscriber loop carrier*) General term for any *pair gain system* using two or more modulated *carriers* to connect two or more subscribers to a *local exchange* over a single pair. The most common version of the technique is the simple 1 + 1 system in which one subscriber is served in the usual way at *audio frequency*, the other being served by two amplitude-modulated carriers, one for each direction of transmission. Power for the remote *modem* is provided by a nickel – cadmium battery, which is trickle-charged over the line.

Other systems serving up to eight subscribers over a single pair are in widespread use. Usually the pair is not used for transmission at audio frequencies, but line-powered repeaters may be used to provide both range extension and pair gain. More recently systems employing digital transmission have been developed, and these are usually compatible with the hardware such as *regenerators* used with standard PCM systems. A *four-wire circuit* is required between the remote terminal and that at the exchange; since a spare is normally provided, at least four pairs are required per system. However, as many as 256 subscribers can be served in this way, so it may sometimes be possible to close a small rural exchange and give the subscribers service from a nearby local exchange.

subscriber's feeder In a CATV system, a connection from a *subscriber's tap* to a system outlet or directly to a receiver. In the latter case equipment such as *filters* may be included.

subscriber's line (US: *subscriber loop* or *access line*) The circuit that connects a subscriber with the *local exchange*. Owing to the use of *pair gain systems* in the *local line network*, a subscriber's line does not necessarily consist of a physical pair of wires.

subscriber's meter A meter associated with a subscriber's calling equipment in an *exchange* to record the call units chargeable to the subscriber.

subscriber's multiple In a manual exchange, the assembly consisting of banks of telephone *jacks* giving outgoing access to *subscribers' lines*. Each line is terminated on a number of jacks connected in parallel and arranged so that at least one can be reached from each switchboard position.

subscriber's store A *store* in which basic data relative to each subscriber may be held, e.g. line category and *class of service*.

subscriber's tap In a CATV-type system, a device such as a *directional coupler* or a resistive tap whereby some fraction of the signal energy in a *spur feeder* is transferred to a *subscriber's feeder*.

subscriber's uniselector A *uniselector* permanently associated with a *subscriber's line* and used to connect it to a free outlet when the subscriber makes a call.

subsequent address message In *common-channel signalling*, a message following the initial address message and containing one or more additional digits of the *address information* and/or the *end-of-pulsing signal*.

subsequent signal unit See *signal unit*.

subsonic frequency See *infrasonic frequency*.

sub-synchronous satellite A *satellite* having a mean *sidereal period of revolution* about its primary body that is a sub-multiple of the *sidereal period of rotation* of the primary body about its own axis.

sub-telephone frequency A frequency below a specified *telephone frequency* band.

sudden ionospheric disturbance A short-lived abnormal increase of the ionisation in the D and E regions of the *ionosphere*, resulting in a sudden radio fade-out.

suffix Of a multi-component signal, that part of the signal which follows the prefix and conveys the required *signalling information*.

super-audio frequency See *ultrasonic frequency*.

superdirectivity A property exhibited by an antenna when its *directivity* in certain directions is markedly higher than the gain obtained with a uniform distribution of the amplitude and phase of the currents in correctly located elements or with a uniform-*aperture* (3) illumination. Superdirectivity is usually obtained when the amplitude and phase of currents or the field over the aperture exhibit rapid variations over distances that are small compared with the operating wavelength, and it results in poor overall efficiency.

supergroup (1) A 60-channel assembly consisting of five *groups* (1) occupying adjacent positions in the frequency spectrum of a carrier transmission system. (2) A standardised 240 kHz frequency band of a carrier transmission system. (3) An abbreviation for a *supergroup link* (see *link*) together with the terminal equipment at its ends.

supergroup distribution frame In a *frequency-division multiplex* carrier system, a frame providing for the interconnection of apparatus transmitting signals with frequencies in the basic *supergroup* range.

supergroup link See *link*.

supergroup reference pilot See *reference pilot*.

supergroup section See *link*.

supergroup translating equipment In a *frequency-division multiplex* carrier system, apparatus that frequency-translates and assembles a number of basic *supergroups* in adjacent positions in a specified frequency range, or carries out the reverse process.

superheterodyne reception A method of radio reception in which the received signal is frequency-changed to an intermediate frequency, usually having a value lower than that of the signal, so that adequate gain and selectivity are more easily obtained.

superimposed ringing A form of *party line* ringing using a combination of alternating and direct currents, both positive and negative, to obtain *selective ringing*.

supermastergroup A 900-channel assembly consisting of three *mastergroups* occupying adjacent positions in the frequency spectrum of a *frequency-division multiplex* carrier transmission system.

superposed circuit An additional *circuit* obtained by using one or more wires of other circuits in such a manner that all the circuits can be used simultaneously without interfering with one another. See also *phantom circuit*.

super-refraction See *standard refraction*.

super-regenerative reception A method of radio reception in which *positive feedback* is used to increase the sensitivity and selectivity of the detector circuit, oscillations alternately being allowed to build up and being quenched at a frequency above the audio range.

270

supersonic frequency See *ultrasonic frequency*.

super-synchronous satellite A *satellite* having a mean *sidereal period of revolution* about its primary body that is an integral multiple of the *sidereal period of rotation* of the primary body about its own axis.

super-telephone frequency A frequency above the band of frequencies effectively transmitted by a given telephone system.

super-trunk feeder In a CATV system, a term proposed for feeders used to interconnect *head ends* or to interconnect a head end and the first *distribution point* in a system.

super-turnstile antenna An antenna consisting of one or more tiers of crossed *batwing antennas* with vertical slots, fed in phase *quadrature* with equal currents to produce a substantially omnidirectional *directivity pattern*.

supervision The process of monitoring and controlling an established call.

supervisory processor A functional unit responsible for call control, including *signalling* and metering.

supervisory relay A *relay* that is actuated by the current fed to a line during a call, and that responds to the signals generated by the subscriber.

supervisory signal The general term for a *signal* (2) used during a call to indicate the state of a *channel, circuit* or other traffic-carrying means.

supervisory tones The audible signals sent to advise callers or operators of the state of a line or other traffic-carrying means.

suppressed antenna See *flush-mounted antenna*.

suppressed-carrier operation A form of amplitude-modulated transmission in which the *carrier* is not transmitted.

suppression loss Of an *echo suppressor*, the specified minimum loss in *decibels* introduced into the return channel to suppress echo.

surface duct See *tropospheric duct*.

surface wave An electromagnetic wave that travels along a surface separating two media in a manner determined by the shape of the surface, the properties of the media, or a combination of these factors.

surface-wave antenna An *end-fire antenna* the radiation from which can be considered to result from an electromagnetic wave travelling along the surface of the antenna or an imaginary surface associated with it.

surface-wave transmission line Deprecated term for *single-wire transmission line*.

suspension strand See *messenger cable*.

switch In an automatic exchange, a device consisting of an

271

assembly of *crosspoints* that may be externally controlled to connect one of a plurality of inlets to one of a plurality of outlets. The term is also used in the US to describe a complete switching system.

switch-hook   A switch forming part of a telephone instrument and operated by the removal of the receiver or handset from its rest position. Sometimes called *cradle switch*.

switchboard   In a manual exchange, a suite of operators' positions from which the interconnection of lines is controlled.

switchboard position   That part of a *switchboard* normally staffed by a single operator.

switchboard section   A structural unit comprising one or more operating positions.

switched range extension   A facility provided by some types of *exchange* whereby range-extension capability is built into the system, the necessary amplifiers being located behind a concentrating switching stage so that their cost is shared by more than one line. See also *range extender*.

switching   Generic term for the process of establishing a transmission path from a particular inlet to a particular outlet of a set of inlets and outlets.

switching centre   A generic term applied to points in a telecommunication network at which *switching* is carried out. See also *exchange* and *classification of exchanges*.

switching congestion   Congestion resulting from inadequacies in *switching* equipment.

switching matrix   An array of *crosspoints* in the form of a matrix in which a given inlet (matrix row) has access to a given outlet (matrix column) via the crosspoint located at the intersection of the row and column in question.

switching network   The *switching stages* and their interconnecting cables in a *switching centre*. Such a network is termed *homogeneous* if every connection between an inlet and an outlet uses the same number of *crosspoints* and *heterogeneous* if different connections may use different numbers of crosspoints.

switching-network plan (US)   See *trunking diagram*.

switching node   A point in a network where *switching* may be carried out.

switching path   A unidirectional means of transmission through a *switching stage* or network.

switching pilot   A *pilot* used to busy the channels of a *carrier transmission* system or to effect a changeover to standby facilities.

switching stage   An assembly of *switches* forming part of a *switching centre* and designed to operate as a unit from the traffic-handling point of view.

switching tone   An audible signal sent to a subscriber or PABX extension user to indicate that his dialled instructions relating to a service such as *call back* or *call diversion* have been received and will be acted upon.

syllabic companding   *Companding* in which the mean level of the signal (over a period commensurate with the duration of a syllable) controls the degree of amplification used in the compression and expansion processes.

syllable articulation   *Articulation* measured using meaningless syllables as the speech units.

symbol   An agreed representation for a concept. A symbol may consist of a single letter, figure, punctuation mark, etc. In the context of digital transmission the word is used to describe a discrete condition assumed by a signal during a *unit interval.*

symbol rate   In the line transmission of digital signals, the number of *symbols* per second. Since each symbol occupies a *unit interval* the symbol rate is numerically equal to the reciprocal of that interval in seconds, and its value is expressed in *bauds.* The term therefore has the same meaning as *modulation rate* in telegraphy.

symmetrical antenna (also termed *symmetrical radiator*)   An *antenna* or *radiating element* consisting of two geometrically similar parts symmetrically disposed on either side of a zero-potential plane and fed symmetrically with respect to this plane.

symmetrical binary code   In *pulse code modulation*, a code in which one digit represents the sign of a quantised sample, the remaining digits constituting a binary number describing its magnitude. Sometimes called *folded binary code.* This method is usually preferred to straight binary (in which the scale of *quantising intervals* from maximum negative to maximum positive is represented by a sequence of binary numbers taken in order) because errors occurring in the most significant digits cause less *click noise* with low-level audio signals.

symmetrical channel   In a public data network, a *channel* in which the send and receive directions of transmission have the same *data signalling rate.*

symmetrical grading   See *grading* (2).

symmetrical radiator   See *symmetrical antenna.*

synchronisation (1) Of rotating machines, a process of adjustment whereby the machines are constrained to run at the same speed. (2) Of signals, a process of adjustment whereby the signals are constrained to be synchronous. By common usage the term is also applied to the process whereby digital signals are made to be *mesochronous*; see *synchronised network.*

synchronisation information In a *digital network*, information obtained by comparing the *phases* of the *clocks* in the network.

synchronisation link In a *digital network*, a selected transmission path joining two *synchronisation nodes* and used for the derivation of *synchronisation information* at one or both nodes. Such a link is termed an *effective synchronisation link* at any node at which synchronisation information derived from it is used to influence the frequency of the *clock* at that node.

synchronisation network A dedicated network consisting of an arrangement of *synchronisation links* and *synchronisation nodes*, and used to synchronise the *clocks* at those nodes.

synchronisation node A point in a *digital network* at which *clock* frequency control information is derived.

synchronisation signal unit In *common-channel signalling*, a *signal unit* containing a distinctive bit pattern that facilitates the rapid establishment of *synchronism* (2) between sending and receiving terminals in a signalling network. Signal units of this kind may also be sent over a *signalling link* to maintain synchronism at times when no signal messages are available for transmission. See also *idle signal unit*.

synchronised network A digital network in which the *clocks* are controlled with the objective of giving them identical rates and specified *phase* relationships. In practice this ideal synchronous condition may not be obtained and the clocks may be *mesochronous*; in common usage such networks are often described as *synchronised*.

synchronised satellite A *communication satellite* controlled so that successive passes through a characteristic point in its orbit occur at specified instants.

synchronising The act of bringing rotating machines or signals into a desired *phase* relationship.

synchronising pilot A *pilot* used to synchronise the oscillators of a *carrier transmission* system or to provide a means of comparing the frequencies and the *phases* of the waves generated by those oscillators.

synchronising signal Any signal used to establish and maintain a desired state of *synchronism* (2).

synchronism (1) In *facsimile telegraphy*, the desired state in which there is identity in frequency and correspondence in *phase* between the scanning process at the transmitting and receiving ends of a system. (2) The state existing when two oscillations have the same frequency and the phase angle between them is zero.

synchronous correction In telegraphy or data transmission, the process whereby the receiver in a *synchronous system* is maintained in a desired *phase* relationship with the transmitter.

synchronous idle character In synchronous data transmission, a control character transmitted to establish *synchronism* (2) between data terminal equipments or to maintain it when no other character is being transmitted.

synchronous margin See *start-stop margin*.

synchronous signalling In *common-channel signalling*, a method of operation in which information in the form of a continuous stream of *signal units* is transmitted at a uniform bit rate over a *signalling channel*, the receiving terminal being operated with the correct time relationship for satisfactory reception of the signal units.

synchronous signals (1) Sine waves having the same frequency and a constant *phase* relationship. (2) Digital signals whose corresponding signal *transitions* have a constant phase relationship.

synchronous system A telegraph, data or PCM system in which the equipment at the transmitting and receiving points is operated continuously at the same rate and with a fixed *phase* relationship.

system routing code (US) In world-zone 1, a code identifying an international switching centre and consisting of the *country code* (i.e. 1) followed by two additional digits.

systematic distortion Of data and telegraph signals, the average distortion occurring when a given signal is repeatedly transmitted through the same system. See also *bias distortion* and *characteristic distortion*.

systematic parity-check codes In data transmission, error control codes in which *parity bits* are generated in conformance with prescribed rules and *information bits* are always transmitted without change.

T

T-antenna An *antenna* consisting of a horizontal conducting element insulated at its ends and connected at its midpoint to a down lead. The element may be made up of a number of conductors connected in parallel.

TE mode A propagation *mode* (2) in a waveguide in which the longitudinal component of the electric field is everywhere zero, and the longitudinal component of the magnetic field is not. For the latter reason this mode has been called the *H mode*, but such usage is now deprecated. The letters TE derive from *transverse electric* mode, because the electric field vector is perpendicular to the direction of propagation.

Modes of propagation in which the longitudinal components

of the electric field are not zero, but are of negligibly small amplitude, are termed normal modes and are usually designated TE_{mn}. The subscripts m and n relate the given field configuration to the waveguide cross-section in the following manner. (a) In a rectangular waveguide m and n indicate the number of half-period variations of the mainly transverse electric field parallel to the narrow and broad sides, respectively, of the guide. (In some other countries, particularly in North America, the opposite convention is preferred.) (b) In a circular waveguide m indicates the number of axial planes along which the normal component of the electric field is zero, and n indicates the number of coaxial cylinders (including the guide wall) along which the tangential component of the electric field is zero.

A third subscript p is added in the case of a resonant cavity consisting of a length of rectangular or circular waveguide, to indicate the number of half-period variations of the field along the waveguide axis.

TEM mode (*transverse electromagnetic mode*) A propagation *mode* (2) in which the longitudinal components of both the electric and magnetic fields are everywhere zero. This mode does not occur in a waveguide but applies to a wave propagating in a homogeneous isotropic medium so that the electric and magnetic field vectors are everywhere perpendicular to the direction of propagation.

T junction A *waveguide* junction in the form of a letter T. See *series T* and *shunt T*.

TM mode A propagation *mode* (2) in a waveguide in which the longitudinal component of the magnetic field is everywhere zero, and the longitudinal component of the electric field is not. For the latter reason this mode has been called the *E mode*, although such usage is now deprecated. The letters TM derive from *transverse magnetic* mode, because the magnetic field vector is perpendicular to the direction of propagation.

Modes of propagation in which the longitudinal components of the magnetic field are not zero, but are of negligibly small amplitude, are termed normal modes and are usually designated TM_{mn}. The subscripts m and n relate the given field configuration to the waveguide cross-section in the following manner. (a) In a rectangular waveguide m and n indicate the number of half-period variations of the mainly transverse magnetic field parallel to the narrow and broad sides, respectively, of the guide. (In some countries, notably in North America, the opposite convention is preferred.) (b) In a circular waveguide m indicates the number of axial planes along which the normal component of the magnetic field is zero, and n is the number of cylindrical surfaces (including the guide wall) to which the electric field is normal.

A third subscript p is added in the case of a resonant cavity consisting of a length of rectangular or circular waveguide, to indicate the number of half-period variations of the field along the waveguide axis.

T-pulse and **2T-pulse**   See *waveform testing*.

T-wire   See *tip wire*.

tailing (US: *hangover*)   In *facsimile*, a defect whereby any abrupt tonal transition on the original document is blurred on the reproduced copy and appears as a relatively slow change from black through grey to white, or vice versa.

talker echo   An *echo* signal in a telephone circuit heard by the person uttering the original sound.

tandem central office   See *tandem exchange*.

tandem-completing trunk (US)   A channel or circuit between a *tandem exchange* and an exchange.

tandem exchange (US: *tandem central office*)   An *exchange* whose primary purpose is to switch traffic between other exchanges.

tandem selection   A method of *trunking* in which two *selectors* are connected in tandem so that the number of outlets available is the product of the availability of both selectors.

tandem selector   A *selector* located at some switching point between the originating and terminating *exchanges*.

tandem switching   The switching of circuits between *exchanges* only.

tangent ray or **tangential wave path**   The propagation path of a *direct wave* that is tangential to the surface of the earth. The path is slightly curved as a result of atmospheric *refraction*.

tank circuit (US)   See *tuned circuit*.

tape callmaker   See *callmaker*.

tape perforator   See *perforator*.

tape printer   Telegraph apparatus that prints characters in line on a moving paper tape.

tape reader or **tape reading head**   That part of an automatic telegraph transmitter which examines a tape and produces electrical signals corresponding to the code combination recorded thereon.

tape relay   A method of telegraph working in which messages arriving on an incoming channel are recorded on tape by a *perforator*, the perforated tape subsequently being fed into a tape transmitter connected to an outgoing channel.

tape transmitter   Telegraph apparatus which automatically transmits signals previously recorded on perforated paper tape.

taper   A length of *waveguide* that changes progressively in size and/or shape.

tapered distribution   A method of illuminating the *reflector* of a *microwave* antenna so that the *field strength* across a given dimension increases from the edges to the centre.

tearing   Break-up of parts of a displayed television picture, owing to partial failure of the line synchronisation.

teleautography   A system of *analogue telegraphy* intended for the immediate transmission of handwritten messages. A continuous signal provides information on the successive positions of the writing instrument as it moves across the paper, so enabling corresponding lines to be produced on a document at the receiving end.

telecommunication   Essentially the transmission of *information* from one point to another by wire, radio, optical or other electromagnetic systems.

teledata   See *teletext*.

telegram   A message transmitted by some form of *telegraphy* and recorded on a form for delivery to the addressee.

telegraph alphabet   See *alphabet* (2).

telegraph channel   A means of unidirectional transmission for a telegraph signal; see for example *voice-frequency telegraphy*. Two telegraph channels working in opposite directions can be associated to form a *telegraph circuit*.

telegraph code   A set of rules specifying how the signal used to represent a telegraph or data message should be formed for a particular *transmission mode*.

telegraph distortion   Departures from the ideal theoretical duration of the *significant intervals* in *telegraph modulation* or *telegraph restitution*.

telegraph key   A hand-operated device used to form *Morse-code* signals.

telegraph modulation   The train of *significant conditions* that corresponds to the signal produced by telegraph apparatus. The term stems from the early days of telegraphy when a direct current was effectively 'modulated' by the telegraph transmitter.

telegraph repeater   Apparatus that receives telegraph signals and retransmits corresponding signals into the next section of line. If the equipment produces a new signal that is virtually free from distortion, it is known as a *telegraph regenerator*.

telegraph restitution   The train of *significant conditions* assumed by telegraph receiving apparatus as a result of the received signal. See note under *telegraph modulation*.

telegraph sounder   A device used in the aural reception of *Morse code* signals, the transitions from space to mark and from mark to space each resulting in a single sound (click).

telegraph transmission speed   A measure of the speed with which messages may be transmitted, usually stated in words per minute. For this purpose a *telegraph word* is defined as five letters together with one letter space.

telegraphy The generic term for all those telecommunication services providing for the reproduction at a distance of written and printed matter, still pictures and similar material. See *alphabetic telegraphy, analogue telegraphy, facsimile (telegraphy)* and *teleautography*.

teleinformatics and **telematics** Relatively new terms used generically to describe non-voice services, particularly those resulting from the merging of computing and telecommunication techniques. Usage has not yet crystallised, but a CCITT Study Group has proposed that the term *teleinformatic services* should include all services other than *telephony*. The term would therefore cover services such as *facsimile, telex, teletex* and *videotex*, some of which are at present regarded as branches of telegraphy.

telemetering or **telemetry** A process in which variable quantities are measured at some remote location, the results of the measurements being transmitted by wire or radio to a central point, where they are displayed and/or recorded.

telephone See *telephone set*.

telephone air-to-air input/output characteristic A plot of the acoustical output level of one *telephone set* as a function of the acoustical input of another set with which it is connected.

telephone channel A means of one-way communication suitable for the transmission of speech. See also *telephone circuit*.

telephone circuit A means of two-way communication suitable for the transmission of speech. Telephone channels and circuits are not always used for the transmission of speech, but may also be used for *voice-frequency telegraphy* and *data transmission*.

telephone exchange See *exchange*.

telephone frequency An *audio frequency* in the band of frequencies transmitted by a particular *telephone channel*.

telephone influence (interference) factor A factor used to assess the total interfering effect of currents induced in a telephone line by the fundamental and harmonic components of the current in an adjacent power line. The factor allows for variation with frequency of both the sensitivity of the average ear and the response of the average telephone receiver. Its value is given by the ratio of the sum of the weighted RMS values of all the sine-wave components of the power wave to the RMS value of the whole wave.

telephone message In call accounting, an effective call over a connection set up between the calling and wanted stations.

telephone receiver A *transducer* forming part of a *telephone set* and used to convert voice-frequency currents into audible sounds.

telephone ringer (US) An electric bell responsive to low-frequency AC or pulsating current and used as a calling device at a telephone station.

telephone set An assembly of apparatus normally provided at each end of a *telephone circuit* to enable a user to make and receive calls. The composition of a telephone set depends on the system with which it is used, but most sets include a *telephone receiver*, a *telephone transmitter*, a bell or buzzer, and a calling device such as a *dial*.

telephone sidetone The ratio of the resulting acoustical output power from the receiver of a given telephone set to the acoustical input power to the transmitter of the same set.

telephone subscriber A customer provided with telephone service under an agreement or contract.

telephone system A telecommunication system in which speech or other sounds are converted into electrical signals that are transmitted to a distant point where they are converted back into reproductions of the original sounds.

telephone transmitter A microphone forming part of a telephone set.

telephony The branch of telecommunications providing for the exchange of *information* in the form of speech.

telephoto or **telephotography** US terms for phototelegraphy; see *facsimile*.

teleprinter (US: *teletypewriter*) A start-stop instrument for *alphabetic telegraphy* consisting of a combined keyboard transmitter, receiver and page printer. Operation of the keyboard causes characters to be printed and corresponding coded electrical signals to be sent to line to operate the printer of a distant machine. Coded electrical signals received from another machine are automatically translated and printed as characters.

teleprocessing Any processing of data using a combination of computers and data transmission facilities. In the US the term *compunication* has been proposed for this concept.

teletex A term provisionally adopted by the CCITT to describe a proposed service enabling subscribers to exchange correspondence on an automatic memory-to-memory basis over telecommunication networks. The service is intended to be complementary to the telex and data communication services and to be able to interwork with them. Its basic purpose, however, is to enable information in page format to be transmitted between terminals on an automatic, 24 hours per day, basis. Information received by a terminal will be stored, and may subsequently be displayed on a viewer and/or used to produce hard copy.

teletext A broadcast service consisting of the transmission of information in coded form within the standard television signal for display as text or pictorial material on the screens of suitably equipped receivers, either in place of, or superimposed on, the normal programme material. In this service the teletext material is transmitted as a pulse-coded signal occupying one of the normally empty forward scanning line periods in the field blanking interval. (*Note* The term teletext is currently used in the UK and some other countries to describe services such as Ceefax and Oracle. However, its similarity to the word *teletex,* especially when spoken, can obviously give rise to confusion, and alternative terms have been proposed for use at the international level. These include *broadcast videography, broadcast videotex, datavision, teledata, tevetex* and *videodif*.)

teletypewriter See *teleprinter*.

television A system for the production at a distance of a transient visible image of an actual or recorded scene.

telewriter Apparatus used to generate the signals required for *teleautography*.

telex A telegraph service enabling its subscribers to communicate directly with one another over the public telegraph network using start-stop apparatus, usually *teleprinters* operating at 50 *bauds*.

Telstar An *active satellite* launched into an inclined *elliptical orbit* in 1962 and used experimentally for the transmission of speech, television and facsimile signals between Europe and the US. The satellite's *orbital period* was 157.8 minutes, and it was simultaneously visible from the earth stations at Goonhilly (UK) and Andover (Massachusetts) only for periods of 30 to 40 minutes three or four times a day.

temperature inversion An abnormal condition in the *troposphere* in which temperature increases with height.

temporarily out of service Designation given to a *subscriber's line* deliberately disconnected from the exchange equipment on a temporary basis.

terminal exchange An *exchange* that receives incoming traffic directed solely to its own subscribers.

terminated level A *signal level* in dBm, obtained as a result of a measurement made across a resistor numerically equal to the modulus of the nominal impedance of the transmission path. The measurement may be made at any point by breaking the transmission path and replacing the disconnected portion by a resistor of suitable value.

terminating A qualifying term applied to *traffic* (or *exchanges*) in a network to indicate that the sinks, i.e. called parties, are located in the network or are directly connected to the exchanges.

terminating set Equipment that terminates the go and return channels of a *four-wire circuit* and enables them to be connected to a *two-wire circuit*.

terminating toll centre code Designation used in North America for the three digits dialled by operators to gain access to the *toll centre* in the area to which the call is routed.

ternary signal A digital signal having three *significant conditions*. See also *n-ary digital signal*.

terrestrial noise Radio *noise* from a source located on the surface of the earth or in its atmosphere, as opposed to *cosmic noise*.

tertiary centre See *classification of exchanges*.

test board See *test desk*.

test busy signal See *blocking signal*.

test desk (US: *test board*) A switchboard equipped with testing apparatus and so arranged that it can be connected to *subscribers' lines* or exchange equipment for testing purposes.

test handset A portable handset usually containing additional apparatus such as a dial, keys, etc., and used in the field or an *exchange* for testing purposes.

test level The absolute level at a given point in a telephone circuit when the origin is energised by a generator having a resistance R equal to the nominal impedance of the circuit, an EMF of $2\sqrt{(R/1000)}$ volts and a frequency of 800 Hz, unless otherwise specified. See also *absolute power* [*voltage*] *level* and *signal level*.

test traffic See *artificial traffic*.

testing In automatic switching, the process of determining the state of a device or traffic-carrying means.

tête bêche In a cabled television system, a method for minimising *crosstalk* between monochrome television signals transmitted in the same frequency range over *pairs* in the same cable. *Vestigial-sideband transmission* is employed, the two carriers differing in frequency by a substantial fraction of the video bandwidth of the signals. The lower-frequency carrier has its vestigial sideband on its lower side, whereas the higher-frequency carrier has its vestigial sideband on its higher side. The full sidebands thus overlap, but the carrier frequency of the unwanted signal in each pair corresponds with a high video frequency of the wanted signal. Since most of the energy in a monochrome television signal is concentrated around the carrier frequency and such signals are much less susceptible to interference at the higher video frequencies, this arrangement reduces the possibilities of crosstalk while permitting the transmission of two signals in substantially the bandwidth occupied by a single signal.

tevetex See *teletext*.

theoretical margin See *margin*.

thermal noise *Noise* due to the thermal agitation of electrons in conductors and semiconductors. The random motion of the electrons increases with temperature, and the resulting noise voltage is given by the expression $V = \sqrt{(4RkT\,\mathrm{d}f)}$, where $\mathrm{d}f$ is the frequency bandwidth in hertz, R is the resistance of the source in ohms, k is Boltzmann's constant and T is the absolute temperature in kelvins. Also known as *Johnson noise* and *resistance noise*.

thermistor A semiconductor device with a high negative temperature coefficient, so that its resistance falls with increasing temperature.

three-condition cable code (US: *cable Morse code*) A *cable code* in which each equal-length *signal element* represents either a dot, a dash or a letter space according to the particular combination of the three *unit elements* comprising it. Each unit element may assume one of three *significant conditions*.

three-party conference or **three-party connection** A PABX facility whereby an extension user already engaged on an established call can set up a further call to a third party in the *hold for enquiry* service, and then (by pressing an auxiliary button and dialling a suitable code) can include the original call in a three-party conversation. Also known as *three-way calling, add-on third party* and *cooption*.

threshold effect In the reception of angle-modulated waves, the inherent suppression of *noise* when the amplitude of a received *carrier* slightly exceeds that of the noise.

threshold element A binary logic device, having m inputs and one output, that takes on its defined 1-state if, and only if, at least n of the inputs stand at their defined 1-states. The term is also used if the inputs are weighted so that a 1-state at a given input contributes a weighted value towards the threshold value that causes the output to take on its 1-state.

threshold frequency Of a photoelectric device, the frequency of incident radiation below which there is no photoemissive output.

through level A *signal level* in dBm, measured with a high-impedance measuring set bridged across the transmission path.

through-pulse-echo testing A technique for assessing the effect of any systematic structural irregularities present in a *coaxial cable* on its performance as a transmission medium for high-speed digital signals. Through-pulse-echo testing is carried out on installed and equalised cable sections. The technique consists of the transmission of high-level, short-duration pulses over a spare coaxial pair to the remote end of a section, where the pulses are regenerated and applied to the end of the pair under test. The received signal is recorded via a sampling technique that may be adjusted in time to exclude the test impulse. The repetition rate of the test pulses is sufficiently low to avoid any possibility of the tails of successive echoes interfering with one another. See also *forward echo* and *structural return loss*.

throughput delay In digital switching, the delay in the passage of a bit through a digital *switching node* owing to the processes of buffering, synchronising and time-slot interchange. A delay of two to four frames in each channel is typical.

ticketing The recording of call details for the purpose of charging.

tie-line or **tie-trunk** (US) A line permanently connecting two *private branch exchanges* or *private exchanges*. Sometimes called an *interswitchboard line*.

tilt Of a *directional antenna*, the angle between the major axis of radiation and a reference axis (which is usually horizontal).

time-and-charge-request call See *advise-cost-and-duration call*.

time-and-distance charging Charging based on both the distance and the duration of a call.

time-assignment speech interpolation A technique that increases the *traffic capacity* of a multichannel transmission system by exploiting the fact that on an average each party to a telephone conversation is silent for about 60 per cent of the time. The essential principle of operation is that of allocating a *channel* to a talker only at those times when he is actually speaking; at all other times the channel is available to carry speech bursts from other conversations. In this way the transmission paths provided by a pool of channels may be shared between a larger number of callers, the channels being switched between talkers by a high-speed voice-operated switching arrangement. Under busy conditions any one channel may thus carry successive speech bursts from a number of different conversations. Control signals transmitted over a separate channel enable the distant terminal equipment to direct the various speech bursts to the correct parties. The equipment requires a finite time to recognise the start of a speech burst and to search for and allocate an available (i.e. idle) channel. As a result some 20 ms is clipped off the beginning of each speech burst. This has an insignificant effect on speech, but makes a TASI channel unsuitable for some forms of data transmission.

TASI was developed for use with long-distance submarine cable systems, where the costs of the complex terminal equipment are more than offset by the savings resulting from the increased transmission capacity.

time congestion ratio The ratio of the time during which *congestion* exists to the total time considered.

time-consistent busy hour See *mean busy hour*.

time-derived channel A channel obtained by the process of *time-division multiplex*.

time diversity The use of a number of paths separated be in the time domain.

time division The technique of separating a number of transmission paths in the time domain.

time-division multiple access A technique used in communication satellite systems whereby earth stations transmit information through the satellite in sequence in the form of non-overlapping *bursts*. The burst from each station occupies a unique time slot in a frame, beginning with a *reference burst* from a nominated station followed by a *standard burst* from each station in turn. See also *frequency-division multiple access*.

time-division multiplex *A multiplex system* in which a number of digital signals are interleaved in time for transmission over a common channel.

time-division switching The connection of inlets to outlets in a switching stage using *time-division* techniques. The signals to be switched may be transmitted over a common highway, each signal occupying a different *time slot*. A particular signal can be connected to a particular outlet by operating the appropriate channel gate at the right instants.

time equaliser A term formerly used to describe an **echo waveform corrector**.

time-out An enforced action taken automatically at the end of a predetermined period. Usually the term is applied to the enforced release of common equipment that has been held for an unduly long period without being used for its correct function.

time-polarity-control coding A method of coding in which a three-level signal is produced, one binary state always being represented by zero signal level and the other state by either the positive or the negative level, the choice between the two being controlled on a time basis alone.

time-quantised control Of *synchronisation* (2) in a digital network, a method in which the control signal is derived from the phase error between clocks (or is utilised for control purposes) only at a number of discrete instants, not necessarily equally spaced in time.

time sharing A method of using common equipment, e.g. a *central processor*, in which each terminal, device etc. is given access for a short interval of time on a cyclic basis.

time slot A recurrent interval of time that can be uniquely defined. Thus the first second of each minute constitutes a time slot having a duration of 1 second.

timing extraction or **timing recovery**   In digital transmission, the process of deriving a timing signal from the received signal.

tinsel cord   A flexible cord in which the conductors consist of thin metal ribbons wound helically on suitable cores.

tip   Of a telephone plug, the rounded contacting part at the point of a plug.

tip wire   That wire of an *exchange* circuit which is connected to the *tip* of a plug or to the corresponding contact of a switchboard *jack*. Also called *T-wire*.

toggle   See *bistable element*.

toll call (US)   A call to a destination outside the *local service area* of the calling station and therefore subject to a separate charge.

toll centre (US)   A class 4C office handling toll traffic for a number of *end offices* and having one or more manual boards to provide operator assistance. See *classification of exchanges*.

toll line (US)   A circuit joining two *toll offices*.

toll office (US)   An exchange whose primary purpose is the switching of toll traffic.

toll point (US)   A class 4P office handling toll traffic for a number of *end offices* and sometimes having operators to handle outward calls only. See *classification of exchanges*.

toll restriction (US)   A PABX facility that prevents extension users from making certain (or any) *toll calls* or reaching a toll operator except via the PABX operator.

toll station (US)   A public telephone station directly connected to a toll switchboard.

toll switching trunk (US)   A line connecting a local exchange (*end office*) to a *toll office*.

tone   (1) A steady sound characterised by its pitch, or the acoustic wave giving rise to such a sound. By extension the term is often used in connection with audio-frequency electrical waves. See *tone receiver*. (2) In *facsimile*, a measure of the brightness of picture elements.

tone calling   The use of an audio tone in place of a telephone bell for attracting the attention of a called party.

tone-on-idle signalling   A method of *signalling* in which the idle state of a circuit is represented by the continuous transmission of a low-level tone.

tone receiver   Apparatus designed to receive an electrical signal at a particular frequency in the audio range.

tone wedge   A wedge of optical densities ranging from black to white in a specified number of linear steps.

tonlar (US)   Tone-operated net loss adjuster: a system for adjusting the overall loss of a telephone circuit by transmitting a tone between conversations.

top-loaded antenna A vertical antenna, usually short compared with the wavelength, and having conductors or a metal plate connected at the top to load it capacitively.

torn-tape relay See *tape relay*.

touch-tone telephone (US) Bell system designation for a telephone equipped with a *keypad* for generating dual-tone calling signals.

traffic The aggregate of calls (including call attempts) offered to or carried by some defined part of a network such as a group of circuits or switches, account being taken of both the number of calls and their duration. In traffic engineering, any occupancy of a circuit or device caused directly or indirectly by a subscriber making or attempting to make use of the system is regarded as a call.

The amount of traffic carried by a group of circuits will always exhibit daily and seasonal variations. Of more significance, however, are the changes that occur with the time of day, leading to the concept of the *busy hour* when the volume of traffic carried is at its maximum. During such a period the numbers of call arrivals and departures are essentially equal and the system is said to be in a state of statistical equilibrium. In this state a measure of the density of the traffic is given by the average number of calls existing simultaneously; see *traffic flow*.

traffic capacity Of a group of circuits or devices, the *traffic intensity* that can be handled for a specified *grade of service*. In the UK and US this refers to the density of the *traffic offered*, whereas some countries refer to that of the *traffic carried*.

traffic carried (US: *carried load*) Traffic that actually occupies a group of trunks or switches. Its average intensity in *erlangs* is given by the average number of simultaneously occupied trunks or switches. The amount or volume of traffic carried by the group in a defined period is given by the sum of the *holding times* of the calls occurring in that period and is expressed in erlang-hours.

traffic flow or **traffic intensity** A measure of the density of the *traffic*, expressed in *erlangs*. For a defined period (such as the *busy hour*) its value is obtained by dividing the *traffic volume* in erlang-hours by the duration of the period. Its value indicates the average number of simultaneous calls existing in the part of the network under consideration. The *instantaneous traffic intensity* refers to the number of simultaneous calls existing at a given instant or to the figure derived from the traffic volume for a very short period.

traffic offered (US: *offered load*)   The total number of calls (including call attempts) submitted to a group of trunks or switches. Its average intensity in *erlangs* is given by the mean number of calls arriving during the mean *holding time*.

traffic unit   Earlier term for the unit of *traffic intensity*, the erlang.

traffic volume (US: *load*)   The amount of *traffic* carried by a particular group of circuits or switches in a defined period, as given by the sum of the *holding times* of the calls occurring in that period. It is expressed in *erlang-hours*.

transceiver   A combination of radio transmitter and receiver in a common case, usually for mobile use, some of the circuits and components being common to both the transmitting and receiving functions.

transducer   General term for any device that accepts energy from one transmission system or medium and delivers related energy to a second system or medium in another form. Loudspeakers, microphones, pick-ups and strain gauges are typical examples of transducers.

transfer of calls (automatic)   A PABX facility enabling an extension user to transfer an incoming call to another extension by using the *hold for enquiry* service and replacing his receiver as soon as the wanted extension has answered. If the transfer fails owing to mis-operation or because the required extension is barred from receiving the particular type of call, the incoming call is automatically routed to the PABX operator.

transfer of calls (via the operator)   A PABX facility enabling an extension user to transfer an incoming *exchange line call* or inter-PBX call within the PBX network by using the operator call-in service.

transfer rate   In telegraphy and data transmission, the average number of binary digits, characters or blocks transferred in unit time between equipment such as *modems* or sources and sinks. *Actual transfer rate* describes the rate disregarding errors, whereas *effective transfer rate* refers to the rate for those digits, characters or blocks accepted as valid at the receiving point.

transformer   General term for a device that transfers energy from an alternating current in a primary winding into one or more secondary windings by means of electromagnetic induction. An *autotransformer* consists of a single tapped inductor in which part of the winding is common to the primary and secondary circuits. In all other cases the primary and secondary windings are insulated from one another.

transient   The short-duration non-cyclic component of current or voltage existing in a circuit during a change from one *steady state*

288

to another. See also *step function*.

transient response   A measure of the ability of a circuit or device to handle sudden changes in the instantaneous level of an input signal, e.g. the time response of an amplifier to a *step function* waveform.

transit   A qualifying term applied to a network (including *exchanges*) to indicate that neither the source of traffic (caller etc.) nor the sinks (called parties etc.) are located in the network. See also *trunk transit network*.

transition   Of a digital signal, a change from one signal condition to another, e.g. from a *mark* to a *space*.

translation   The act of converting *information* in one form into an alternative form. For example, the function carried out by a telegraph or data receiver whereby the text of a message is derived and recorded from the incoming digital signal. See also *translator* and *frequency translation*.

translator   In automatic switching, apparatus that examines input signals and changes them to other signals needed to control the subsequent setting up of a wanted connection.

transliteration   The conversion of characters in one alphabet into the corresponding characters of a second alphabet.

transmission   The process of sending information in the form of electrical signals over wires, *waveguides, radio links* or other forms of communication system.

transmission band   A band of frequencies within which a system or device has characteristics making it suitable for *transmission*, for example the band within which the *attenuation* is less than a specified value.

transmission bridge   Apparatus provided in an *exchange* with the primary purpose of dividing a connection into incoming and outgoing sections for *signalling* purposes while permitting the through transmission of speech-frequency currents. The transmission bridge may also control the holding and release of a connection and provide feed current for the microphone in the subscriber's telephone.

transmission level   See *relative level*.

transmission line   General term for some means of conveying electromagnetic energy from one point to another, sensibly without radiation. See *coaxial line, waveguide, strip line* and *optical fibre*.

transmission loss   See *loss*.

transmission measuring set   Apparatus used to measure the insertion loss or gain of a transmission path, and consisting essentially of a calibrated signal generator and a level-measuring set.

transmission mode One of the possible field configurations of a travelling wave in a *transmission line*. See *TE mode, TEM mode* and *TM mode*.

transmission performance Of a telephone circuit used for speech, a measure of the effectiveness of the circuit determined by comparison with a reference system such as *NOSFER*. The circuit is used to replace part of the reference system, and the transmission performance rating is then given by the constant frequency loss that has to be added or subtracted from the system to obtain equivalent performance.

transmission plan A scheme that defines the allocation of transmission parameters such as *attenuation, noise* and *crosstalk* to the various parts of a network. Sometimes called an *attenuation plan*. The plan adopted by the CCITT for circuits between international transit exchanges is shown in *Figure T.1*.

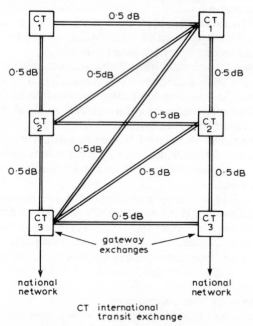

Figure T.1 Transmission plan

transmission units A collective term used to describe the *bel*, the *neper* and their submultiples the *decibel* and the *decineper*. Strictly speaking there can be no such thing as a transmission unit since transmission is not a quantity that can be measured. Physical quantities such as power, voltage and current can be measured, however, so a transmission parameter such as *attenu-*

ation can be expressed as a ratio of two values of an appropriate quantity. Since such a ratio may be quite large it was natural for the early telephone engineers to choose logarithmic scales for the expression of attenuation. The bel and the neper are in fact merely the fundamental units of scales based on the use of common logarithms and natural logarithms, respectively. The usage that developed in English-speaking countries was for unqualified expressions in decibels to refer to ratios of powers, but for similar statements in nepers to refer to ratios of voltage, current or related field quantities. The official ITU definitions were appropriately worded and were accompanied by notes on the need for caution if either unit were used in circumstances where a power ratio was not the square of the corresponding voltage or current ratio.

In 1968 the CCITT approved a Recommendation that only the decibel should be used as a transmission unit in international contexts. The continued use of the neper as the natural unit for use in theoretical and scientific fields was recognised, however.

transmitted wave See *refracted wave*.

transmultiplexer Equipment that transforms signals formed by *frequency-division multiplex*, for example a *group* or *supergroup*, into corresponding *time-division multiplex* signals having a similar structure to those formed by PCM multiplex equipment. It can also carry out the inverse operation.

transparent codes In digital transmission, codes having the ability to represent and faithfully transmit any input sequence of digits.

transponder In a *communication satellite*, equipment that accepts signals received from the earth, translates them to another frequency band where necessary and amplifies them for re-transmission to earth via the satellite's antenna system.

transposed multiple A form of *grading* used with *line concentrators* (1), in which a subscriber shares some outlets with one group of subscribers and other outlets with another group of subscribers.

transposition Originally, the ordered interchange of conductor positions in successive lengths of an overhead line in order to minimise *induced interference* and *crosstalk*. The term is now also used to describe the arrangement of the *multiple* (2) of a switching stage in order to improve the crosstalk characteristics.

transposition section A length of *open-wire* line in which a specified *transposition* pattern is completed.

transversal equaliser An adjustable equaliser based on some form of transversal circuit arrangement, and hence possessing the property that its loss and delay characteristics can be varied independently across its working frequency range. The basic

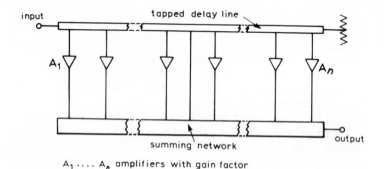

input

tapped delay line

A_1

A_n

summing network

output

$A_1 \ldots A_n$ amplifiers with gain factor
in the range −1 to +1

Figure T.2   Block diagram of transversal equaliser

arrangement of a transversal equaliser is illustrated in block form in *Figure T.2*. It will be seen that it consists of a terminated *delay line* with a number of tappings symmetrically disposed on either side of a central tapping, from which the main portion of the output signal is derived. Signals taken from the other tappings may be added to this main signal in a summing network after each has been individually scaled in amplitude and possibly changed in sign. The signal available at the central tapping will be a delayed replica of the input signal. The signals taken from the tappings in the first half of the line will not be delayed as much as the main signal, and they may therefore be regarded as an array of advanced or leading echoes of the main signal. In the same way the tappings in the second half of the line will provide an array of delayed or trailing echoes. Combinations of leading and lagging echoes, adjusted in amplitude and changed in sign as required, can be added to the main signal to cancel out (to a first approximation) distortion present in the input signal.

The behaviour of a transversal network can also be considered in the frequency domain. *Figure T.3* shows how the addition of a pair of echoes with even symmetry about the main signal results in a cosine loss characteristic but has negligible effect on the phase characteristic. If the echoes have odd symmetry the loss characteristic is effectively flat but the delay characteristic exhibits a cosine shape. It follows that arrays of echoes with even symmetry and constant spacing will produce harmonically related cosines of loss, whereas arrays with odd symmetry will produce harmonically related cosines of delay. In order to equalise a system with a bandwidth of B Hz the spacing between the taps must give a delay t such that $t = 1/2B$. This is equivalent to sampling the input signal at the *Nyquist rate*, and it is then possible to completely equalise the system provided that

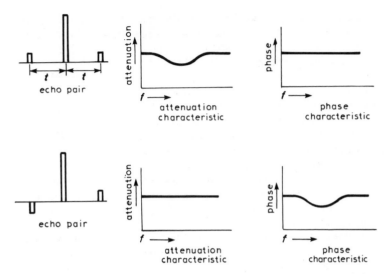

Figure T.3 Relationships between echo pairs and loss and phase characteristics

sufficient echoes of appropriate amplitude are available. In practical designs the number of tappings provided may be reduced, especially where the nature of the distortion present in the input signal can be predicted with a fair degree of accuracy. Similarly, equalisers with arrays of leading (or lagging) taps only, can be used to produce desired loss characteristics where the phase response is not of importance.

Because they are capable of simultaneously producing variable loss and phase characteristics, transversal equalisers are suitable for the correction of *linear waveform distortion*, and they find application in both television and data transmission systems.

transverse electric hybrid wave In radio-wave propagation, an *electromagnetic wave* in which the electric field is linearly polarised normal to the plane of propagation and the magnetic field is elliptically polarised in this plane.

transverse electric mode See *TE mode*.

transverse electromagnetic mode See *TEM mode*.

transverse electromagnetic wave An *electromagnetic wave* propagating in a homogeneous isotropic medium and having both its electric and magnetic fields everywhere perpendicular to the direction of propagation and to each other. This is the normal mode of propagation of a wave in free space.

transverse gyro frequency See *gyro frequency*.

transverse judder See *judder*.

transverse magnetic hybrid wave In radio-wave propagation, an *electromagnetic wave* in which the magnetic field is linearly polarised normal to the plane of propagation and the electric field is elliptically polarised in this plane.

transverse magnetic mode   See *TM mode*.

trapped mode   A propagation mode of an electromagnetic wave confined within a *tropospheric duct*.

travelling plane wave   An *electromagnetic wave* conveying energy away from a source, and characterised by field components that vary linearly in phase and decay exponentially in amplitude with distance in the direction of propagation.

travelling-wave antenna   An antenna for which the fields and currents that produce the *directivity pattern* can be regarded as due to one or more travelling waves, usually propagating in the same direction along the antenna. Also known as a *progressive-wave antenna*.

trembler bell   A non-polarised bell in which the operating current is rendered intermittent by contacts associated with the movable striker arm.

triangular random noise   *Random noise* having a spectral distribution in which the power per unit of bandwidth is proportional to the square of the frequency.

trigger   To initiate some action in a circuit, the action then continuing under its own control.

trigger circuit   A circuit that can be put into one or more states by the application of a suitable trigger excitation; see *bistable element* and *monostable element*.

trombone working   A method of working in which calls between subscribers served by the same *satellite exchange* have to be completed via junctions to the parent exchange. The method may appear to be wasteful of junction capacity but it can lead to savings in plant at the satellite exchange by eliminating the first *selectors*, access to the parent exchange being given directly from the subscribers' *uniselectors*. Moreover, only a small proportion of the total traffic generated by a satellite exchange normally consists of own-exchange calls.

troposcatter (US)   See *tropospheric scatter link*.

troposphere   The lower portion of the earth's atmosphere in which temperature generally falls with respect to height and in which convection effects such as cloud formation occur. It is bounded at its upper surface by the *tropopause*, a region above which temperature either rises slightly with respect to height, or remains constant. The height of the tropopause varies from some 9 km at the poles to about 17 km at the equator.

tropospheric duct   A layer in the *troposphere* in which abnormal variations in *refractive index* exist, usually as a result of one or more temperature inversions (temperature rising with altitude). Waves of sufficiently high frequency entering the layer at low angles are refracted between the upper and lower boundaries, and hence are able to follow the curvature of the earth. A layer having the earth as its lower boundary is called a *ground-based duct* or *surface duct*. Such a duct—typically formed by a layer of warm air over a cold sea—can extend the range of a *microwave* radio station far beyond the normal line-of-sight limit. A duct in which the lower boundary is also formed by an abnormality in refractive index is called an *elevated duct*.

tropospheric reflection Partial or total reflection of radio waves by discontinuities between air masses of different *refractive index* in the *troposphere*.

tropospheric scatter link A *microwave* radio link relying on energy scattered by inhomogeneities in the *troposphere* to provide communication between a transmitter and a receiver located beyond the *radio horizon*. In operation, a beam from a high-power transmitter feeding a large-aperture antenna is directed at a region of the sky above the receiving site. Sufficient energy is scattered downwards to provide a usable signal at the receiving antenna, the *main lobe* of which is directed at the area of the sky illuminated by the transmitted beam. In practice only a minute fraction of the transmitted energy reaches the receiver, a figure of one picowatt per watt of transmitted energy being fairly typical. Tropospheric scatter links are a useful way of providing communication facilities in circumstances where normal links cannot be provided, for example to offshore oil platforms.

tropospheric wave A wave whose propagation between two points on or near the surface of the earth is primarily determined by the distribution of *refractive index* in the *troposphere*.

trunk General term for a permanent connection between any two *switching stages* in an *exchange*. In North America the term is also used instead of *trunk circuit*.

trunk circuit A traffic artery between two *exchanges* or *switching centres*. In the UK the designation applies to circuits between exchanges more than 24 km (15 miles) apart.

trunk code (US: *area code*) A *routing code* consisting of one or more digits used to designate a called *numbering-plan area* within a country or a group of countries covered by one overall numbering scheme. In the UK the digit 1 is used to identity a London number, two digits are used for each of several major cities, and three digits are used for all the remaining areas. In the North American integrated numbering scheme a three-digit trunk code is used for each of the numbering-plan areas, which vary in size from part of a city to a whole state.

295

trunk concentrator See *concentration*.

trunk control centre Old designation for an *auto-manual exchange* controlling the trunk traffic of a number of exchanges.

trunk dialling See *subscriber trunk dialling*.

trunk exchange An exchange to which *trunk circuits* are connected but which does not provide for the termination of subscribers' lines.

trunk feeder See *feeder* (1).

trunk group (US) A set of *trunks* normally treated as a unit from a traffic point of view, in which all the paths are interchangeable unless sub-grouping is employed.

trunk-junction circuit A junction circuit between a *local exchange* and a *primary centre* (such as a group switching centre) which can form part of a long-distance connection. See *Figure T.4*. (*Note* The word 'toll' has been used in this context in some CCITT literature in the past, but such usage would appear to be unwise in view of the wider meaning of the term in North America.)

trunk offering An exchange facility enabling an operator to intrude into an established connection to offer one of the parties an incoming long-distance call.

trunk prefix One or more digits (preceding the *trunk code*) to be dialled when making a call to a subscriber in the same country but outside the local area. In the UK the trunk prefix is a single zero.

trunk transit network Designation for the four-wire-switched network enabling any two *group switching centres* in the UK to be interconnected by not more than five transit links. *Figure T.4* is a diagram of the network showing the five links as basic routes. Because so many auxiliary routes are provided, only a very small percentage of the traffic actually requires a five-link route.

trunking (1) That aspect of *exchange* design which is concerned with the provision of equipment to meet traffic requirements with a specified *grade of service*. (2) By extension, the interconnections between the various ranks of switching equipment.

trunking diagram (US: *switching-network plan*) A block diagram showing the *switching stages* and interconnecting *trunks* in an *exchange*, or a part of one.

truth table In binary logic, a table describing a logic function in terms of the *logic state* caused at the output of an element by each combination of logic states applied to its inputs. The term refers only to logic states and should not be used to describe a *table of combinations* (which lists the relationships between the

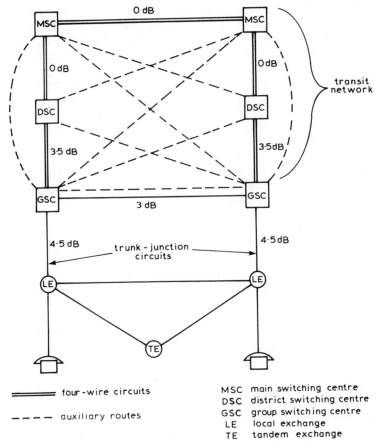

Figure T.4 Trunk transit network

Table T.1

Table of combinations	Truth table assuming positive logic: AND function	Truth table assuming negative logic: OR function

Inputs A	B	*Output*	*Inputs* A	B	*Output*	*Inputs* A	B	*Output*
H	H	H	1	1	1	0	0	0
L	H	L	0	1	0	1	0	1
H	L	L	1	0	0	0	1	1
L	L	L	0	0	0	1	1	1

297

electrical levels at the output and inputs of a device capable of performing a logic function), since the function actually performed depends on the significance ascribed to the levels, i.e. to the logic convention in use. *Table T.1* shows a table of combinations and truth tables for a device capable of performing the AND function if the positive logic convention is applied at both inputs and output, or the OR function if the negative logic convention is applied. It should be noted that other functions are possible if the convention applied at the inputs differs from that applied at the output.

tuned circuit (US: *tank circuit*) A series or parallel circuit consisting of an inductor and a capacitor whose values are adjusted to make the circuit resonant at the frequency of an applied sinusoidal signal.

tuned-radio-frequency reception A method of reception in which all the amplification of the received signal prior to detection is made at *radio frequency*.

tuning The act of adjusting the value of the capacitance or inductance of a *tuned circuit*.

tuning probe or **tuning screw** In a *waveguide*, a component whose degree of penetration into the electromagnetic field in the guide can be adjusted in a controlled manner.

tunnel diode A semiconductor junction diode so fashioned that some electrons are able to pass through the depletion layer, giving the device a negative resistance over a part of its operating range. Also called an Esaki diode after its inventor. Tunnel diodes are used for low-noise amplification and as oscillators at *microwave* frequencies.

turnstile antenna An *antenna* consisting of one or more tiers of crossed horizontal dipoles fed in phase *quadrature* with equal currents to produce a substantially omnidirectional *directivity pattern*.

turret A PBX switchboard in the form of a desktop cabinet.

twin cable Designation given to a cable containing a number of twisted *pairs* not laid up in the form of *quads*.

twinned binary code A *pseudo-ternary code* in which the three signal levels are formed by delaying the binary input signal by one bit and subtracting it algebraically from the original. The term is also used in connection with coding in which the binary input signal is delayed by one bit and added algebraically to itself. In this case the result is a three-level signal, which is the same as that produced by *biternary coding*.

twinplex See *four-frequency diplex telegraphy*.

twist A length of *waveguide* with a deliberate progressive rotation of the cross-section about the longitudinal axis.

two-condition cable code   A *cable code* in which each equal-length *signal element* represents either a dot, a dash or a letter space according to the particular combination of the two *unit elements* comprising it. Each unit element may assume one of two *significant conditions*.

two-condition telegraph code   A code in which each *signal element* can assume one of two *significant conditions*.

two-frequency operation   A method of operating a *radio link* in which the frequency used for transmission is different for each direction of transmission.

two-frequency signalling   A method of in-band AC *signalling* using two frequencies.

two-motion selector   An electromagnetic selector in which the wipers have two senses of motion; see for example *Strowger selector*.

two-out-of-five code   A binary-coded decimal code in which each decimal digit is represented by five binary digits, of which two are of one kind (usually 1s) and three are of the other kind.

two-source frequency keying   A form of *frequency shift keying* in which the marking and spacing waves have frequencies derived from independent sources so that phase continuity of the output wave is not maintained.

two-step relay   A *relay* provided with two sets of contacts and a double-motion armature such that one set of contacts is operated by a specified value of magnetic flux and both groups by a larger value.

two-tone keying   A form of digital *modulation* in which a carrier is modulated with one tone for the *mark* condition and a different tone for the *space* condition.

two-way simplex system   Old designation for a telegraph system consisting of two unidirectional channels operating in opposite directions between two stations and hence providing *duplex* operation.

two-wire circuit   A *circuit* using two conductors (or two groups of conductors in the case of a *phantom circuit*) to provide simultaneous transmission in both go and return directions in a common frequency band.

two-wire repeater   A *repeater* suitable for use in a *two-wire circuit*. Such a repeater either must contain one amplifier with its input and output terminals in one pair of conjugate branches of a circuit and the lines in another conjugate pair, or it must contain a separate amplifier for each direction of transmission and suitable hybrid terminations. In the US the two types are designated 21-type and 22-type repeaters, respectively.

U

UT chart A geographical chart with contours predicting the worldwide value, at an instant specified in Universal Time, of some ionospheric quantity such as the *critical frequency* (1).

ultra high frequency band The band of frequencies extending from 300 to 3000 MHz in the radio spectrum. See also the table under *band*.

ultrasonic frequency A frequency above the range audible to the average human ear. The term is used in connection with waves propagated in gases, liquids and solids, rather than the electrical analogues of such waves. Also termed *super-audio frequency*. The term *supersonic frequency* is now deprecated because of the use of supersonic in connection with aircraft speeds.

umbrella antenna A top-loaded *antenna* consisting of a vertical conductor connected at its top to a number of radially disposed conductors that slope down towards the ground but are not connected to it.

unabsorbed field strength The *field strength* to be expected at a given receiving point if a radio wave were to experience no absorption between the transmitting and receiving aerials.

unbalanced circuit A circuit in which the two sides are electrically dissimilar with respect to some common reference point. For example, a two-wire line in which each conductor has a different capacitance to ground.

unbiased telephone ringer (US) A telephone bell in which the clapper-driving element occupies a central position so that the bell can be operated by alternating current. The term is also applied to bells that are very weakly biased to prevent bell tinkling during dialling.

unblocking signal See *blocking signal*.

uncommitted logic array An array of transistors and resistors formed in a single chip, with terminations that can be interconnected in a manner specified by the customer.

underground cable Cable installed in ducts, tunnels, etc. so that it can be removed without disturbing the ground; compare with *buried cable*.

underlap In *facsimile*, a defect arising when the width of the scanning lines is less than the *scanning pitch*.

undetected error rate See *residual error rate*.

undulator An instrument used to record *Morse code* signals, and consisting of an inking stylus resting on a moving paper tape. The stylus is moved laterally across the tape between two positions corresponding to the *mark* and *space* of the received signal.

unguarded interval Any short interval of time during which a circuit or device can be erroneously seized. Such an interval can be caused by a fault or may occur very briefly during the transition from the busy to the idle state.

unidirectional antenna An *antenna* having a single well-defined direction of maximum *gain* (2).

uniform encoding In *pulse code modulation*, the representation of uniformly quantised samples of an analogue signal by character signals according to a defined code.

uniform linear array An *array* consisting of a line of equally spaced and identically oriented elements having the same current amplitudes and equal phase increments between excitation currents.

uniform plane wave In radio propagation, a *plane wave* in which the electric and magnetic field strengths have constant amplitudes over the equiphase surfaces. In simpler terms, a wave that is travelling in a straight line and is not being attenuated.

uniform quantising *Quantising* in which all the quantising intervals are equal.

uniform-spectrum random noise See *white noise*.

uniform waveguide A *waveguide* having substantially constant physical and electrical characteristics throughout its length.

unilateral control Between two *synchronisation nodes*, a method of operation whereby the frequency of the clock at only one of the nodes is influenced by timing information derived from the clock at the other node (compare with *bilateral control*).

unipole antenna (also termed *monopole antenna*) An open *antenna* consisting of a radiating element perpendicular to the earth or some other conducting surface. The element is fed at the earth end by an unbalanced feeder and behaves as one half of a dipole, the other half of which is represented by the image of the element in the earth or conducting surface.

uniselector An electromagnetic *selector* in which the *wipers* can move in the rotary sense only.

unit automatic exchange Designation used in the UK for an unattended automatic exchange providing service to a small community.

unit call See *hundred call seconds*.

unit disparity code A binary code in which the number of 1s differs from the number of 0s in each character by plus or minus one.

unit element Of a character signal in telegraphy, a *signal element* having a duration equal to the *unit interval*.

unit impulse A *pulse* of vanishingly small width and infinitely great height so that the product of its height and width is unity.

Also known as a *delta impulse* or *Dirac pulse*. This concept is of considerable importance in communication theory because the spectrum of such a pulse contains all frequencies from zero to infinity at constant amplitude. Real pulses approaching this ideal as closely as practicable are used for testing purposes.

unit interval (US: *signal interval*)   The shortest interval of time between the ideal instants at which the transitions in a digital signal should occur.

unit pulse   See *unit impulse*.

unit step function   A *step function* in which the steady signal value after the transition is equal to one unit on some specified scale.

unit type cable   A cable in which *pairs* are stranded into groups (units) each containing a given number of pairs, the units themselves being stranded together to form the cable.

unperturbed orbit   The idealised path that would be followed by a *satellite* if it were subjected only to the gravitational attraction of the larger body concentrated at its centre of mass.

unreasonable message   In *common-channel signalling*, a *signal message* with an inappropriate or incorrect *information content* or one appearing at an inappropriate place in the signal sequence. See also *reasonableness check*.

unrestricted extension   A PABX extension that can make *exchange line calls* without the intervention of the PABX operator.

unshift-on-space   A shift from *figures case* to *letters case* while the printing position of a telegraph receiver is advanced as the result of the reception of a *space* signal.

unsymmetrical grading   See *grading* (2).

untimed call   A call, the charge for which does not depend on the call duration.

uplink   A unidirectional transmission path from an *earth terminal* to a *communication satellite*. The link includes the transmitter, the antennas and the satellite's receiver.

upset duplex system   A DC telegraph system permitting a station between any two *duplex* equipments to transmit signals by opening and closing the line and thereby upsetting the duplex balance.

upward modulation   See *positive modulation*.

urgent fault alarm   An audible signal sounded in the apparatus room and accompanied by a visual indication on the relevant equipment when a fault condition classified as urgent occurs. If the apparatus room is not normally staffed (e.g. in the case of a PBX), the audible alarm may be located in the switchroom and extended to the apparatus room when maintenance staff are present. Also called *emergency alarm* (US) and *prompt alarm*.

302

usage (US)   The *traffic* (load) carried by a group of circuits or switches (servers), usually expressed in *hundred call seconds*.

user   Of a *common-channel signalling* system, a sub-system such as a telephone or data call control system that makes use of the message transfer facilities of the signalling system. Some of the functions of a user may be provided as a part of a particular common-channel signalling system; see *user part*.

user part   Of a particular *common-channel signalling* system, a part of the system that is permanently allocated to a particular *user* and serves as an interface between the user and the signalling system. Also known as a *service-oriented part*.

V

V antenna   An antenna resembling a letter V and consisting of a pair of straight conductors parallel with the ground and fed at the junction of the two arms.

VL43   A variable-length code in which blocks of four or eight binary digits are represented by three or six ternary digits respectively. This is a state-dependent code like *MS43*, but has a lower variation of *digital sum* and a higher density of transitions for *timing recovery*.

VODAS (US)   A system for preventing *singing* in a two-way telephone circuit by permitting transmission in only one direction at a time. The name is derived from the expression 'voice-operated device anti-sing'.

VOGAD (US)   A device used to give a substantially constant volume output for a wide range of speech input levels. The name is derived from the expression 'voice-operated gain-adjusting device'.

VOLCAS   Apparatus that switches loss out of the transmitting branch of a telephone circuit and simultaneously inserts loss into the receiving branch under control of the subscriber's speech. The term is derived from the expression 'voice-operated loss control anti-sing'.

vacant-code tone (US)   A tone indicating that a caller has dialled a number that is spare.

vacant-number signal   A *signal* (2) sent back from a distant exchange to indicate that the *address information* applies to a number not allocated to a subscriber. This causes the exchange nearest to the caller to connect a suitable tone to his line. Some systems do not employ this signal, but a suitable tone is returned to the caller directly from the distant exchange.

van Duuren ARQ system An *error detecting and feedback system* widely used on radio telegraph circuits and based on the use of a '3 out of 7' *constant disparity code*. If a character violating the '3 out of 7' rule is received at either station, message transmission is automatically interrupted and a signal requesting retransmission of the last *n* characters is inserted. The duration of the interruption and the number of characters retransmitted depend on the transmission time between the stations. Continuously updated storage of the last few characters transmitted has to be provided at both stations to enable the system to work.

vane attenuator A strip of absorptive material parallel to the narrow wall in a rectangular *waveguide* and capable of being moved in a direction normal to its surface to vary the *attenuation*.

vane wattmeter An instrument for measuring the power flowing in a *waveguide* by using the electromechanical force exerted on one or more vanes of metal or dielectric material.

varactor A semiconductor device designed to be used as a voltage-dependent capacitor. The capacitance of a reverse-biased junction diode is dependent on the value of the bias because the latter controls the width of the depletion region. Varactors are widely used for tuning purposes, in AFC circuits, as *parametric amplifier* elements, etc.

variable-length coding The production of a pseudo-ternary signal by using the input data to form *code words* of several different lengths. Since the data must normally be transmitted at a constant rate the length of each code word must be proportional to the number of bits it represents; see *VL43*.

varioplex A device used with early *time-division multiplex* telegraph systems to enable the channels to be distributed automatically between the users in a variable manner according to the number of users transmitting at any given time.

vertex feed Of a *microwave* antenna, a *front feed* located on the axis of the main reflector and energised by a coaxial or waveguide feeder passing through the vertex of the main reflector.

vertex plate A plate located near the vertex of a reflector of a *microwave* antenna to reduce undesired reflection of energy back to the *driven element*.

vertical-incidence ionospheric recorder See *ionospheric recorder*.

vertical-incidence ionospheric sounding Measurement of ionospheric properties using radio signals transmitted vertically upwards.

vertical monopole See *vertical unipole*.

vertical polarisation *Linear polarisation* in which the direction of the electric field is vertical or, by extension, is perpendicular to some other chosen plane of reference.

vertical unipole An antenna consisting of one or more vertical radiating elements fed at the base by an unbalanced feeder and behaving as one half of a dipole, the other half of which is represented by the image of the element in the earth.

vestigial sideband A *sideband* reduced to a vestige owing to the severe *attenuation* of some of its spectral components, usually those corresponding to the higher frequencies of the modulating wave.

vestigial-sideband transmission A method of operation employing a *carrier*, one complete *sideband* and its corresponding *vestigial sideband*. Also known as *asymmetric-sideband transmission*. This method requires less bandwidth than the use of two complete sidebands but is nevertheless suitable for the transmission of a modulating signal having a DC component, as in the case of television.

via net loss (US) The smallest loss allowable between *trunk exchanges* according to the North American *transmission plan*. The value in any particular case is given by the expression $VNL = xl + y + z$, where x is a factor appropriate to the type of transmission plant, l is the length in miles, and x and y are additions allowing for circuit variations and the use of two-wire switching.

vibrating circuit A telegraph receiving arrangement that includes a local timing circuit to improve the performance when the definition of the received signals is poor.

vibrating relay A telegraph *relay* with additional windings excited by a local timing circuit to increase its sensitivity and to reduce any distortion present in a received *line signal* connected to its normal windings.

video Pertaining to the picture and synchronising signals in television, or to equipment handling such signals.

video frequency A frequency in the band occupied by the combined picture and synchronising signals in a given television system. The video band extends from DC up to the highest frequencies present in the picture signal—typically around 6 MHz.

videography A term proposed for use at the international level as the common name for services providing for alphanumeric and/or graphic displays on suitably equipped television sets or other viewers; see for example *viewdata* and *teletext*. The proposal is thus to create a generic term for *interactive* services using the public telecommunication networks and *non-interactive* services provided by broadcasting authorities.

videotex A term proposed for use at the international level instead of *viewdata*.

viewdata A term presently used in the UK to describe a service enabling a subscriber to obtain information over the public telecommunication network for presentation in alphanumeric and/or graphic form on a visual display unit, usually a specially equipped television receiver. Viewdata services are being developed by a number of countries and will be marketed under a variety of trade names, e.g. Prestel (UK), Telset (Finland), Bildschirmtext (West Germany) and Vista (Canada). These services are in an evolutionary stage, and they may be expanded to provide additional facilities such as message transmission between terminals and access to computers for purposes other than simple information retrieval.

virtual call The transfer of data between two terminals in a *packet-switching* network, the call being established and terminated at the user's request by means of agreed data *protocols*. The term 'virtual' is used because, although the call appears to provide a connection between the terminals, the network transmission facilities are allocated to the connection only when packets are actually being transferred over it.

virtual data circuit The transmission path allocated as required for the transmission of the packets comprising a *virtual call*. See also *permanent virtual circuit*.

virtual data connection See *data connection*.

virtual decision value In *pulse code modulation*, one of two hypothetical *decision values* lying at the ends of the working range used in quantising or encoding. The hypothetical values are obtained by extrapolation from the real decision values.

virtual height Of an ionised layer, for a given frequency: the apparent height of the layer calculated from the time interval between the transmission of a signal and the reception of its ionospheric echo at vertical incidence. The transmitted wave is assumed to have the velocity of light *in vacuo* over the entire path. In practice it will travel slightly more slowly in any ionised region, so the value obtained for the virtual height will always be greater than the true height if the signal travels through or penetrates into an ionised region.

virtual switching points Hypothetical points marking the interconnection of international and national circuits in an international *switching centre*, and defined for the purpose of specifying the *relative levels* required at these points.

vocoder Equipment for *articulation* testing using synthetic speech made up from recorded speech elements.

voice calling A facility available on some subscribers' telephone installations whereby a terminal (extension telephone) equipped with an integral loudspeaker can be called and an announcement can be made via the loudspeaker before the handset is lifted for call-answering purposes. Typically the announcement might be a request for a secretary's presence in an inner office. This type of facility can be extended so that an announcement can be broadcast to all the free terminals of a group for paging purposes, for example.

voice frequency   A frequency lying in the band required for the effective transmission of speech, usually taken as 200 to 3500 Hz.

voice-frequency electronics (US)   General term for devices that permit the use of *subscribers' lines* having a higher loop resistance than that for which the exchange equipment was designed. See *range extender, dial long lines* and *ringer isolator*.

voice-frequency signalling   A method of *signalling* in which alternating currents having frequencies in the telephone speech band are used for the transmission of information relating to the set-up, control and release of calls.

voice-frequency telegraphy   A system of *alphabetic telegraphy* in which modulated carriers in the *voice-frequency* range are used for transmission. For 50-*baud* amplitude or frequency-modulated systems the CCITT has recommended carrier frequencies based on odd multiples of 60 Hz, starting at 420 Hz and finishing at 3180 Hz. It is thus possible to transmit 24 telegraph (telex) signals over a standard 4 kHz channel of an FDM carrier transmission system.

volatile store   A *store* that loses its information content if the power is removed.

voltage level   Of a signal at some point in a transmission system, the ratio of the peak voltage of the signal to a specified reference value, in *decibels*.

voltage standing-wave ratio   See *standing-wave ratio*.

volume   (1) The loudness of a sound. (2) The magnitude of an *audio-frequency* wave as measured in *volume units* on a standard volume indicator.

volume compression and expansion   See *companding*.

volume equivalent (US)   A measure of the performance of a complete telephone connection in terms of the loudness of speech transmitted over it. The measurement is made by adjusting the loss of a reference system so that it gives equal loudness.

volume indicator or **volume meter**   A voltmeter, with standardised electrical and dynamic characteristics, that is used in a prescribed manner to measure the comparative levels of audio signals (speech and music) in terms of the apparent loudness of the sounds they represent. The indicating instrument and associated circuits are arranged to have a time constant of about 0.2 seconds so that the reading corresponds with an integration of peak values over this period—approximately the time constant of the human ear.

volume unit   The unit in which a standard *volume indicator* is calibrated. For a sine wave this corresponds to one *decibel* relative to a reference power of one milliwatt in 600 ohms.

W

wait on busy   See *camp on*.

waiting-in-progress signal   A *signal* (2) sent in the backward direction to indicate that the call has been placed in a waiting queue because the called subscriber is busy but has the *camp on* facility.

waiting system   See *delay system*.

waiting-time jitter   That component of the total timing *jitter* produced in the *justification* process which occurs because justification cannot be carried out on demand but has to wait until one of the preassigned *justifiable digit time slots* appears. *Figure W.1* illustrates the production of jitter in the justification

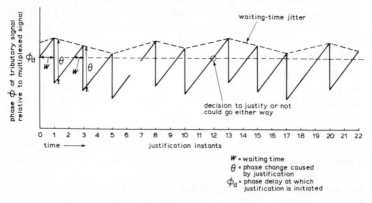

Figure W.1   Waiting-time jitter

process, and shows how it consists of a component θ equal to the *phase delay* produced by justification, together with an irregularly varying component (the waiting-time jitter) due to the waiting delay W. At times when W approaches zero the decision to justify or not may be influenced by circuit noise and can go either way. This introduces a non-repetitive random component

308

into waiting-time jitter, which makes it a difficult impairment to correct.

waiting traffic   In a *delay system*, the average number of calls occurring during a period equal to the average delay of delayed calls.

walkie-talkie   A portable two-way radio set designed to be carried by one person.

wander   General term for slow variations about the mean value of a parameter of a recurrent phenomenon such as a digital signal; see for example *low-frequency wander*.

warn pulse or **warn tone**   See *intrusion tone*.

waste traffic   *Traffic* that occurs when a device is taken into use for the purpose of setting up a call but is subsequently released without effectively contributing to the establishment of the call.

watch receiver   A separate telephone earpiece provided in addition to a normal handset, usually to assist a customer with hearing problems. It can enable a person to listen to the incoming speech with both ears or can be held against the microphone of a suitable hearing aid.

wave   A travelling disturbance whose intensity at any point in a medium or space is a function of time. Waves may be electromagnetic, acoustic, mechanical, etc. Propagation of the latter classes involves displacement of the medium in which they travel, whereas the propagation of electromagnetic waves is characterised by variations of the electric and magnetic field intensities from their equilibrium values.

wave antenna   See *Beverage antenna*.

wave impedance   See *characteristic wave impedance*.

wave tilt   Of a radio wave travelling along the surface of the earth, the forward inclination of the *wavefront* caused by the proximity of the ground.

wave-trap   A *tuned circuit* used as a *band rejection filter* to reduce *interference* in a receiving system.

waveband   A band of *wavelengths* defined for some given purpose, for example the medium waveband used for broadcasting.

waveform   The shape of a wave obtained by plotting some characteristic (usually the instantaneous amplitude of the voltage, current or power) against time.

waveform amplitude distortion (US)   See *amplitude/amplitude distortion*.

waveform corrector   Generic term for a device used to remove or reduce *linear waveform distortion*. Waveform correctors are essentially equalisers operating in the time domain to correct simultaneously *amplitude/frequency distortion* and *phase/frequency distortion*. The term gained currency in the context of television transmission, where early correctors were sometimes called *time equalisers*. See *adaptive equaliser, derivative equaliser* and *transversal equaliser*.

waveform distortion Generic term for unwanted changes in the *waveform* of a signal caused by its transmission through a device or system. The term is widely used in connection with *video frequency* television signals, where any change in the shape of the waveform constitutes an impairment. Non-linear effects and *linear waveform distortion* are treated separately for measurement and specification purposes; see *waveform testing*.

waveform monitor A high-quality oscilloscope for displaying the *waveform* of a video signal such as an *insertion test signal*.

waveform response The output *waveform* produced by a device or system in response to an input signal having a closely specified waveform.

waveform return loss The *return loss* determined by means of a *video-frequency* television test signal. It is given by the ratio of the peak-to-peak amplitudes of the 'picture' portions of the incident and reflected waveforms, and will be numerically equal to the return loss measured in the usual way only if the return loss is independent of frequency.

waveform testing A method of determining the *transmission performance* of a system by observing and/or measuring its *waveform response* as displayed on a suitable high-quality oscilloscope. For very accurate results the display can be photographed, the measurements of waveform features being carried out using a travelling microscope. For routine tests transparent masks can be designed to fit in front of the display, and they can be marked with outlines within which the waveform should fit for a predetermined degree of distortion; see *K-rating system*. The method was developed for use with *video-frequency* television links because it gives a sensitive measure of transmission performance that can be directly related to the picture impairments the links produce. Steady-state tests of the attenuation/frequency and phase/frequency characteristrics of a system, on the other hand, yield relatively little information on the effect they will have on a transmitted picture. The essential difference between the two approaches is that the former method operates in the time domain and the latter in the frequency domain. Because of the reciprocal nature of time and frequency it is possible for a relatively small departure from the ideal attenuation and phase characteristics to cause a disproportional degree of picture impairment. Conversely, quite large departures from the ideal characteristics may have an insignificant effect on picture quality. It follows that the specification of the performance of a link intended for the transmission of signals sensitive to waveform distortion, e.g. television, is best done in terms of its waveform response. The precise details of the waveforms used for specification and testing purposes must be related to the parameters of the signals the link will transmit, and should be selected so that they are sensitive to forms of distortion known to cause significant picture impairment. Many types of waveform can be devised, but most signals used to test for linear waveform distortion are built up using one or more of the four basic shapes described below. (A staircase waveform is normally used to test for non-linearity distortion; see *crushing*.)

(a) *T-pulse*: a pulse of approximately sine-squared shape having a duration at half-amplitude equal to one half-period of the nominal upper cut-off frequency of the TV system to be transmitted. For example, a half-amplitude duration of 100 nanoseconds corresponding to a frequency of 5 MHz is specified by the CCITT for links suitable for 625-line television signals. The amplitude/frequency spectrum of this pulse falls with increasing frequency, and is 6 dB down at 5 MHz. Nevertheless it provides a sensitive measure of amplitude/frequency and phase/frequency distortion in the upper part of the video band.

(b) *2T-pulse*: identical with the T-pulse except that its half-amplitude duration is a whole period of the upper cut-off frequency of the system to be transmitted. As a result the pulse contains no energy at frequencies outside the system passband, and it is very useful for routine tests.

(c) *Half-line bar*: a smooth bar having a duration approximately equal to half a line period of the TV system to be transmitted. Its transitions are shaped by a network identical to that used to shape the 2T-pulse, and hence the spectrum of the bar contains negligible energy outside the system passband. The bar explores system performance in the lower part of the video band down to the line repetition frequency. The bar is normally associated with a T- or 2T-pulse and a line-synchronising pulse to form a composite *pulse-and-bar signal*.

(d) *Low-frequency square wave*: used to explore system performance at frequencies between the field repetition rate and the line repetition rate of the system to be transmitted.

wavefront Of a travelling wave, an imaginary surface at which the wave has everywhere the same *phase* at a given instant.

waveguide A *transmission line* consisting of a system of boundaries for guiding electromagnetic energy, and generally taking the form of a hollow metallic conductor or a rod of dielectric material. Rectangular or circular cross-section metallic tubes of prescribed dimensions are most generally used at frequencies in the *microwave* region of the spectrum. At infra-red and optical frequencies dielectric filaments are used; see *optical fibre*. See also *single-wire transmission line*.

waveguide bend A length of *waveguide* in which the direction of the longitudinal axis changes gradually; see *E bend* and *H bend*.

waveguide corner A length of *waveguide* in which the direction of the longitudinal axis changes abruptly. Also sometimes called an *elbow*.

waveguide dispersion In an *optical fibre*, the spreading in time of the energy in a short pulse transmitted along the fibre as a result of variations with *wavelength* of the optical field distribution between the core and the cladding.

waveguide mode A particular field configuration in a uniform *waveguide*; see *TE mode, TEM mode, TM mode, hybrid mode* and *evanescent mode*.

waveguide wavelength For a travelling wave in a uniform *waveguide* at a given frequency and for a given *mode* (2): the distance along the guide axis between adjacent points at which the phase of a specified field component differs in phase by 2π radians.

waveguide window A gas- or liquid-tight barrier transparent to electromagnetic waves.

wavelength Of a sinusoidal wave, the distance between two points of corresponding *phase* in consecutive cycles. This is equal to the velocity of propagation divided by the frequency, and in the case of an electromagnetic wave propagating *in vacuo* its value in metres is given by dividing 3×10^8 by the frequency in hertz.

wavelength constant See *phase-change coefficient*.

weighting Artificial adjustment of measured values to allow for their significance in a particular context. For example, the disturbing effect of *noise* or *interference* in a telephone or television channel varies with frequency, so values are measured using appropriate weighting networks whose characteristics with respect to frequency are closely specified.

wet contact A contact through which a direct current is maintained in order to prevent the formation of a resistive skin.

Wheatstone automatic system A telegraph system in which signals formed in accordance with the *Morse code* are transmitted automatically by means of a previously perforated tape, and are received and recorded automatically either on a tape suitable for automatic printing or on an inked paper for interpretation by an operator.

whip antenna A simple *vertical unipole* antenna supported on an insulator.

white noise *Random noise* whose spectral distribution over the frequency range of interest is such that the noise power per unit of bandwidth is independent of frequency. Also known as *flat random noise* or *uniform-spectrum random noise*. White noise is widely used for system tests; for example, it is possible to load a wideband system with such a signal but to filter out the noise present in a defined narrow band of the transmitted frequency range. Measurements of the noise power present in this narrow band at the receiving end of the system will give an indication of *crosstalk* or *crossmodulation* produced by the system. This type of test is sometimes called a *notched noise test*.

white recording [transmission] (1) In an amplitude-modulated *facsimile* system, recording [transmission] in which the maximum values of signal amplitude correspond to the whitest areas of the picture. (2) In a frequency-modulated facsimile system, recording [transmission] in which the lower signal frequencies correspond to the whitest areas of the picture.

white signal In *facsimile*, the signal produced by scanning the whitest areas of the original document.

who-are-you signal A signal sent from a calling telegraph or data terminal to a called terminal to initiate the automatic return transmission of an *answer-back code*.

wiper Of a *selector*, a moving contact that engages with the contacts of a *bank*.

wire-photo See *facsimile telegraphy*.

wired broadcasting The distribution of programmes to a number of receiving points using a line network. In the UK the term is applied to systems distributing broadcast sound and television programmes. The systems have to be licensed and may not distribute any programmes other than those radiated by the broadcasting authorities.

wired program control A method of control using hardware in the form of wire strappings, ROM, etc. to store a *program*, which can therefore only be altered by wiring or component changes.

wobble modulation *Frequency modulation* of a carrier at a frequency that is low compared to that of a signal subsequently used for *amplitude modulation*.

wobbulator A signal generator whose frequency can be periodically swept across a selected range—for example by the scanning voltage of an oscilloscope—in order to display the response of a device or system being tested.

word In data processing, a series of characters that it is convenient for a given purpose to regard as a unit. An *alphabetic word* contains only letters from the same alphabet, whereas a *numeric word* contains digits and sometimes space characters and special characters.

word articulation See *articulation*.

words per minute A measure of *telegraph transmission speed* in terms of an arbitrary telegraph word consisting of five letters and one letter space. For start-stop 50-*baud* telegraph systems using a 1½-unit *stop signal* the speed computed in this way is 66⅔ words per minute. With 50-baud 5-unit synchronous transmission it is 100 words per minute.

working fill See *fill*.

world numbering plan The *numbering plan* formulated by the World Plan Committee of the CCITT, according to which the world is divided into nine *world numbering zones*:

1 North America	6 Australasia
2 Africa	7 USSR
3 Part of Europe	8 North Pacific (Eastern Asia)
4 Remainder of Europe	9 Far East and Middle East
5 South America	

Each geographical zone is allocated a single numeral, which forms the first digit of the *country code* for every country in that zone. In the case of North America and the USSR the single numeral itself forms the country code.

world zone number A single digit identifying a world numbering zone.

write To insert data into a *store*.

writing bar Of a facsimile *continuous recorder*, a conductor forming the second electrode in conjunction with a helix or a bar used to project the recording medium on to the helix.

writing speed Of a *facsimile* receiver, the linear speed at which the recording medium is scanned.

X

X operation Of a *relay*, the early operation of one contact with respect to the remainder of a group of contact units, either by means of an armature with double motion (see *two-step relay*) or by means of mechanical adjustment.

X-press callmaker UK designation for a *callmaker* incorporated in a standard pushbutton telephone, able to store up to ten telephone numbers and having the *repeat last number* facility.

X wave Abbreviation for extraordinary wave; see *magneto-ionic double refraction*.

XL callmaker UK designation for a desktop *callmaker* equipped with a monitor loudspeaker and having the *repeat last number* facility.

XY switch A *selector* in a flat assembly in which the *wipers* move under remote control in a plane, first in one direction and then in a second direction normal to the first.

Y

Y operation Of a *relay*, the late operation of one contact unit with respect to the remainder of a group of contact units.

Yagi antenna An *end-fire array* consisting of a dipole element and a number of secondary elements arranged in line; see *Figure Y.1*.

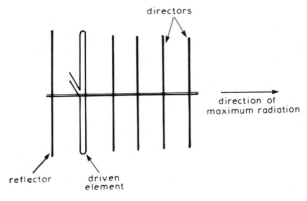

Figure Y.1 Yagi antenna

The director elements consist of unfed dipoles, but the reflector element may be an unfed dipole (as shown) or a plane reflecting surface. Usually the driven element is folded to offset the impedance changes produced by the parasitic elements. Yagi antennas have quite good *directivity* and gain and are widely used for television reception. For further information see the companion *Dictionary of Audio, Radio and Video*.

Z

Z component One of the components into which a radio wave entering the *ionosphere* may be resolved when the direction of propagation is parallel to the earth's magnetic field. See also *magneto-ionic double refraction*.

Z condition In a *start-stop system*, the significant condition of the

315

element that follows a character signal or block signal. The Z-element prepares the receiving equipment for the reception of a subsequent character signal or block.

Zener diode A semiconductor diode that exhibits a sharply defined avalanche breakdown at a certain reverse bias known as the *Zener voltage*. Zener diodes are widely used to provide reference potentials in stabilising circuits and can be used directly for stabilisation if the load current variations are not too large.

zero-disparity code A *binary code* in which every code word has an even number of digits and is comprised of equal numbers of 1s and 0s. Hence 001011, 101010 and 000111 could be three words of such a code.

zero-minus call (US) A call in which the single digit zero is dialled to gain the attention of an operator.

zero-plus call (US) A call in which the digit zero is dialled as the first part of a code to gain the attention of an operator.

zero suppression In digital transmission, the technique of forcing the transmission of a 1 whenever the density of 1s in the signal falls below the threshold at which satisfactory signal *regeneration* is possible.

zone centre A term formerly used in the UK to describe a *trunk exchange* that served as the *main switching centre* for all the *group switching centres* in a given region.

zoned antenna A *microwave* antenna in which the *reflector* or *lens* has a discontinuous surface and is composed of zones or steps designed to provide an *aperture illumination* with a desired phase distribution.

Appendix   Common Abbreviations and Acronyms

In accordance with international usage, the abbreviations and acronyms (other than those relating to the decibel) are shown in capitals. An asterisk (*) indicates that the name or term is given an entry in the main part of the dictionary.

AAR	automatic alternative routing
ACC	automatic carrier control
ACD	automatic call distribution*
ACG	adjacent charging group
ACPI	automatic cable pair identification
ACRE	automatic call recording equipment
ACS	advise called subscriber
ACU	acknowledgement signal unit*
ADC	advise duration and charge (see advise-cost-and-duration call*)
ADH	A-digit hunter
ADI	alternate digit inversion*
ADQ	almost differential quasi-ternary code*
AEN	articulation reference equivalent*
AER	alarm equipment rack
AFC	automatic frequency control*
AFN	all-figure numbering*
AGC	automatic gain control*
AHT	average holding time
AIOD	automatic identified outward dialling*
AIS	alarm inhibit signal
AM	amplitude modulation*
AMA	automatic message accounting*
AMC	automanual centre
AMI	alternate mark inversion*
AML	actual measured loss
AMSU	automanual switching unit
AMVF	amplitude-modulated voice frequency
ANA	automatic number analysis*
ANC	all-number calling*
ANI	automatic number identification*
ANIK	designation for Canadian satellite
APC	automatic phase control
APD	avalanche photodiode*
APS	addressed packet system
ARCOM	Arctic communication satellite
ARQ	error correction by automatic repetition (see van Duuren ARQ system*)

317

ASK	amplitude shift keying*
ASS	analogue switching subsystem
AST	anti-sidetone
ASU	apparatus slide-in unit
ATB	all trunks busy
ATE	artificial traffic equipment, *or* automatic telephone exchange
ATR	automatic traffic recorder
ATS	applications technology satellite
BBC	British Broadcasting Corporation
BCC	block check character
BCD	binary coded decimal*
BCH	bids per circuit per hour
BCPS	basic call processing subsystem
BCS	bridge control system
BEL	bell character
BER	bit error rate
BFL	busy flash
BFO	beat frequency oscillator*
BH	busy hour*
BLA	blocking acknowledgement signal
BLO	blocking signal*
BLU	bipolar line unit
BPC	binding post chamber
BS	backspace character
BT	barred trunk, *or* busy tone*, *or* block terminal
BXB	British crossbar
CAM	content-addressable memory
CAMA	centralised automatic message accounting
CAN	cancel character
CANTAT	transatlantic cable system between UK and Canada
CATV	community antenna television system*
CAX	community automatic exchange
CB	central battery
CBS	central battery signalling*
CBX	centralised private branch exchange; see centrex service*
CC	call check
CCB	coin collecting box
CCIR	International Radio Consultative Committee*
CCIS	common-channel interoffice signalling
CCITT	International Telegraph and Telephone Consultative Committee*

CCM	call count meter
CCMB	completion of calls meeting busy
CCP	cross-connection point*
CCS	common-channel signalling*, *or* hundred call seconds*
CCTV	closed-circuit television*
CDF	combined distribution frame*
CDO	community dial office
CDT	control data terminal
CEF	cable entrance facility*
CEPT	Conference of European Posts and Telecommunications*
CFC	coin and fee checking
CFDE	call failure detection equipment
CFL	call failure signal
CFSK	coherent frequency shift keying
CGS	circuit group congestion signal
CHDB	compatible high-density bipolar*
CHT	call holding time
CLF	clear forward signal*
CLI	calling line identification*
CLR	recording completing trunk*
CNI	changed number interception*
COF	confusion signal*
COMSAT	Communications Satellite Corporation*
COS	class of service*
COT	continuity signal
CR	carriage return character
CSA	called subscriber answer
CSB	called subscriber busy
CSC	coin slot control
CSH	called subscriber held
CSO	centralised service observation
CSS	cordless switchboard section
CSU	central switching unit
CTC	chargeable time clock*
CTS	cable turning section
CVSD	continuously variable slope delta modulation*
CWI	calls waiting indicator*
dB	decibel*
dBK	figure of merit*
dBm	decibels relative to one milliwatt
dBm0	decibels relative to one milliwatt at a point of zero relative level (see signal level*)

dBm0p	decibels relative to one milliwatt at a point of zero relative level and psophometrically weighted for telephony
dBm0ps	decibels relative to one milliwatt at a point of zero relative level and psophometrically weighted for sound-programme transmission
dBq	absolute voltage level of audio-frequency noise in decibels relative to a reference voltage defined by the CCITT and measured with a quasi-peak noise meter without a weighting network
dBr	relative level in decibels
DCE	data-circuit terminating equipment*
DCO	digital central office
DCSCS	data code and speed conversion subsystem
DDD	direct distance dialling*
DDI	direct dialling-in*
DEL	direct exchange line*
DEMUX	demultiplexer
DEXT	distant-end crosstalk
DID	direct inward dialling*
DJSU	digital junction switching unit
DLE	data link escape character
DLL	dial long lines*
DLS	digital line system
DLU	data line (terminating) unit
DM	delta modulation*
DME	digital multiplex equipment (see muldex*)
DMNSC	digital main network switching centre
DNCC	data network control centre
DNSC	digital (or data) network service centre
DOD	direct outward dialling*
DP	distribution point*
DPC	data processing centre
DPCM	differential pulse code modulation*
DPE	data processing equipment
DQ	directory enquiry
DRS	data relay satellite
DSA	dial service assistance
DSB	double sideband
DSBSC	double-sideband suppressed carrier
DSC	district switching centre*
DSE	data switching equipment (or exchange)
DSI	digital speech interpolation*
DSS	digital switching subsystem
DSV	digital sum variation*

DSX	digital signal cross-connection equipment
DTE	data terminal equipment*
DTMF	dual-tone multifrequency*
E	erlang*
EAS	extended area service
EAX	electronic automatic exchange
EBCDIC	extended binary-coded-decimal interchange code
ECM	effective calls meter
ECO	electronic central office
ECS	European fixed-service satellite system*
EDC	error detection and correction
EEL	exclusive exchange line*
EET	equipment engaged tone*
EHF	extra high frequency (see band*)
EIRP	effective isotropically radiated power*
EMI	electromagnetic interference*
EMSS	emergency manual switching system
EN	equipment number
ENQ	enquiry character
EOT	end of transmission
EPSS	experimental packet-switching service
EQ	enquiry
ERL	echo return loss
ERP	effective radiated power*
ESA	European Space Agency*
ESC	escape character
ESRO	European Space Research Organisation (see European Space Agency*)
ESS	electronic switching system, or echo suppression system
ET	engaged tone (or test)*
ETX	end of text
FAX	facsimile
FCC	Federal Communications Commission
FDM	frequency-division multiplex*
FDMA	frequency-division multiple access*
FEC	forward error correction
FEXT	far-end crosstalk*
FLS	free-line signal
FM	frequency modulation*
FOT	optimum traffic frequency
FR	forced release*
FRB	faultsman's ring back

FRXD	fully automatic reperforator – transmitter
FS	final selector*
FSK	frequency-shift keying*
FSU	final signal unit*
FXT	fixed time call
GDF	group distribution frame*
GE	gateway exchange*
GOM	group occupancy meter
GOS	grade of service*
GRP	group reference pilot*
GSC	group switching centre*
HC	heat coil*
HDB	high-density bipolar*
HDLC	high-level data link control
HES	house exchange system
HF	high frequency (see band*)
HFDF	high-frequency distribution frame
HLL	high-level language (see programming*)
HRC	hypothetical reference circuit
HRDP	hypothetical reference digital path
HRP	hypergroup reference pilot
HRX	hypothetical reference connection*
HTE	hypergroup translating equipment
IAM	initial address message*
IATAE	international accounting and traffic analysis equipment
IBA	Independent Broadcasting Authority
ICB	incoming calls barred
ICC	international control centre
ICECAN	Iceland – Canada cable
IDD	international direct dialling
IDF	intermediate distribution frame*
IDN	integrated digital network*
IDP	interdigit pause*
IDU	idle signal unit*
IEC	International Electrotechnical Commission*
IFRB	International Frequency Registration Board*
INTELSAT	International Telecommunications Satellite Organisation*
INWATS	inward wide-area telephone service
ISB	independent-sideband transmission*
ISC	international switching centre
ISD	international subscriber dialling

ISDN	integrated-services digital network*
ISO	International Standards Organisation*
ISU	initial signal unit*
ITC	International Teletraffic Congress*
ITSC	international telephone service centre
ITU	International Telecommunications Union*
IXSD	international telex subscriber dialling
JCN	junction
JRS	junction relay set
JTE	junction tandem exchange
KLU	key and lamp unit*
KP	start-of-pulsing signal*
KTS	key telephone system
LAMA	local automatic message accounting*
LB	local battery*
LC	line circuit*
LCC	late-choice call
LCCM	late-choice call meter
LCM	last calls meter
LCU	line control unit
LE	local exchange*
LED	light-emitting diode*
LF	low frequency (see band*), or line finder*, or line feed character
LFJ	local feed junctor
LLE	long line equipment
LMS	level-measuring set*
LND	local number dialling
LOS	line of sight*
LSB	lower sideband
LSC	local switching unit
LSS	loop switching system*
LST	loudspeaking telephone
LSU	line selection unit, or lone signalling unit
LTB	last trunk busy
LTE	local telephone exchange
LUF	lowest useful high frequency*
MAC	measurement and analysis centre
MAR	miscellaneous apparatus rack
MARECS	European maritime satellite system*
MARISAT	maritime satellite service*

MATV	master antenna television system
MAX	mobile automatic exchange
MBD	manual board
MCA	malicious call alarm
MCC	maintenance control centre
MCVF	multi-channel voice frequency
MCW	modulated continuous wave*
MDF	main distribution frame*
MF	multi-frequency, *or* medium frequency (see band*)
MFSS	multi-frequency signalling system*
MH	manual hold*
MKR	marker*
MML	man – machine language
MNDX	mobile non-director exchange
MNSC	main network switching centre
MOJ	metering over junction
MRF	message refused signal
MSC	main switching centre*
MSU	main switching unit
MTS	mobile telephone service
MTX	mobile telephone exchange
MUF	maximum usable frequency*
MUM	multi-unit message
MUSA	multiple-unit steerable array (see musa array*)
MUX	multiplexer
MXE	mobile electronic exchange
NAK	negative acknowledgement signal
NBFM	narrow-band frequency modulation
NCC	network coordination centre
NEXT	near-end crosstalk*
NIB	negative impedance booster
NLC	new line character
NMC	network management centre
NNC	national network congestion signal
NND	national number dialling
NPA	numbering-plan area*
NRZ	non-return to zero*
NSS	network synchronisation subsystem
NSU	network service unit
NTI	noise transmission impairment*
NU	number unobtainable (tone)*
NUL	null character
OAU	operator assistance unit

OBH	office busy hour
OCB	outgoing calls barred
OCS	overload control subsystem
ODD	operator distance dialling
ONI	operator number identification*
OPA	operator priority access
ORE	overall reference equivalent
OTC	originating toll centre
OTS	orbital test satellite*
OWF	optimum working frequency*
PABX	private automatic branch exchange*
PAD	packet assembly/disassembly facility*
PAM	pulse amplitude modulation*
PATX	private automatic telex exchange
PAX	private automatic exchange*
PBU	pushbutton unit
PBX	private branch exchange*
PCC	personal code calling
PCM	pulse code modulation*
PCP	primary cross-connection point
PDD	post dialling delay*
PDM	pulse duration modulation*
PDN	public data network
PDX	private digital exchange
PFM	pulse frequency modulation*
PLA	programmable logic array*
PLJ	permanent loop junctor
PM	phase modulation*
PMBX	private manual branch exchange*
PNSC	packet network service centre
PPM	periodic pulse metering, *or* pulse position modulation*
PPS	pulses per second
PPU	preprocessor utility
PRF	pulse repetition frequency*
PROM	programmable read-only memory*
PRRM	pulse repetition rate modulation
PSD	post sending delay*
PSE	packet switching exchange
PSK	phase-shift keying*
PSP	presending pause
PSTN	public switched telephone network
PT	packet terminal
PTM	pulse time modulation*

PU	processor utility
PWM	pulse width modulation (see pulse duration modulation*)
QAM	quadrature amplitude modulation*
QDPSK	quaternary differential phase shift keying
QFM	quantised frequency modulation
QOS	quality of service
QUAM	quantised amplitude modulation
RAM	random-access memory*
RCB	renters coin box
RDF	repeater distribution frame*
RFI	radio-frequency interference
RG	release guard*
RHT	register holding time
RI	radio interference*
RIS	recorded information service
RLG	release guard signal*
ROM	read-only memory*
RRE	receiving reference equivalent
RSS	route switching subsystem
RTLP	reference transmission level point
RTNR	ringing tone no reply
RWT	right when tested
RZ	return to zero*
SAC	special area code, or serving-area concept*
SALT	subscriber's apparatus line tester
SAM	subsequent address message*
SCA	short code address
SCAN	switched circuit automatic network
SCE	signal conversion equipment
SCFM	sub-carrier frequency modulation
SCP	secondary cross-connection point
SCPC	single channel per carrier (see SPADE*)
SCS	separate-channel signalling
SCU	system-control signal unit
SDF	supergroup distribution frame*
SDR	signal-to-distortion ratio
SHF	super high frequency (see band*)
SIS	signalling interworking subsystem
SIT	special information tone
SLU	special line unit

SNR	signal-to-noise ratio*
SOH	start of heading
SPC	stored-program control*
SPL	splice*
SPN	service protection network
SRE	sending reference equivalent
SRL	structural return loss*
SSAC	alternating-current signalling system
SSB	single sideband*
SSBSC	single-sideband suppressed carrier
SSC	sector switching centre
SSDC	direct-current signalling system
SSMF	multi-frequency signalling system
SSN	switched service network
SST	subscriber transferred signal
SSTDMA	satellite-switched time-division multiple access
SSU	subscriber's switching unit, *or* subsequent signal unit*
STD	subscriber trunk dialling*
STE	supergroup translating equipment*
STR	sidetone reduction
STX	start of text
SUB	substitute character
SVI	service interception
SXS	step by step*
SYN	synchronous idle character*
SYU	synchronisation signal unit*
TAS	telephone answering service
TASI	time-assignment speech interpolation*
TASS	teleprinter automatic switching system
TAT	transatlantic telephone cable
TCBH	time-consistent busy hour (see mean busy hour*)
TCC	toll centre code
TCMF	touch-calling multi-frequency
TDF	trunk distribution frame
TDM	time-division multiplex*
TDMA	time-division multiple access*
TDMS	telegraph (or transmission) distortion measuring set
TIDF	trunk intermediate distribution frame
TIE	time interval error
TIS	telephone information service
TKO	trunk offering*
TMS	transmission measuring set*
TOS	temporarily out of service*

TRC	telegram retransmission centre
TRS	telephone repeater station
TSC	transit switching centre
TSO	telephone service observations
TSS	toll switching system
TST	time-space-time switching
TSU	trunk switching unit
TTR	trunk (or transmission) test rack
TXD	digital telephone exchange
TXE	electronic telephone exchange
TXK	crossbar telephone exchange
TXS	Strowger telephone exchange
UAX	unit automatic exchange*
UBA	unblocking acknowledgement signal
UBL	unblocking signal*
UFI	upstream failure indication
UHF	ultra high frequency (see band*)
ULA	uncommitted logic array*
USB	upper sideband
VDA	verbal delay announcement
VDT	visual display terminal
VDU	visual display unit
VF	voice frequency*
VFO	voice-frequency oscillator
VFT	voice-frequency telegraphy*
VHF	very high frequency (see band*)
VLF	very low frequency (see band*)
VNL	via net loss*
VNN	vacant national number signal
VSB	vestigial sideband*
WADS	wide-area data service
WARC	World Administrative Radio Conference
WATS	wide-area telephone service
WBS	wideband system
WCI	waiting-calls indicator
WRU	who are you*
XBT	crossbar tandem
XCU	crosspoint control unit
XD	ex-directory
XFC	transferred-charge call
XPD	crosspolarisation discrimination*

XPI	crosspolarisation interference*
XPT	crosspoint*
YAG	yttrium aluminium garnet (laser material)